DAVID: WARRIOR AND KING

Frank G. Slaughter

DAVID

WARRIOR AND KING

A BIBLICAL BIOGRAPHY

CLEVELAND AND NEW YORK

THE WORLD PUBLISHING COMPANY

Published by The World Publishing Company
2231 West 110th Street, Cleveland 2, Ohio

Published simultaneously in Canada by
Nelson, Foster & Scott Ltd.

Library of Congress Catalog Card Number: 62-9050

SECOND PRINTING

2HC762

To Rebecca

CONTENTS

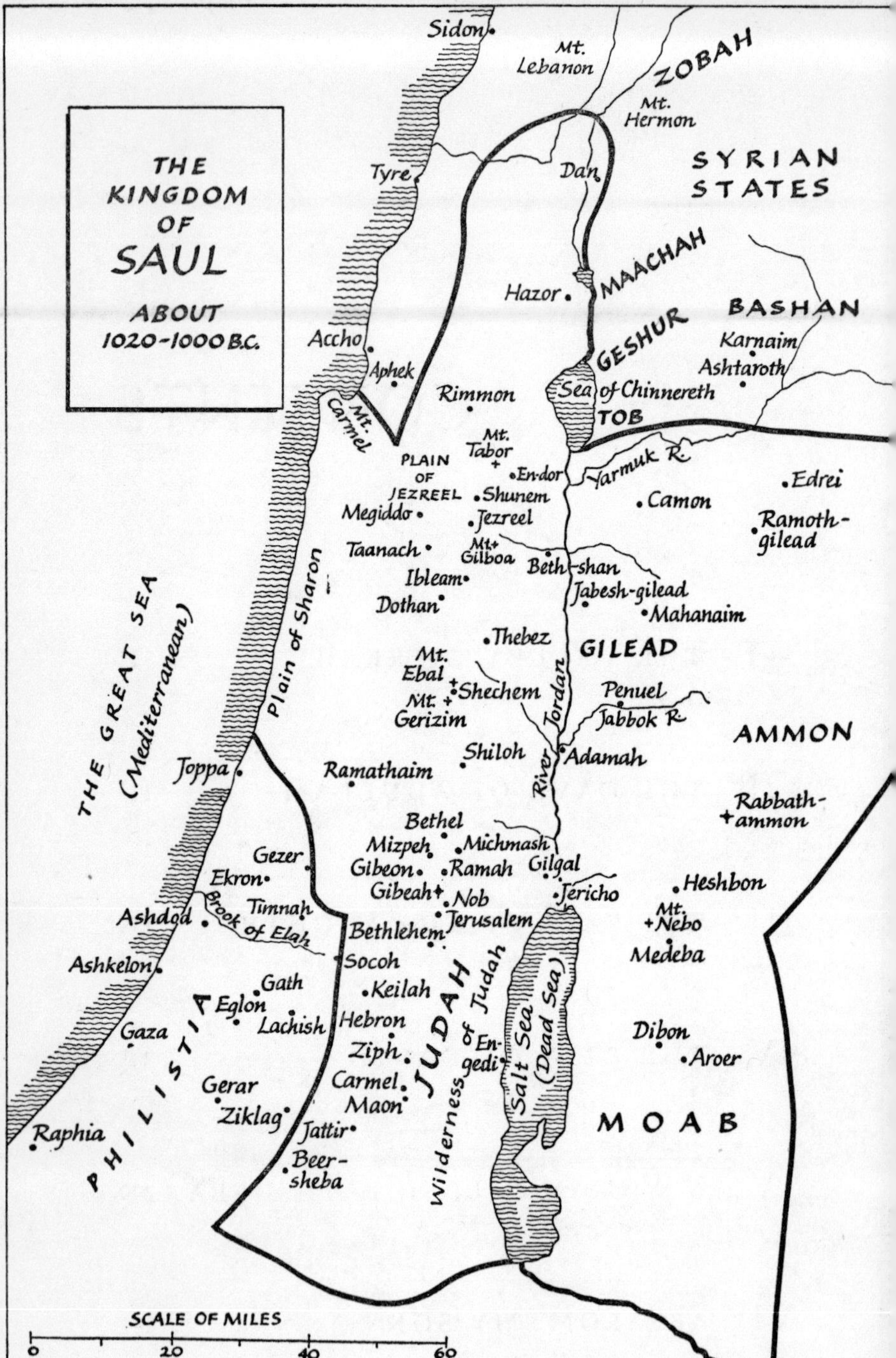

THE KINGDOM OF SAUL
ABOUT 1020-1000 B.C.
Sidon
Mt. Lebanon
ZOBAH
Mt. Hermon
SYRIAN STATES
Tyre
Dan
MAACHAH
Hazor
BASHAN
GESHUR
Karnaim
Ashtaroth
Accho
Aphek
Rimmon
Sea of Chinnereth
TOB
Mt. Carmel
Mt. Tabor
PLAIN OF JEZREEL
En-dor
Yarmuk R.
Edrei
Shunem
Camon
Megiddo
Jezreel
Ramoth-gilead
Taanach
Mt. Gilboa
Beth-shan
Ibleam
Jabesh-gilead
Dothan
Mahanaim
Plain of Sharon
THE GREAT SEA (Mediterranean)
Thebez
GILEAD
Mt. Ebal
Shechem
Mt. Gerizim
River Jordan
Penuel
Jabbok R.
AMMON
Shiloh
Adamah
Joppa
Ramathaim
Rabbath-ammon
Bethel
Mizpeh
Michmash
Gezer
Gibeon
Ramah
Gilgal
Ekron
Gibeah
Nob
Jericho
Heshbon
Timnah
Brook of Elah
Ashdod
Jerusalem
Mt. Nebo
Bethlehem
Medeba
Ashkelon
Socoh
Gath
Keilah
JUDAH
Wilderness of Judah
Salt Sea (Dead Sea)
Eglon
Lachish
Hebron
Gaza
Dibon
Ziph
En-gedi
Aroer
PHILISTIA
Gerar
Carmel
Maon
Ziklag
MOAB
Raphia
Jattir
Beer-sheba
SCALE OF MILES
0
20
40
60
EDOM
Morgan

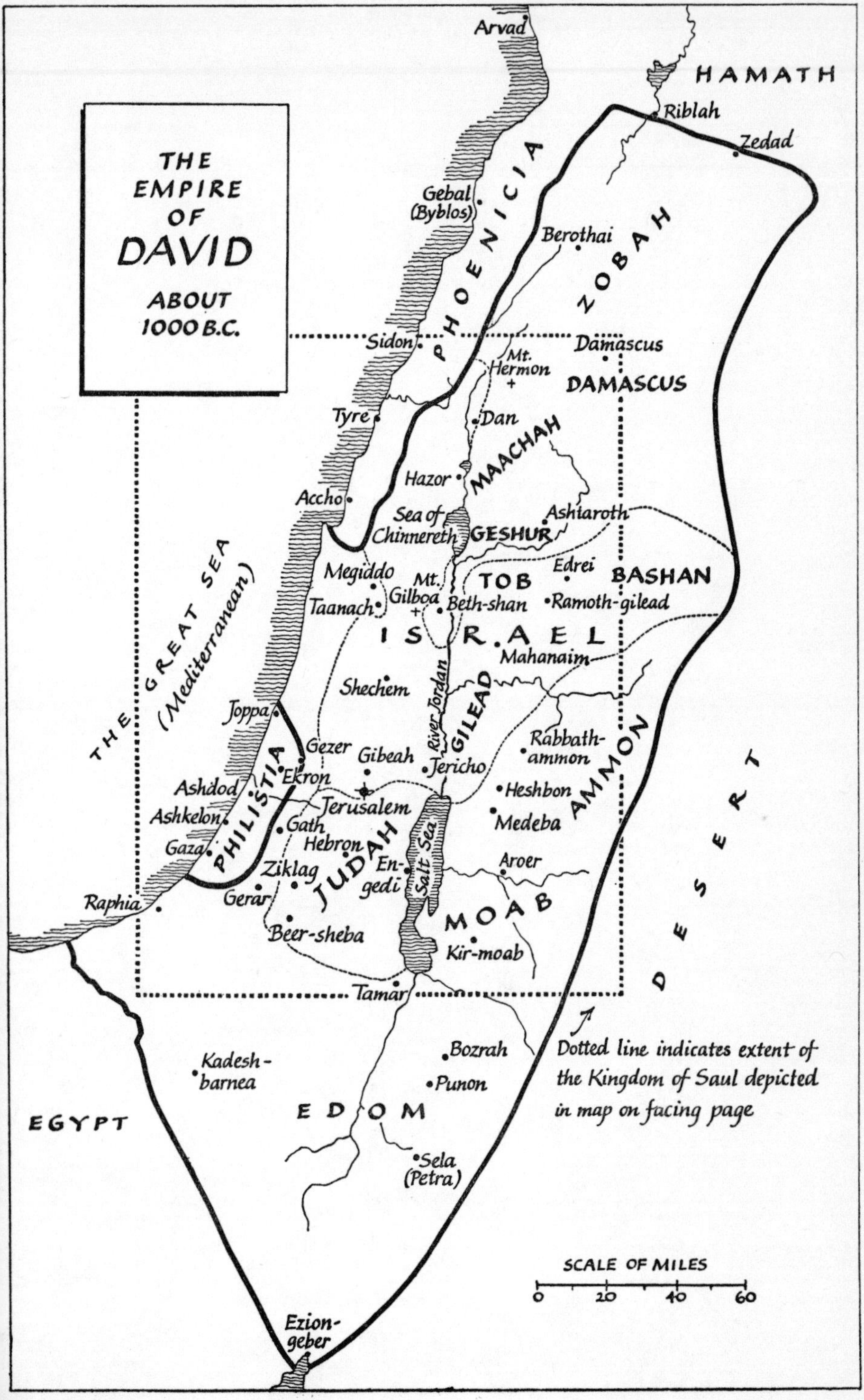
THE EMPIRE OF DAVID
ABOUT 1000 B.C.
HAMATH
Arvad
Riblah
Zedad
PHOENICIA
Gebal (Byblos)
Berothai
ZOBAH
Sidon
Damascus
Mt. Hermon
DAMASCUS
Tyre
Dan
MAACHAH
Hazor
Accho
Sea of Chinnereth
GESHUR
Ashtaroth
THE GREAT SEA (Mediterranean)
Megiddo
Mt. Gilboa
TOB
Edrei
BASHAN
Taanach
Beth-shan
Ramoth-gilead
ISRAEL
Mahanaim
Shechem
River Jordan
GILEAD
Joppa
Gezer
Gibeah
Jericho
Rabbath-ammon
AMMON
Ekron
PHILISTIA
Ashdod
Ashkelon
Jerusalem
Heshbon
Medeba
Gath
Hebron
Gaza
JUDAH
Salt Sea
En-gedi
Aroer
Ziklag
Gerar
Raphia
MOAB
Beer-sheba
Kir-moab
DESERT
Tamar
Bozrah
Kadesh-barnea
Punon
EGYPT
EDOM
Dotted line indicates extent of the Kingdom of Saul depicted in map on facing page
Sela (Petra)
SCALE OF MILES
0 20 40 60
Ezion-geber

I.

THE VALLEY OF ELAH

"And Saul and the men of Israel were gathered together, and pitched by the valley of Elah, and set the battle in array against the Philistines." I SAMUEL 17:2

CHAPTER 1

"And Obed begat Jesse, and Jesse begat David."
RUTH 4:22

FOR MORE THAN an hour David had patiently followed the bloody trail left by the jackal and its prey. Dawn was just breaking, and the hills around Bethlehem were shrouded with early morning mist. Ordinarily, David loved this time of day, when the fog and the half-light created a mystical world, a perfect backdrop for the exciting battles and hunts he dreamed of as he watched over the flock. But the jackal he had glimpsed a short while ago was no creature of his imagination. The shepherds of Bethlehem had been hunting the hoary old plunderer for years. An ever-present threat to both shepherd and flock, it was an enemy to be destroyed ruthlessly. This morning David had seen it carry off a lamb, and he was determined to hunt it down.

Already tall for his age, David was lithe and wiry, his well-shaped head crowned by a mass of dark curls, his eyes clear and bright. He held his sling loosely, and the round stone forming its missile was already settled in the pocket that fitted the palm of his left hand. The boy's long fingers were graceful and flexible from many hours of plucking the strings of the *kinnar*, a lyre or harp much favored by the Israelites.

For more workaday purposes, such as summoning the sheep, David used the shepherd's pipe, fashioned from the hollow papyrus reeds that grew on the banks of streams and in low, marshy areas. Or he might employ the *challil,* with which he was also adept. Made from a block of wood carved to fit the hand and hollowed out, it sounded soft and pleasant when the musician blew upon it.

David leaped lightly from rock to rock, his eyes ever alert for the telltale smears of blood that showed where the jackal had dragged its victim. Although he had to be careful not to touch the bloodstains with his foot, for blood was a source of defilement and must be strictly avoided, he was certain that he was moving faster than the jackal, which would have to drag its victim; for the weight of even a young lamb was more than the old veteran raider could carry in its mouth.

David did not worry about what his father Jesse would say when he reported another loss. He had always been careful in shepherding the flock and lost fewer lambs than almost any of the shepherds in that area. Besides, jackals were a hazard the shepherds of Bethlehem could well appreciate; they were as much to be feared as those human jackals, the Philistines, who prowled the area in marauding bands, falling upon whatever households or villages they could find that had been left defenseless.

Since the prophet Samuel had anointed Saul, the son of Kish, some years before as king of both the northern and southern tribes at Gilgal, near the Jordan River, the Israelites had freed themselves to a degree from the Philistine confederation of five cities, Gath, Ekron, Ashkelon, Ashdod, and Gaza, which had held them under tribute. Nevertheless, a Philistine garrison remained at Bethlehem, as well as at Beth-shan in the north, and at Michmash and Geba. In these cities the *mesibim* collected the taxes which the proud sons of Israel hated to pay as tribute to a foreign overlord.

The old sanctuary at Shiloh had been destroyed by the Philistines and, though the prophet Samuel dwelt at Ramah not far away, there was now no place to which all of Israel could look as the earthly dwelling place of their God, Yahweh. David was too young to remember the days when, once a year at the time of the vintage, every family in Israel hoped to make the journey to Shiloh to celebrate with a great feast of thanksgiving another harvest from the vineyards and fields that dotted the hillsides. But many long nights he had sat by the hearth and listened as his wizened old grandfather Obed recited in a quavering voice the thrilling stories of Israel's past.

Those had been the days of the *shophetim* or judges, when tribe often fought against tribe; only when a great leader arose did the whole people join forces long enough to throw off their oppressors. Though fiercely independent, the men of Israel had finally come to see that only by joining forces for their common defense could they survive in a land largely controlled by the Philistines. By then, however, the Philistines had forbidden them to work in iron; no smiths were allowed in the land except the Kenites to the south, who had been smelters of copper and brass since the time of Moses.

David's father, Jesse, was one of the elders of Judah who had chosen Saul to be king, first over the southern tribes, and later over all of Israel. The boy had listened, spellbound, as his father told of the ceremonies at Mizpeh and Gilgal when Saul had been crowned, and the glorious victories over the Philistines by which the Son of Kish had earned the adoration of Israel and become one of its greatest heroes. To David, Saul was even greater than Gideon who, with three hundred hand-picked men, had routed the Midianites during a night attack in the Vale of Jezreel, several days' journey to the north. Nor did the youth trouble himself, as did his elders, with misgivings about the king's failure to weld the quarreling tribes into a single powerful nation.

As David neared the top of one of the highest hills, the going became much rougher. Jagged gray rocks dominated the landscape now; dark spots among the boulders marked the shallow caves where both human and animal marauders often found hiding places.

David's left hand tightened upon the sling, setting the round stone firmly in the pocket of the weapon. He had been taught its use by a Benjaminite who had served his father as a shepherd, the men of Benjamin being the most skilled of all the tribes in handling the sling. During the long hours of watching over the flock, when he was not singing to the music of the harp or dreaming, as boys do, of battles in which he was the champion, David had perfected his skill with the weapon of the shepherds. Now he could strike a target more than a hundred cubits away with rarely a miss and guide the sheep to and from the pastures by casting stones to either side of them.

A low warning growl made David stop in his tracks, every sinew of his body tense and waiting. The odor of the jackal's lair came to his nostrils now, and he crept forward, the fingers of his right hand holding the cords of the sling tightly. Along with the jackal's stench, he could detect the sickly sweet smell of blood and freshly torn flesh from the lamb.

Rounding a jutting cliff, David halted as his eyes searched the rocky crevices lining the crest of the hill. To the east, the hills of Moab were a ragged purple line in the morning sun. At the foot of the hills, he could see the lead-blue sheen of the Salt Sea, sometimes called the Dead Sea, separating part of Judah from Moab. From far below, the voices of women working in the vineyards and gardens that lined the hillsides floated up to his ears. But when he reached the very top of the hill, there was no sound except the gentle rush of the wind and the flow of breath through his own nostrils.

Then the warning growl sounded again, a deep menacing rumble. David saw the spot from which it came—a crevice in the rocks that marked the entrance to the animal's lair. He felt a rising excitement, a throbbing beat which he recognized as that of his own pulse in his ears. Though he had hunted the jackal more than once, he had never before identified its lair. Now that he had found it, the battle lines were drawn; there could be no retreat.

Without taking his gaze from the dark shadow marking the inner recess of the jackal's den, David stooped to pick up a pebble; he tossed it with a circle-swing of his arm toward the cave. The stone disappeared into the crevice, and a sharp growl told him it had struck its mark. With his eyes still fixed on the opening of the cave, he picked up another stone and threw it into the crevice. The growl of the jackal was louder now and he saw a sudden movement in the shadows as if it were tensing itself to spring. At the third stone, the raging animal, as he had hoped, came bounding from the cave to attack the human who had dared to track it to its den.

David had been waiting eagerly for just this to happen, but the size of the jackal, the bared fangs, and the blood-flecked gray muzzle startled him. For an instant he stood immobile, frozen in his tracks by a sudden rush of fear. The marauder was halfway across the rock-littered space between them before he was finally able to shake off his paralysis and get his sling into position.

Once, twice, David whirred the sling in a circle, then snapped it with a crack as the stone left the pocket. There would be no time to place another missile in the sling. With lightning speed he dropped the weapon and reached for the long knife at his belt. Though made of bronze—for the Philistines destroyed all weapons of iron found upon their Israelite subjects, and killed the owners of such weapons as well—the knife was honed to such a sharpness that David could have shaved himself with it, had the soft down upon his cheeks acquired the stiffness of a man's beard.

Knife in hand, David conquered the almost overpowering impulse to flee, and set himself to meet the slashing attack of the jackal. But the knife proved to be unnecessary. Driven by the power of the youth's strong arm and the tremendous momentum imparted to it by the leverage of the sling, the stone had struck the animal directly between the eyes. As the jackal charged, every muscle in its body suddenly went limp, and it fell to the rocky floor almost at David's feet. In fact, he needed only to take one step forward and slash the animal's throat with the knife.

Jubilant, he leaped back to avoid the spout of warm red blood that gushed from the wound, and gave a wild shout of triumph. This was a feat of which a man could boast for the rest of his life, a story to be told around campfires for many years. He felt a tremendous sense of power flow through him and shouted aloud once again, as if to let all the world know that, in destroying the jackal which the shepherds of Bethlehem had hunted vainly for many years, he had crossed the threshold between boyhood and manhood.

Physically David was still a boy. The down on his cheeks was a year or more away from becoming a man's beard. His body was lanky and his legs a little long in proportion to the torso, giving him the awkward grace of a stripling. But his heart had been put through the tempering fires of sudden danger and paralyzing fear, and had come out stronger than before, like iron from the furnace of a smith. Though still a youth, he had met a man's enemy and defeated it; no one could wrest from him the glory of that feat.

Once again he shouted jubilantly and, as a song was never far from his lips, the surging elation within him found natural expression in the strains of a poem of triumph, a song needing only the strings of the harp that he had left behind him where the sheep were grazing to become a paean of victory and praise for God:

"Blessed be the Lord, my strength,
Who trains my hands for war,
And my fingers for battle;
He is my rock and fortress,
My stronghold and my deliverer.
He is my shield and in him I take refuge.

Bow the heavens, O Lord, and come down!
Touch the mountains that they smoke!
Flash forth the lightning and scatter them,
Send out thy arrows and rout them!
Stretch forth thine hand from on high.

I will sing a new song to thee, O God;
Upon a ten-string harp, I will play to thee,
Who gives victory to kings,
Who rescues David, his servant.
Happy the people to whom such blessings fall!
Happy the people whose God is the Lord!"

CHAPTER 2

"I will send thee to Jesse the Bethlehemite: for I have provided me a king among his sons."

I SAMUEL 16:1

THE CARCASS of the jackal was too heavy to drag down the mountainside, but David had no intention of descending without some proof of his feat. He knew his brothers would never accept his own account of the event; more than once they had accused him of lying, because his fluency with words sometimes led him to describe events with more freedom of expression than had been given to them. With his bronze knife, he hacked off the head and forepaws of the animal, very much as warriors of that day were accustomed to cut off the heads and the hands of their victims as easily carried proof of their prowess. Bearing these, he ran joyfully down the hillside, already rehearsing in his mind the story of the chase and kill he would tell to his household that night.

As he approached the meadow where the sheep were grazing, David caught sight of his elder brother, Eliab. Wanting to surprise Eliab with his feat, he hid the head and the paws of the wolf behind his back as he approached.

"A fine shepherd you are!" Eliab growled when David was within earshot. "Is this the way you guard the flock?"

"A jackal came and stole one of the lambs," David explained. "I went in search of it."

"Was it the same one that stole a lamb several weeks ago, the fellow with the gray muzzle?"

"Yes."

"The old ones are dangerous if you corner them. We will organize a hunt before I go back to the army and drive him out of the rocks so we can kill him."

"You need not trouble yourself about the jackal." David produced the head and the forepaws of the animal. "I tracked him to his lair and made him come out so I could kill him."

Eliab stared at the blood upon David's knife. "With a bronze knife?"

"I struck him between the eyes with a stone," David explained, holding up the sling. "When he fell to the ground, I cut his throat."

"It was a dangerous task. You should never have attempted it alone."

"There was only one wolf," David said with a shrug. "I have heard you tell more than once how you fought several Philistines at the same time and conquered them all."

"That is different. I am a soldier and trained in the use of arms while you—" Eliab stopped and looked at David more closely. "You have grown a great deal since I saw you last," he admitted. "In fact, you have almost the tallness of a man, if not quite his breadth through the shoulders."

"I will have that, too," David said confidently. "One day I will be as strong as you are."

"If the Lord wills," Eliab agreed. "Father wants you back at the house. I will stay with the flock until you return."

David was not loath to go home for he was anxious to display his trophies. Yet he could think of no reason at the moment for such a summons during the middle of the day.

"Why am I being sent for?" he asked.

"I don't know," Eliab told him. "The prophet Samuel is there; perhaps he wants you to sing songs for him."

David picked up the lyre from the rock where he had left it. "I will come back as soon as I can," he promised.

"See that you do," Eliab said. "It is not fitting that a warrior of Saul's army should tend sheep upon the hillside."

Bethlehem meant "House of Bread," a name the town had borne since the earliest days because of the fertility of the land surrounding it; the region was a pleasant and prosperous one where few lacked enough to eat or drink. Built upon two hilltops with a saddle or ridge between, the town stood almost as high as the Jebusite stronghold of Jerusalem, which was about a two-hour walk to the north. On the north and south, the hills upon which Bethlehem stood were quite steep, but to the east the slopes leveled off to a plain. Here there were rich fields of grain and verdant pastures for the flocks, as well as terraced vineyards.

Although Bethlehem was not a heavily fortified town, its site on a wedge-shaped bed of rock gave it something of a defensive position: during the several centuries that the Hebrews had been in Canaan and in possession of most of the region, the inhabitants of Jerusalem had not troubled them here. The Bethlehemites suffered only from the Philistines to the west, who used the valleys that cut through the central highlands of Judah as highways for incursions into the inland areas and the fertile lands of the Jordan Valley.

As he hurried home, David paused here and there to tell friends the story of his conquest of the jackal. And if the tale grew a little in the telling, it was no more than was natural for a boy of his age. Outside the gate he came upon three of his best friends and companions, his cousins Joab, Abishai, and Asahel, with whom he had grown up, gone to school, and played at games of war. David's quick intelligence had made fast work of lessons, but Joab's broad shoulders and stocky frame enabled him to triumph at games of strength, while the swift feet of Asahel usually brought him in first in a race.

By the well at the gate of the city, whose waters the youth remembered as being sweeter than any other when he returned from driving the flocks to the grassy uplands or from playing at war with his fellows, a group of girls had paused to gossip. When they saw David they whispered and nudged each other, admiring his lithe grace. But when he brought the head and forepaws of the wolf from behind his back, they ran screaming and giggling ahead of him, bringing others out to discover the cause of the excitement and admire the prowess of the hunter.

Running lightly through the narrow streets, humming the victory song he had just composed, David climbed the slope to where his father's house stood in the highest area of the town. Unlike more temporary structures, built of sun-baked brick, which were subject to erosion by the spring rains and sometimes collapsed upon the occupants, the house of Jesse was constructed of uncut field stones set in mortar. Like his father, Obed, and his grandfather, Boaz, Jesse was a man of some substance. His eight fine sons, of whom David was the youngest, were the treasures of his old age.

The house of Jesse was built in two stories, with a stairway of stone blocks leading up the outside wall to the roof. Constructed from beams of cedar covered with planking and then overlaid with tiles, the roof was sturdy, and here the family often slept in summer, as was local custom. The houses in this area were set close together and often had common walls, so David could visit his friends in the long summer twilight by stepping from rooftop to rooftop, traveling what was popularly known as the "Road of the Roofs."

The main part of the house surrounded an open courtyard, shaded by the spreading branches of a huge terebinth tree. To one side was the stone-lined and plastered cistern into which water from the roof poured during the rainy seasons. At other times, it was filled from the large urns or ollas which David's sisters and the serving-women carried each morning to the well beside the gate.

Jesse was sitting upon a bench beneath the terebinth tree that shaded the courtyard; beside him was a tall man with the flowing gray beard and hair of a Nazarite, as those who dedicated themselves entirely to the service of God were called. The guest was not luxuriously dressed; in fact, his robe was of poorer stuff than that of his host, and his sandals of rough leather were worn from much walking. Yet in spite of his outward appearance, David saw at once that here was a man of power and fierce pride; it shone from his deep-set eyes and was again emphasized in the craggy outlines of his face.

All of Israel knew the story of the prophet Samuel; in the course of time it had become almost a legend. His mother, so the story ran, sad because the Lord had not blessed her with a child, had prayed at the ancient shrine of Shiloh, long since destroyed by the Philistines, that she be given a man-child. In return for the gift, she promised that the boy would be dedicated from his birth to the service of the Lord.

Samuel had served the old High Priest Eli at the shrine of Shiloh during his boyhood years, in fulfillment of his mother's promise. There, as he rested one night from his task of serving before the altar, a voice had spoken to him, calling him to the service of God. As spokesman for the Lord in Israel, Samuel had remained steadfast even during the troubled times when the Philistines had captured the Ark of the Covenant, symbol of God's own presence. For desecrating the sacred symbol of Israel's faith, the Philistines were so harassed by plague and pestilence that they sent it from their territory, first to Beth-shemesh and later to Kirjath-jearim, where it had remained. Under Samuel's guidance as both prophet and judge, the Israelites had driven the Philistines from a good position in the central highlands and reclaimed the cities taken from them by the enemy.

Only when Samuel became old, and his sons, Joel and Abiah, had proved themselves unfaithful as judges, had the people reluctantly faced the fact that, with the death of the old prophet, they would no longer have a leader. In a congregation assembled at Marah, they had begged Samuel to select a king who would be leader of all the people, as Samuel himself had been when younger. And with many misgivings lest naming a temporal leader rather than a prophet of God would bring misery upon the people, Samuel had anointed as king a Benjaminite, Saul the Son of Kish.

It had seemed a wise choice at the time, for Saul was tall, handsome, and strong, his bearing regal in every way. Moreover, since he came from one of the smallest, yet most warlike, of the tribes, no charge of favoring one over the other because of wealth or influence could be made. And yet it was no secret that, from the first, discord had flared between Samuel and Saul.

Saul was a man of action, a soldier first and a priest afterward, while Samuel sought to keep the people in the old ways when the voice of God alone had guided them. Lately, the chasm between the king and the man who had chosen him had steadily widened, with Samuel remaining at his old home in Ramah while Saul often sulked in his palace at Gibeah, north of Jerusalem, gripped by the black moods of depression and melancholy that were his greatest weakness.

"You were overlong in coming, David," Jesse said, as the youth crossed the courtyard to where the two older men were sitting. "It is not courteous to keep a guest waiting."

"I was stalking a jackal that had stolen a lamb," David explained, bowing courteously to the guest.

"Did you find it?" Samuel's voice was deep, as David had always imagined the voice of God himself would sound, if the Lord were one day to speak to him from a burning bush as he had spoken to Moses on Mount Sinai.

"Yes, my lord Samuel." David took the head and the forepaws of the animal from behind his back. "I tracked him to his lair and killed him. Here is the proof."

"By the tents of Israel!" Jesse exclaimed. "That is a feat of some importance! We have been trying to kill that fellow for a long time."

David felt a warm sense of pride at his father's words of praise; as the youngest of eight boys, it sometimes seemed that he was at the foot of the ladder with little chance of climbing up.

"Is this your youngest son?" Samuel asked of Jesse.

"Yes. You have seen all the others."

"Come closer, my boy," the old prophet ordered. "Let me see you more clearly."

David approached and stood facing the old man. He could not help wondering why Samuel was subjecting him to such a close scrutiny. In fact, under the prophet's probing gaze, he had the strange feeling that his very soul was being turned and examined and his innermost thoughts made known. For a long moment there was silence; then Samuel spoke.

"This is he whom the Lord has chosen," he said. "Call in your family, Jesse, and I will anoint him."

The rest of the family gathered around quickly while David, still not sure what was happening, stood before the old prophet. When all were in the courtyard except Eliab, who was minding the sheep, Samuel took from his robe a small horn filled with oil and, removing the stopper, tilted the container above David's head, letting the contents pour out upon the youth's mass of dark curls.

"I anoint thee, my son David, in the name of the Most High," Samuel said, repeating the sacred ritual of selection for a special purpose. "May the spirit of the Lord be with you always, to guide and protect you in all of your endeavors. And may you serve only the Most High forever."

The ceremony of anointing with oil was usually carried out at some significant high point in a man's life, so David naturally concluded that in this case it marked his emergence from boyhood into the status of young manhood. Only later was he to realize its true significance.

CHAPTER 3

"The Spirit of the Lord departed from Saul, and an evil spirit from the Lord troubled him."
I SAMUEL 16:14

THE SOUL OF Israel's king was deeply troubled, but the reason lay where he was unwilling to look.

Being a practical man, Saul told himself there was no point in believing the rumors, carefully concealed from him and therefore all the more likely to reach his ears, that the prophet Samuel had already anointed another as King of Israel. But deep in his heart, he remembered the circumstances under which Samuel had chosen him; particularly, how the fact that he had been named as the future king was kept from the people until he had performed the great military feat of relieving the besieged city of Jabesh-gilead and had been hailed as a hero.

With the army behind him and with Israel safe, at least for the time being, from the depredations of the Philistine kings, Saul could take comfort in the fact that he was a hundred times stronger than Samuel could possibly be. In fact, his spies in Ramah assured him that the old prophet was growing steadily more feeble with the passage of the years and hardly ever ventured out, except occasionally to visit such old friends as Jesse of Bethlehem.

If it came to an actual contest between him and Samuel, Saul was sure that the people would be overwhelmingly on his side. Some time earlier he had gained a significant victory over the

Amalekites and taken their king, Agag, as a prisoner to be ransomed. The Amalekites had thwarted the children of Israel when they had sought to enter Canaan from the south during their escape from Egypt, forcing them to take a long and arduous journey to the east. But that had been centuries ago, and neither Saul nor the people could see why the curse of *herem*, under which every living thing taken from a vanquished enemy must be destroyed, along with his possessions, should be invoked as in the time of Joshua. It seemed much more sensible to sacrifice the enemy's cattle in a great feast of victory and use the ransom paid for King Agag to build stronger fortifications for Saul's capital at Gibeah.

"Blessed be ye of the Lord," Saul had greeted Samuel jubilantly when the prophet appeared at Gilgal where the king had decreed a great celebration in honor of the victory over the Amalekites. "I have performed the commandment of the Lord."

But Samuel was not to be put off so easily. "What does this bleating of sheep mean, then?" he demanded sternly. "And the lowing of oxen that I hear?"

Too late Saul remembered the curse that God had put upon the Amalekites and his own obligation as the Lord's Anointed to carry it out. In the excitement of battle, the glory of victory, and the satisfaction of capturing a king whose ransom would be great, he had conveniently forgotten.

"They have brought the sheep and oxen to sacrifice to the Lord, thy God," he said lamely.

To the old prophet, whose own hands had crowned Saul as king, the words betrayed a grave weakness. Samuel had won his own victories by serving the Lord in everything, judging the people wisely and sending them into battle with the assurance that God would give them victory. To Saul, however, the Lord of Hosts was not a personal god, guiding his every action, but the god of Samuel, a vengeful, often seemingly irascible deity with whom he had never felt the true communion that would have let him rule as the dispenser of divine will to his people.

"Does the Lord have as great delight in burnt offerings and sacrifices as in obedience to his voice?" Samuel demanded. "To obey is better than to sacrifice, and to hearken, better than to eat the fat of rams. For rebellion is like the sin of witchcraft and stubbornness as iniquity and idolatry. Since you have rejected the word of the Lord, he has also rejected you from being king."

The words penetrated even Saul's anger at the old prophet for treating him in front of the people as if he were only a boy to be reprimanded. "I have sinned in transgressing the commandment of the Lord and your word," he confessed. "But it was because I feared the people and obeyed their voice. Pardon my sin, I pray you, and turn again with me that I may worship the Lord."

"The Lord has rent the Kingdom of Israel from you this day and has given it to a neighbor of yours who is better than you," Samuel repeated. "He is the strength of Israel and he will not lie nor repent."

Saul made one last attempt to patch up the quarrel, knowing the effect that news of it would have upon the nation and upon his army. "I have sinned," he said. "Yet honor me now before the elders of the people and before the people themselves. And turn again with me that I may worship the Lord."

Samuel felt only pity now for the man who had failed both him and God, as he had feared would be the case when, long ago, he had yielded to the desires of the people and crowned a national hero as king. He could not help Saul now, Samuel knew; the voice of the Lord had made it abundantly clear that the Son of Kish had utterly failed in his sight as a leader of the people. But God had not decreed that Israel itself should be destroyed and, for the time being at least, it had seemed expedient to Samuel for Saul to continue at the head of the nation. There he could at least inspire their fervor in battle against their traditional enemies, who were reported to be massing for still another attack.

"I will worship with you," Samuel told the penitent king finally. "Let us go out together."

There at the ancient shrine of Gilgal, upon the sacred altar made of twelve stones taken from the dry bed of the Jordan after the children of Israel led by Joshua had crossed over, Samuel performed the sacrifices and worshiped with Saul for the last time. But he had not finished punishing Saul; when the ceremony was finished, Samuel ordered Agag brought before him.

The king of the Amalekites came in chains, yet there was no

fear in his bearing; he knew how much Saul wanted the ransom his people would pay for his return. But when he saw Samuel, his confidence began to desert him, for the two had been enemies for many years and he knew the prophet to be stern and unrelenting.

"Surely the bitterness of our past quarrels is over," he said ingratiatingly, but found no answering warmth in Samuel.

"As your sword has made women childless, so shall your mother be childless among women," the old prophet told him sternly. Turning, he drew from its scabbard Saul's great iron sword, relic of a previous victory over the Philistines and, swinging the weapon in his hands, hewed off the head of the Amalekite king at one stroke.

Sulking in his chamber at Gibeah later, Saul found it easy to blame Samuel, rather than himself, for all his troubles. Had the prophet not come to Gilgal that day, the people would have gorged themselves upon the flesh of the Amalekite cattle. Their money pouches would likewise have been heavy with Amalekite gold, and a sizeable fortune in jewelry could have been traded to the caravan owners who passed every day on the highway between the nearby fords of the Jordan and the cities of the seacoast. What troubled him most, however, was the knowledge that he had failed Israel as a king.

Vaguely Saul sensed that a true leader should be more than just a warrior who could inspire them to battle. The periods between wars with the Philistines had grown longer and longer as his own military strength developed and his enemies grew more wary of his power. In such times of peace, the nation needed a leader who embodied an inspiration and an ideal which could hold them together as securely as did the excitement of battle in time of war. Such a man, he suspected now, must take on many attributes of a god, attributes he could not hope to gain except through divine favor.

Had he paused to examine the ancient records, Saul would have discovered that time and time again God had given Israel victory or defeat, depending upon whether or not the people and their leaders had obeyed him or had gone astray by following the false gods of Canaan and Philistia. More than once in Israel's history, an oppressor had been allowed to enslave the people in order to bring them back to a realization of their obligation to the deity who had spoken to Moses from the burning bush and had led them on the long journey out of subjection in Egypt.

As he sought now to discover just when his path and that of Samuel had first diverged sharply, Saul realized that it must have been on an occasion not long after his being anointed as king. He had waited then at Gilgal for Samuel to appear and perform the sacrifices, invoking the Lord's favor in a battle to be fought soon with the Philistines. But Samuel had been late in arriving, and Saul had grown impatient. Finally, afraid that his armies would be whittled down by the daily increasing defections, he had performed the sacrifices himself. It had seemed the only sensible thing to do under the circumstances, but now Saul could not escape the conviction that somehow he had failed in a crucial test, a test which would decide whether or not he was a king whose line was worthy to rule the nation in the years to come.

Suddenly oppressed beyond endurance by the weight of his thoughts and his guilt, Saul strode to the door of his chamber and threw it open. The night breeze cooled his flushed face somewhat, for the fortress stood on a crest almost as high as that of Jerusalem a short distance to the south, and the wind freshened rather sharply at sundown. Much of the land he ruled was visible from this height, and as he looked upon it, Saul could tell himself, in justification of his stewardship, that from the wilderness of Shur in the desert waste of the Negeb to the south, as far north as the new land wrested by the sons of Dan for themselves where the Jordan burst from the earth in a great spring beyond the lovely lake called Chinnereth, no Israelite was enslaved by his enemies. Most of this had been accomplished by armies under his own leadership, which made it all the more difficult to accept the fact that his son Jonathan, the bravest warrior in all of Israel, would never sit upon his father's throne, because Saul himself had not been able to be at one and the same time both prophet to understand the will of God, and soldier to fight in battle.

A violent anger began to swell deep within Saul, anger at Samuel, at his own fate, and even at God. Lifting his eyes to the star-studded canopy of the heavens, he shouted a curse of defiance over and over again until the courtyard of the palace rang with the sound of his rantings, and soldiers came tumbling from their quarters, hurriedly girding on armor and weapons as they ran. But they saw only the king standing upon the balcony outside the door of his chamber, shouting an angry challenge to the skies. And with a sense of foreboding, because they could no longer deny that their ruler was a madman, they crept silently back to their sleeping quarters.

Only Saul's personal servant, Jethro, dared approach his master during one of his rages. The two had been together on that day long ago when they had come to the house of Samuel at Ramah while searching for some mules which had escaped from the pasture, and the prophet had anointed Saul as King of Israel. Jethro had served Saul well since then, and he did not desert the king now in his hour of deepest melancholy and rebellion.

"An evil spirit from God troubles you, my lord," the servant said soothingly. "Command your servants to find a man who is a cunning player upon the harp. Then, when the evil spirit is upon you, he shall play and you shall be well."

"Find me such a man and bring him to me," Saul ordered.

"I have seen a son of Jesse, the Bethlehemite, who is cunning in playing as well as having a comely appearance."

"What is his name?"

"He is called David, my lord. His brothers are among the soldiers and he sometimes visits them."

"Dispatch a message to Jesse," Saul directed. "Tell him to send me David, his son."

"It shall be done, my lord," Jethro said, not knowing that he was working out the pattern of God's will which had begun to be traced that day when Samuel had visited Bethlehem and had anointed the youngest son of Jesse in the courtyard.

CHAPTER 4

"And Jesse took an ass laden with bread, and a bottle of wine, and a kid, and sent them by David his son unto Saul." I SAMUEL 16:20

David was in the hills with the sheep when word came to him that King Saul demanded his presence at Gibeah. The few occasions when he had visited the army camp at Gibeah, carrying food, clothing, and money to his brothers, had been exciting times, and as he ran down the hillside toward Bethlehem, he was dreaming of the day when he, too, would gird himself with armor and take up the javelin and spear, the sword of bronze, the bow and quiver and bronze-tipped arrows, the bronze helmet and round shield that made up the armament of the soldiers of Israel in the field.

David had often tried his brothers' weapons when they were at home between campaigns against the Philistines, the Amalekites, or the Ammonites who lived in the mountainous districts to the east across the Jordan. He was slenderer than his brothers, however, and unaccustomed to the use of their weapons, so when they returned to camp, he had taken up once again the sling with which he was as skilled as any of the "Sons of Benjamin," as that tribe was called, the greatest marksmen with that weapon in all of Israel.

David was growing fast, however, and as he hurried home now, in answer to his father's summons, he dared to hope the call to

Saul's city of Gibeah meant that he, like his elder brothers, would now go into training to become a warrior in the army. With his vivid imagination, he had no difficulty picturing himself leading troops upon the field of battle or perhaps riding in a chariot, as King Saul sometimes did, all the while striking great blows against the enemy with his sword.

Jesse met his youngest son in the courtyard, where the servants were already loading a pack mule with freshly baked loaves of bread, a bottle of wine, and a tender young kid, its hooves securely tied together so that it could not escape.

"The mule is almost ready," Jesse told him. "You can leave at once."

"I must get my weapons," David said. "They are all polished and sharpened."

"You will need no weapons except your sling to drive away jackals or bears on the way to Gibeah. And perhaps your knife."

"But King Saul has sent for me to become a soldier in the army!"

"Saul needs only the sweet music you coax from the harp and the pipes," Jesse explained. "And the songs you sing."

"A singer of songs!" David exclaimed in disgust. "What honor can come from that?"

"Much, if you please the king. They say Saul is troubled by an evil spirit and sometimes does not seem to know what he is doing. I knew his servant Jethro of old, and once, when Jethro was here, he heard you sing. He must have told the king about you, for he sent word that he hoped you could soothe Saul's troubled spirits with your playing and singing."

Slowly, almost with dislike, David picked up the harp. It was a beautiful instrument, made of sandalwood which he had purchased with his own money. The sounding board was highly polished, the strings had been twisted from gut and allowed to dry, the horns attached to the sounding board tipped with a paper-thin inlay of gold. There was not another harp quite like it in all of Bethlehem, and until now it had been among David's proudest possessions. Little pleasure showed in the young man's face, however, as he placed it now among the few things he would carry to Gibeah. His heart had been set on acting quite another role, for, in spite of his skill with musical instruments and in composing songs, David was an active and eager youth, able to hold his own even with sturdy playmates like Joab and Abishai in the martial games that the youths of the village liked to play.

"If you please the king, he might make you his armorbearer," Jesse suggested, hoping to ease some of David's disappointment. "Then you would have a chance to practice with the weapons of war."

David's mobile face brightened a little. "Surely the king will not want me to sing all the time," he agreed. "Eliab is with the army; he can teach me to use the weapons of war." And happy now at the prospect, he left for Gibeah, leading the pack mule.

Upon a hill north of Jerusalem, from which he could look down upon that city, David paused to let the pack mule rest. Situated on several hills, with a broad and heavily battlemented wall and several springs to furnish water, Jerusalem appeared from that distance to be impregnable. David knew Saul had considered attacking the city more than once, but had given up the idea when it became evident that storming the thick walls would be nothing less than suicide for the attackers. Nevertheless, he remembered, Joshua had captured more than one Canaanite stronghold by stealth, and David considered now how such a move might be used against Jerusalem.

A large spring bubbled from beneath the edge of the wall, and David realized, from many hours of exploring the caves in the hills outside Bethlehem, that such springs sometimes marked the opening of caverns in the rocky base of the hills themselves. But he could see no sign of any such opening so far as Jerusalem was concerned and, finally tiring of a fruitless fancy, turned his eyes eastward to where the deep slate-blue of the Salt Sea merged with the pinkish-brown of the mountains in the Land of Moab beyond it. In the afternoon sunlight, the shadings of color upon the mountains were fascinating to one whose temperament included a natural love of beauty. Between where David stood and Moab the Jordan curved in a lazy arc, looking like a vast necklace with its jewels of emerald green studding the fertile banks, where, even in winter, frost almost never came.

Much of Israel's history in this Promised Land of Canaan had taken place within David's present range of vision. To the northeast, his eyes, sharp from watching for marauders such as the jackal he had killed, could make out some of the points where the Israelites had fought long ago to secure the eastern bank of the Jordan before crossing to attack the citadel of Jericho. A slash in the hills far away could only be the bed washed out by the turbulent stream of the Jabbok upon whose banks Jacob had wrestled all night with the angel. Beyond it the hills of Gilead shut away the battlements of the city of Jabesh, where Saul had first gained glory as the deliverer of Israel. David's vivid imagination had no difficulty in re-creating that tense battle and the great victory which had led the people to name Saul their king.

In the near foreground, the eastern flank of Judah's hill country descended to the deep cleft of the Jordan Valley, with the fertile oasis of Jericho hidden by the yellow hills of the forbidding mountain called Quarantaria towering over the city. From where he stood he could look almost directly down into a secluded miniature valley among these hills where a small village lay. Hedges of prickly pear set off garden patches and fields, and the white and red blossoms of the almond trees alternated with the silvery-stippled hues of the olive and the more intense green of the carob that grew here and there in dense clusters.

Remembering, somewhat belatedly, that night usually brought a sharp drop in temperature at this elevation, David tightened the lead-rope of the animal and began to descend from the elevation upon which he had been standing, following a trail which led back to the main road between Jerusalem and Gibeah, a little north of the former city. Here and there black goats, grazing upon patches of grass along the way, snorted at the sight of the tiny caravan and went bounding off down the hillside. David did not let himself be distracted, however, but held tightly to the lead-rope lest the pack mule shy away, for a misstep here could mean a broken bone for man as well as beast, a disaster in either case.

On a rounded elevation where the village of Anathoth stood, David paused again to survey the territory allotted to the tribe of Benjamin, of which Saul was the most distinguished member. Impressive among the range of heights for which the territory of Benjamin was noted was Gibeah, where Saul was building a fortress as his center of government. But across a narrow plain from the Benjamite capital rose the commanding height of Mizpeh, at the summit of which Saul had been crowned king of all the tribes, the first ruler in Israel's history after God himself.

At the foot of the slope leading up to Saul's fortress, David paused while the thirsty pack mule drank from a small brook leading away from a spring. Kneeling at the edge of the brook, he himself drank deeply and then got to his feet, dusting off the leaves and small sticks which had clung to his robe, for he wanted to make the best possible appearance when he entered the city of Gibeah. The mule trotted along the banks of the small brook to crop the green grass growing there and David followed it, picking up the lead-rope once more. But when he started to climb the farther bank, he was startled to see a girl standing upon the slope a little above him, studying him curiously.

She appeared to be about fourteen, several years younger than he, and she possessed an oddly fragile sort of beauty. Her kiton, or tunic, was of rich material, and she carried herself with a degree of self-confidence and poise considerably greater than he would have expected in a girl of her age.

"Who are you?" the girl asked.

"My name is David," he answered. "My father, Jesse, is one of the elders of the congregation at Bethlehem."

The girl was not impressed. "Are you going to Gibeah?"

"Yes."

"Then I will walk with you."

David shrugged. "If you like."

The girl ran down the slope and began to caress the ears of the mule. "You are pretty—for a boy," she confided, studying David's face.

"I am not pretty!" David said indignantly, then burst out laughing. The girl joined him and the sound of their merriment filled the small glen in which the spring lay.

"I like you, David," she confided. "Do you like me?"

"I suppose so," he said diffidently. Then, growing bolder: "Yes, I do."

"My name is Michal."

"It is a pretty name. And you are pretty."

The girl seemed to take the compliment as a matter of course; obviously people had told her this many times before. "Why are you going to Gibeah?" she asked.

"To play and sing for King Saul."

He saw her eyes widen with surprise and pleasure. "Would you sing a song for me?" she asked eagerly.

David could think of no particular reason why he should not humor this elfin creature. Besides, he found himself liking her, for she was not at all like his sisters and the girls he knew at Bethlehem. From the pack on the mule's back he took his harp and tuned it quickly. When he touched the strings, a fragile cascade of sound rippled through the glen and the girl Michal clapped her hands and laughed aloud with pleasure. He looked around for something to sing about, and his gaze fell upon the spring, with the tiny brook draining away the water that flowed from it. And like the spring, as it bubbled from the earth, the words suddenly welled up in his mind and he began to sing softly:

"As the hart pants after the water brooks,
So pants my soul after thee,
My soul. . . ."

Michal interrupted the song before he could go on. "I like that part about the hart and the water brook," she cried. "Last week I saw a little fawn here drinking from the brook with its mother. I wanted it as a pet, but it bounded away before I could catch it."

"My cousin Asahel could have caught it for you," David assured her. "He can outrun even a jackal."

Michal's face clouded. "I hate jackals almost as much as I hate the prophet Samuel."

For a moment David was too startled to speak. "Why should you hate Samuel?" he finally managed to ask.

"Because he rebuked my father for performing the sacrifices when Samuel was late in coming and the Philistines were almost upon us."

The incident was well known to David for he had heard his father and Samuel talking of it in Bethlehem. "Is King Saul your father?" he asked.

"Yes." She was suddenly gay once more. "If you are to play and sing for him you must be going to live in the palace. Then we can come to the spring every day to look for the fawn and you can sing more pretty songs to me."

"Michal!" a girl's voice cried sharply. "What are you doing?"

David looked up to see a girl of about his own age, or perhaps a little older, standing on the rocky slope above the spring. She was so beautiful that for a moment she almost took his breath away. Hers was a lush and almost petulant beauty, quite different from the younger girl's elfin grace and delicacy.

Michal hurried up the slope to where the older girl stood. "This is David, Merab!" she cried excitedly. "He has come to sing songs for our father!"

Merab sniffed scornfully. "He looks more like a shepherd to me. Why did you run away? I have been looking everywhere for you."

"You know I always come to the spring," the younger sister protested. "I saw the fawn here not long ago."

"It will be time for the evening meal before we get back home," Merab scolded. "Come along now." She had still given no sign that she had even seen David, except for the sniff of disdain when Michal had spoken his name and the observation that he looked more like a shepherd. Had she not been so breathtakingly lovely, he would have resented her scorn of him, but it was hard to think ill of such a beautiful girl.

As the two sisters turned up the slope, Michal called back to him. "I will look for you in the palace, David," she promised. "And I will be listening to hear you sing."

CHAPTER 5

"And David came to Saul."
I SAMUEL 16:21

THE HILL upon which the small city of Gibeah stood had once been a field of lentils, and orderly rows of these plants still covered the lower part of the slope. The hilltop, however, had been leveled and the walls of the fortress raised upon the site of an older fortification constructed by the Philistines and destroyed by the men of Benjamin when they had taken Gibeah for themselves. The new citadel, occupying the very top of the cone-shaped hill, was small compared to Jerusalem, the entire area encompassing a space of only about sixty by fifty paces.

Though the walls were very roughly built, they were strong and broad, with towers at each corner from which archers and spearmen could rain down weapons upon an invader. The presence of an outer rampart, into which slots had been cut to allow the release of arrows without exposing the defenders too much, also made it possible for the garrison to move rapidly from place to place within the city, using the wall as a road. Saul's palace was actually a part of the fortress, and was built of large stones with a stairway of stone leading to the upper story. From an elevated platform here, the sentries always on duty could examine a wide sweep of the territory occupied by the tribes of Israel and catch sight of an enemy force in time to give ample warning.

When he had brought food to his brothers on his previous visits, David had always stopped upon the lower slopes to survey the army encampment. The soldiers were quartered in the small city that clustered around the citadel like sheep gathered around the shepherd at night for protection against jackals and wolves. The youth's heart was beating rapidly now as he approached the gate of the citadel and was stopped by a soldier of the guards, a man of Judah who knew David from his earlier visits.

"Why does the son of Jesse seek to enter the palace of King Saul?" the soldier asked. "Your brothers are quartered in the city."

"The king sent for me," David said proudly.

"So?" The man was plainly unimpressed. "For what reason?"

"To play and sing so that his troubled spirits may be eased."

"By the tents of Israel!" the guard exclaimed. "That is a worthy feat, if you can accomplish it! The evil spirit has not let go of the king for days; half the servants in the palace bear the marks of his anger."

"In all of Israel no one can play upon the lyre as I can," David dared to boast. "The king heard of my playing and sent for me."

"Enter, then," the guard told him. "You will find his servant Jethro in one of the rooms on the west side of the court."

King Saul's capital and palace, David discovered, though much larger than his own home in Bethlehem, was no more luxurious. He had no difficulty in finding Jethro, as he had been instructed, and gave the servant the gift of wine and bread and the kid that Jesse had sent to the king.

"You will live in the servants' quarters of the palace and eat with us," Jethro informed him. "Sometimes the king awakes from his sleep with the spell of the evil spirit upon him, so you must be ready to play and sing for him at any hour of the day or night."

"Let me stay in the camp of the soldiers outside the wall during the day," David begged. "I want to learn how to use the weapons of war."

"King Saul did not send for you to fight," Jethro said with a shrug. "He has bigger and stronger men for that."

The idea of living and eating with servants was not particularly attractive to David, for his father was one of the elders of Judah, the largest and richest of all the tribes, and his family as noble as any in Israel. He had no choice, however, unless he returned to Bethlehem, and if Saul were as easily angered as the guard at the gate and his own servant had said, such an act of defiance might bring retribution upon himself and his family. Under the circumstances it seemed wise to remain and accept things as they were.

The evening meal consisted of a savory stew and crusts of freshly baked bread, still warm from the oven, which were used to scoop the stew out of the common pot from which the servants ate. There was also goat's milk cooled in the spring that furnished water for the palace, and a rather thin mixture of wine and water.

As yet David had seen no sign of King Saul, Michal, or Merab. "Does the king know I am here?" he asked Jethro when the meal was finished.

"I told him you had arrived and described the gifts you brought," the servant said. "But Saul is in a black mood tonight. I cannot tell what he is liable to do."

"Perhaps I should sing for him to ease his spirit," David suggested.

"His daughters and his favorite wife are with him now," Jethro explained. "Michal tells him stories she makes up about the animals that drink at the spring near the foot of the hill. She is often able to cheer Saul when he is oppressed by the evil spirit."

"Why can't I go down into the camp and see my brothers, then?" David asked.

"You will stay in the palace," Jethro told him sternly, quite out of patience with his questioning. "If you are not here when the king calls, he might order the guard to cut off your head."

The threat was sufficient to quiet even David. Settling in a warm corner of the room, he tuned his harp by tightening the sandalwood pegs that controlled the tension of the strings. When he began to strum the instrument and sing softly to himself, the servants gathered around to listen. The presence of an audience always encouraged him, and soon the rather austere servants' quarters were filled with music and singing as he led them in the stirring war chants of Israel and other lyric poems. Some of these were so old that they were said to have been brought out of Egypt by those who had followed Moses in the great exodus from that land, so stirringly described in the ancient records of the Hebrews.

One song David particularly loved. It was said to have been composed as a hymn to the sun by a Pharaoh in Egypt who had given up the worship of the old gods for a religion based on the sun and its warmth, and upon one deity, above all, who made the sun to shine. The lines were lovely, and as David began to sing them, a hush fell upon the group of servants gathered around him:

"Thy dawning is beautiful in the horizon of the sky,
O living sun, beginning of life.
When thou risest in the eastern horizon,
Thou fillest every land with thy beauty.

Thou art beautiful, great, glittering, high above every land,
Thy rays, they encompass the land,
Even all that thou hast made.
Thou art the sun and thou carriest them all away captives;
Thou boundest them by thy love.
Though thou art far away, thy rays are upon the earth;

Though thou art on high, thy footprints are the day.
Bright is the earth when thou risest in the horizon.
When thou shinest by day,
Thou drivest away the darkness.
When thou sendest forth thy rays,
The land is in daily festivity.

All cattle rest upon their pasturage,
The trees and the plants flourish,
The birds flutter in their marshes,
Their wings uplifted in adoration to thee.
All the sheep dance upon their feet,
All winged things fly,
They live when thou hast shone upon them.

The boats sail upstream and downstream.
Every highway is open because thou dawnest.
The fish in the river leap up before thee,
Thy rays are in the midst of the great green sea

How manifold are thy works!
They are hidden from before us,
O sole god, whose powers no other possesseth,
Thou didst create the earth according to thy heart.
Men, all cattle large and small,
All that are upon the earth,
That go about upon their feet;
All that are on high or that fly with their wings.

How excellent are thy designs, O Lord of Eternity!
Thy rays nourish every garden;
When thou risest, they live,
They grow by thee.
Thou makest the seasons:
Winter to bring them coolness,
And heat that they may taste thee.
Thou didst make the distant sky to rise therein,
In order to behold all that thou hast made,
Thou alone, shining in the form as the living sun.

Dawning, glittering, going afar and returning
Thou makest millions of forms
Through thyself alone;
Cities, towns and tribes,
Highways and rivers
All eyes see thee before them,
For thou art of the day over the earth.
Living and flourishing forever and ever."

When the last note of the harp had died away, there was silence in the room. Even the servants, many of them captured Philistine slaves who did not worship the god of Israel, could appreciate the beauty of the words and the skill of the musician. Finally, Jethro got to his feet to go to his own sleeping-place in the chamber beside that of his master. As he passed David, he gripped the young man by the shoulder in a gesture that spoke far more than words could have done. And as if Jethro's departure were a signal that they should all be seeking their sleeping-pallets, the group began to disperse.

David was not sleepy, however. The words of the long-dead Pharaoh had filled him with a strange restlessness and, laying down the harp, he left the room. The cool night breeze that descended upon the hill country with the setting of the sun blew through the long passageway outside. He went out into the corridor, which he knew led to the walls of the fortress. Soon he came to a door that opened onto the broad, flat space atop the battlements. To David, who in good weather had often slept under the stars with the flock, the night was the most beautiful part of the sequence of light and darkness that formed each day. And nowhere, he was sure, did the soft white glow of the moon shine with greater brilliance than upon the land he loved.

The moon had not yet risen tonight, and as he stood there, wrapped in his heavy cloak, which served as an outer garment by day and a blanket by night, he let his eyes and thoughts wander among the stars that twinkled overhead. Somewhere in that vast canopy with its millions of gleaming points of light, he remembered hearing a swarthy caravan driver say that there was a single star which seemed never to vary but always showed the north to those skilled in finding it. Using this star alone as their guide, the caravan driver had said, Phoenician seafarers could guide their ships across the trackless seas far out of sight of land, just as a caravan driver guided himself along the Way of the Sea, the oldest and most famous highway in all the world, on which commerce flowed between Egypt, Damascus, and the land of Mesopotamia.

The tale of a star that could guide men by night across the sea had seemed but an idle boast when David had first heard it, for the Phoenician traders who sometimes paused in Bethlehem to buy and sell told many fabulous tales of other lands so strange and foreign to his experience that they were almost impossible to believe. But standing tonight upon the height of Gibeah, and remembering how a Pharaoh in far-away Egypt had nonetheless realized, as did the Israelites, the oneness of God for all people, it somehow did not seem at all fanciful that this same god would have placed a star in the heavens by which men could guide themselves on journeys far from home. Nor was it unbelievable any more that these same stars might be other worlds peopled with men and animals whose shapes could be entirely different from those of men and beasts here on earth, as he had heard swarthy traders from Capthor claim that their wise men believed.

Lost in contemplation of the heavens, David did not realize he was not alone, until the crunching of a pebble beneath a leather-soled sandal startled him out of his reverie. He looked up quickly to see a man of about his own height, standing only a few paces away along the broad, flat surface of the wall.

TER 6

"The soul of Jonathan was knit with the soul of David, and Jonathan loved him as his own soul."
I SAMUEL 18:1

I AM JONATHAN," the man said. "Who are you?"

David was so excited at the thought of finding himself in the presence of the king's eldest son—and Israel's greatest hero—that he forgot to answer. Although only in his early twenties, Jonathan, with no one except his armorbearer to support him, had once discovered a small garrison of Philistines in the hills between Michmash and Gibeah and, attacking in the darkness, had destroyed fully twenty of the enemy. In fact, the daring foray had stirred such fear in the hearts of the Philistines that when Saul had followed with the army, the enemy had been defeated in a great battle and driven back as far as Bethaven, a town north of Gibeah which, in the time of Joshua, had been known as Ai.

During this same battle Saul had vowed that none of his men should eat any food but, not knowing of the curse, Jonathan had broken the order. Saul would have destroyed his own son, but the people had refused to let him execute one who had been a hero of the battle; since that day, Jonathan's name had been sung in Israel by the minstrels as frequently as that of Saul himself.

"Who are you?" Jonathan asked again in an amused tone.

"My name is David," the youth stammered. "I am the son of Jesse, the Bethlehemite."

"I know your brothers, Eliab and Abinadab. They are among our best fighting men."

"As I shall be one day soon."

"You would be a soldier, then?"

"I am already more skilled with the sling than even the men of Benjamin," David boasted. "With one blow I killed a jackal that carried off a lamb, and I have fought against a lion and a bear, conquering them both."

"Come here where I may see you in the light of the lamp!" Jonathan commanded in a tone of some amusement.

David moved to where the light of an oil lamp spilled through the doorway of a room opening out upon the walls. He and Jonathan, he realized, were of about the same height, but Jonathan was stockier and thicker through the shoulders.

The king's son studied him for a moment. "You will never be as broad of shoulder as I am, David," he said finally. "But I suspect you will be quicker of movement, which may even up the difference."

"Surely I cannot hope to equal the feats of the bravest man in Israel," David protested. Now that he had seen the king's elder son closely, he was shocked by his own temerity in boasting about such things as killing a jackal.

"Don't let my father hear you," Jonathan warned. "Since his quarrel with Samuel, he is much troubled about his own actions."

"What right does an old man who can barely walk have to criticize the king of Israel?" David demanded indignantly.

"Nay, David," Jonathan said in a tone of mild reproof. "Samuel may be old, but he still speaks with the voice of God. And we must never forget that without the Lord's favor our strength is as nothing."

"But Saul has driven back the Philistines—with your help, of course—until they fear him and will not come against him any more."

"My father has done well," Jonathan admitted. "But he has been troubled lately because Samuel says none of his own blood shall be king after him."

"Surely no one in Israel would be better fitted to rule after Saul than you!" David protested.

"You have fierce loyalties, my friend David," Jonathan said with a smile. "I like that, for I am much the same way myself. But our people need something more than a warrior to lead them against the Philistines and perform mighty feats of arms. At the moment, neither of those things seems to be quite enough."

"What do you mean?"

"Before my father was anointed King of Israel, the country was in grave danger of existing no longer as a separate people. Samuel had done well in his time, but he was getting old and the tribes were beginning to go different ways. The Ark of the Covenant had even been captured by the Philistines and dishonored, although the enemy soon saw their mistake in offending the Most High and brought it back to our borders. But we are a people of fierce pride, David, and it is hard to take a loose confederation of tribes and mold them into a single people who can fight as one and, more important, live as one."

"Surely Saul has accomplished that."

"He did at first, by being the greatest warrior in Israel," Jonathan agreed. "But now that the Philistines have been pushed back, the tribes are drifting apart again. My father never speaks of it to me, but I am sure his fits of anger and sadness are caused by the realization that, as a king, he has not been able to hold Israel very close together."

"That is Samuel's fault. He should have stayed with your father and revealed God's will."

"Things might have turned out differently if he had," Jonathan agreed. "But I think Samuel was testing my father's trust in God when he delayed coming to Gilgal to make the sacrifices before we went to fight the Philistines at Michmash."

"As he tested Gideon of old?"

"I see you know the ancient stories. Gideon obeyed the Lord, even to cutting his forces down to three hundred men, and was granted a great victory over the Midianites. But my father was impatient and performed the sacrifices himself, lest the men become afraid and run away before the battle. To Samuel that meant he trusted more in himself than he did in the Lord."

"Yet you won the battle," David reminded him.

"But only when I forced my father to attack after I and my armorbearer had destroyed a garrison of the Philistines."

"My father and Samuel are old friends," David said. "He might be able to convince the prophet that King Saul is truly repentant and wishes to follow the way of the Lord."

Jonathan gave him a keen look. "You spoke of Samuel just now as an old man and very feeble. Have you seen him lately?"

"About six months ago when he came to Bethlehem to anoint me."

David saw Jonathan stiffen as if he had been struck by an unseen arrow. "What is wrong?" he started to ask, but the other man interrupted him.

"Come into my room," he said, his voice taut and a little hoarse.

Jonathan's quarters were as sparsely furnished as the rest of the palace, containing little more than the military gear hanging from racks upon the wall, a pallet for sleeping, and a bench which obviously served also as a chair. Still unable to understand the reason for the sudden change in Jonathan's manner, David watched him pull a heavy set of draperies across the door leading to the balcony before he turned once again to face the youth.

"This anointing," Jonathan said, in a low voice. "Tell me exactly what happened."

David described how in Bethlehem the old prophet had poured the small horn of fragrant oil over his head in the ritual of anointing.

"Did Samuel say why he did it?" Jonathan asked.

"No."

"And you did not ask?"

"No. Do you think it really meant anything?"

Jonathan did not answer the question; instead he asked another one: "Have you told anyone here of this?"

"No. I didn't think it was important. Was it?"

"It may have been the most important thing that has happened to Israel in a long time," Jonathan told him solemnly. "Do you remember how my father was selected as king?"

"Of course. I once composed a song about it."

"Tell me how it happened as you heard it."

"But surely you know—"

"Tell me how it was told to you, anyway."

David shrugged. "According to the story, some asses belonging to Kish, your grandfather, strayed from the pasture, and Saul went in search of them with a servant."

"With Jethro, yes."

"On the way they heard that the prophet Samuel lived nearby and went to ask him if he would help them find the animals. Samuel had been told by God to anoint a king in Israel—" David stopped and his eyes widened.

"Go on," Jonathan urged.

"Samuel had been told by God to anoint a king in Israel. He anointed your father and later, when the people gathered at Mizpeh to select a king by lot, your father's lot was taken."

"The Lord has acted in the same way again, David. For several months, rumors have been going around that another king has been chosen to rule over Israel after my father and that Samuel has anointed him. You must be the one."

"But only you should succeed Saul!"

Jonathan shook his head slowly. "I was at Gilgal when Samuel came there after my father broke the commandment of the Lord and performed the sacrifices before the battle. He told my father then: 'The Lord would have established your kingdom upon Israel forever, but now your kingdom shall not continue. The Lord has sought him a man after his own heart and has commanded him to be captain over his people because you have not kept that which the Lord commanded you.' "

"But Saul was only doing what he thought should be done," David protested.

"Since that day at Gilgal, I have known I would never rule over Israel, David," Jonathan said solemnly. "The Lord has spoken and you have been chosen."

"But I know nothing of law or ruling!" David cried, suddenly a little afraid in the face of Jonathan's revelations.

"Remember, Samuel did not publicly name my father as king until after he had been chosen by lot at Mizpeh," Jonathan said. "Your time will come when the Lord is ready for you to rule."

Like any boy of his age, David had dreamed of being a king, reveling in the vicarious feeling of power, the surging sense of self-importance that went with the dream. But he was also an intensely loyal person and could not for long take any pleasure in what must certainly be a bitter disappointment to the friend he had made tonight. Stirred by a generous impulse, he said, "Let me go to Samuel and tell him it is all wrong. When he knows you are everything a king of Israel should be, he will surely ask the Lord to relent and let you follow your father."

But Jonathan only shook his head. "It was all determined when Samuel anointed you in Bethlehem, David. I ask only to serve my people and be your friend."

"You shall always be that!" David exclaimed.

Jonathan's dagger was hanging upon the wall in a scabbard. Drawing out the weapon, David pricked his thumb with the point and watched the drop of blood form upon his skin. "Here," he said, handing Jonathan the dagger. "We will swear blood brotherhood together and nothing can ever come between us."

Jonathan hesitated for a moment. "I have every reason to hate you," he warned. "I might even break the bond some day and kill you so that I could take the throne of Israel for myself."

"If it were in my power to give it to you, I would do it now," David assured him.

Jonathan took the dagger and pricked his own thumb. Silently they pressed the two drops of blood together and watched them mix.

"Let us swear the oath of Jacob," David suggested and together they recited the words: " 'The Lord watch between me and thee, when we are absent one from another. God is witness betwixt me and thee.' "

David had acted impulsively in swearing the pact of friendship, urged on by his deep admiration for the king's son. Jonathan, however, was older and an experienced judge of men; he had seen in the youth a deep-rooted loyalty and sense of honor which had stirred him profoundly. Both were a little self-conscious as they wiped the blood from their thumbs.

"Promise me one thing," Jonathan said. "Tell no one about what happened when Samuel came to Bethlehem. My father is not always himself, and if it were known that you will one day be King of Israel, you might find yourself in grave danger."

"You have my promise," David assured him. "But when I see Samuel again, I shall still ask him to let you succeed your father. After all, I am young and, even if God does intend for me to rule one day, there is still plenty of time."

"We will obey God's will," Jonathan said simply. "No one can do more."

CHAPTER 7

"And Michal Saul's daughter loved David."
I SAMUEL 18:20

WHEN DAVID AWAKENED the next morning in the room where the servants slept, the events of the night before seemed hardly more than a dream—until he pressed his thumb against a crust of bread as he was eating the morning meal, and felt a twinge where the point of Jonathan's dagger had penetrated the flesh.

There was little luxury about the food served to those in the palace. A few crusts of bread, perhaps dipped into a jar of the honey-like spread called *dibash* made in the region around Hebron by boiling down the juice of grapes until it almost crystallized into sugar, a handful of dates or dried figs, and the whole washed down with cool goat's milk, water, or wine completed the morning's repast. Having always been a mighty trencherman, David found the king's table rather meager compared to the plenteous amount of food that had always been readily available to him in Bethlehem.

"When will the king send for me?" he asked Jethro as they were eating.

"Last night Michal charmed him with her tales and he slept well," the old servant said. "Tonight—" he lifted his hands in an eloquent gesture and let them fall.

"Then let me go down into the town and practice the arts of war with the soldiers," David suggested.

"I told you last night—" Jethro stopped, his lips pursed in thought. "Come with me," he said peremptorily and left the room.

At the extreme corner of the courtyard Jethro opened a heavy door. David saw that it was an armory, the walls lined with weapons and armor hanging from pegs.

"If it is weapons you must have, try these," Jethro told him. "They belong to the king and his bodyguard, and they are rusty from not being polished. I will send one of the kitchen maids with wool fat and a cloth that you can use for polishing."

David had no choice except to obey, although left to himself, he could have chosen far more exciting tasks than polishing rusty armor. His vivid imagination soon turned even that chore into an exciting game, however, as he mentally reconstructed the battles in which the weapons and armor had taken part. The few round shields of iron, he decided, had undoubtedly been captured from the Philistines, perhaps during the great victory at Michmash where Jonathan had become a hero. Before that victory, the Philistine overlords had held much of Israel in subjection, enforcing their rule by denying to the Hebrews the right to use their own blacksmiths for the manufacture of tools and weapons, as well for the sharpening of hoes and other farming implements. For many years, the Israelites had been forced to take their tools down to the coastal cities where the Philistines lived and pay high prices to have them sharpened. As for weapons of iron, these had been almost nonexistent and, what was more important, very few among the Hebrews had been allowed to develop the skills of a smith which would have enabled them to manufacture the badly needed tools and weapons for themselves.

To a certain degree, Saul's victories had relieved the pressure upon the Israelites in the matter of tools and weapons, but most of the javelins and spears in the armory still had points of bronze, often chipped and dented. The alloy made by smelting copper from Caphtor with tin—sometimes brought in Phoenician ships from a distant land called Tarshish—was not nearly so hard as iron, though much easier to fashion into tools, weapons, and armor. As for the arrows, hundreds of which were stored in the armory, many of them still had points made from flakes of sharp flint, often stained with the blood of previous victims.

The helmets arranged about the wall had been fashioned, as a rule, from bronze, which was easily handled. Although little more than rough metal caps, they did fulfill an important purpose by protecting the head of the warrior in battle. Most of them had extensions down the sides to cover the ears and the upper part of the neck, but only a few boasted a nosepiece extending down in front of the face between the eyes to guard that portion of the body from sword cuts.

The shafts of the spears were for the most part made of hickory, oak, or ash, with the head swaged onto the shaft by heating, and then secured in place by metal nails. Most of the swords were of bronze, too, although there were a few of iron, again captured from the Philistines who controlled the great mines and smelters located to the south in the area called the Negeb and the Arabah. All were double-bladed and usually wielded with both hands, particularly the iron ones which, David knew, were fashioned largely in the Philistine city of Gezer, across the mountain range in the *Shepheleh,* the foothills leading down into the coastal plain west of Bethlehem.

Even to David's eyes, untutored in matters of weapons and warfare, it was obvious that the Hebrews would have to endure considerable hardship in battle because of the dearth of iron weapons. The few sets of armor made from that metal, with front and back plates to protect the chest, and skirts or tunics of metal scales sewed upon a thick woolen fabric for the lower body and upper thighs, were obviously far superior to their bronze counterparts. If he ever became king and leader of the armies, David promised himself, one of his first acts of war would be to lead an attack upon the smelting and ironworking centers of the Philistines in order to capture not only weapons and armor but, more important, skilled smiths who would be kept as slaves to fashion the protection the Israelites so sorely needed when going into battle.

David could envision the time when the warriors of Israel would also be equipped with chariots, of which only a few existed in all the land. Then they would be able to launch swift forays even as far as the coastal plains, and capture more of the vehicles, until at last they were strong enough to rout their ancient enemies from the five great cities that constituted the Philistine stronghold and drive them into the sea. Only then would Israel be an independent nation, as it had been when Joshua led his warriors in the battles of conquest which had secured for their heritage the promised land of Canaan, as well as the fertile plains along both sides of the Jordan, part of which were now held by the Amorites of Moab.

David worked steadily as he dreamed, and by midafternoon the armor and weapons had been polished until the metal shone brightly. He stayed on in the armory, however, playing at battle himself, jabbing with a spear at an imaginary enemy and slashing the air with the great swords. It was while he was thus fighting an imaginary foe that he saw a pair of bright eyes peering through the partly opened door, and recognized Michal by her giggle.

"You are my prisoner," he told her loftily, pretending to menace her with a spear. "Come in and surrender."

She came meekly into the armory but her eyes were bright with mischief and her lips quivered as she tried to hold back the inevitable giggle.

"How long have you been out there?" he demanded.

"Long enough to watch you kill two Philistines and one Amalekite."

David could not help laughing at the sally. Nor could he keep from admiring the girl as he went to put up the spear. Slim and graceful, she wore a tunic of bright blue with a band of the same material about her hair. The belt or girdle about her waist was of leather imprinted with a floral design, such as was used by Phoenician workers in leather, and her sandals were of the same pattern.

"I was on my way to visit the doe and her fawn that come to the spring at the foot of the hill about this time every day," she confided. "Then I heard strange noises coming from the armory and I stopped by to see whether or not a goat had been penned up here."

David snorted with disdain. "You were snooping—as you always are. I have sisters, so I know."

Michal began to giggle again. "You don't know how funny you looked, David, stomping around and jabbing and growling at the air!" Then her face sobered. "But you will be a great warrior. I know you will."

It was on the tip of David's tongue to tell her that he would one day take her father's place, but he remembered his vow to Jonathan and banished the thought from his mind. Besides, he did not want to hurt Michal.

Then another thought came to him, a thought that had never entered his mind before. When he became king, he could choose the most beautiful women of the kingdom to be his wives—even Michal, if she were not already married. And when he looked at the girl again and saw the slim loveliness of her body in the simple tunic, the laughter in her eyes, and the dark, curling locks of her hair, he could think of no one at the moment he would rather choose than her.

"Why are you looking at me so strangely?" The girl's voice broke into his dream.

"I was wondering how one girl could be such a nuisance," he said in a tone harsher than he had intended it to be, because she had come so close to reading his thoughts.

He saw her lips quiver and knew he had hurt her feelings. "I am sorry, Michal," he said impulsively. "I didn't really mean that."

"Are you sure?" Her eyes were bright with unshed tears.

"Yes."

Suddenly she smiled and was herself again. "Then I forgive you, but only if you promise to go to the spring with me."

"Jethro told me not to leave the armory, lest the king call for me."

"Father went to the camp to talk to Abner, the chief captain, about better weapons for the men," she told him. "I am sure he will not return before the evening meal. Besides, you have finished here already."

Michal knew of a path down the hill that did not traverse the main streets of the small city of Gibeah, so they would not be likely to meet her father or Jethro. As they approached the spring, she put her hand upon David's arm to hold him back. "Walk softly," she warned in a whisper. "The doe and its fawn come to drink here every day about this time."

Stealing through the rank vegetation that grew along the banks of the small watercourse, they approached the spring, hand in hand. Although he had often boasted of how he could track a jackal to its lair, David saw nothing unusual until a sudden quick gasp of breath from the girl beside him and a warning pressure of her hand upon his arm brought him to a stop.

"Look beside the brook, just below the spring," she whispered.

He was able to see the deer now, with the smaller, daintily graceful figure of the fawn beside it. The two had been drinking from a pool, but the mother must have suddenly caught the scent; she stood now, every sinew tense, searching the underbrush with her eyes as she tried to identify the unseen danger. Beside her the fawn was still drinking, its senses not yet as acute as the mother's.

Instinctively David's right hand reached for the sling that hung at his belt, along with a handful of round pebbles in a pouch. Michal did not realize his intention until one of the stones dropped from the pouch into his hand preparatory to his loading the sling.

"No!" she cried in horror. At the sound of her voice, doe and fawn fled instantly into the underbrush.

"You!" Michal was a bundle of fury, beating at his chest with her fist. "You beast! Why did you drive them away?"

David was forced to seize her hands in order to defend himself, but she still struggled. Then suddenly all the fight seemed to go out of her and she buried her face in the cloth of his tunic, sobbing in great spasms that shook her entire body as he stared down at her in amazement, unable to understand her reaction.

The instinct to launch a missile at the deer had been as natural to him as breathing. Time and again he had brought down game with his sling while watching the sheep; always a feast of rejoicing had followed with the neighbors being invited to share the good fortune of Jesse's family, and he who had produced the feast being lauded as the guest of honor. He had never thought of the hunt as an act of killing before, although he had known moments of pity when he looked down to see the body of a coney or squirrel jerking at his feet. But with Michal sobbing against his breast, he knew that he would never kill again without feeling something of the pain he brought to his victim.

In an instinctive attempt to comfort the girl, he put his arm about her shoulders and soothed her until gradually she stopped weeping. When finally she looked up, her eyes still red and filled with tears, he did something he could not have explained either then or for a long time afterward. He bent his head and kissed her awkwardly, tasting the salt of her tears upon his lips and the surprising softness of her mouth against his own. It had been a wholly instinctive gesture of sympathy on his part, but Michal's response surprised and startled him; her lips clung to his and her arms went about him, holding him tightly as if she never intended to let him go.

For only a moment did they remain thus; then, in a sudden rush of embarrassment, David released the girl and stooped to pick up the sling which had dropped from his hand when he had taken her into his arms. He was purposely a long time in the process and carefully attached the weapon to his leather belt before looking up and meeting her eyes. When he did so, he saw in them a look—he realized in a moment of startled awareness—of complete possessiveness.

"I—I am sorry about the deer and its fawn, Michal," he stammered. "You see, I'd never noticed before how beautiful they were."

"And like a man you thought only of killing," she said in a tone of amused tolerance, a note he remembered hearing in his mother's voice when his father had done something foolish. And though he did not have the experience to understand it, he nevertheless realized that, no matter what their ages, she was far older and wiser than he, in a way that women are always older and wiser than the men they love.

"I could use a meal of venison," he grumbled. "Your father doesn't set a very lavish table, if you must know."

Michal's laughter pealed out and she was herself again. "We will set a better one in our house," she promised. "I will have the servants give you roast flesh every night for supper and bread baked in the oven."

"Our house?"

"We are betrothed, of course," she said matter-of-factly. "It cannot be made public until Merab is married, but that will not be long. Many men desire her already and she is only waiting for a prince or a king to ask for her."

"But you are the daughter of a king and I am only the son of a shepherd." It was not quite the truth, for Jesse was as well off, and his family as noble as any in Judah.

"When you please Father with your music, he will surely make you a prince of his court," Michal assured him. "Then, when the right time comes, you can send the matchmaker to ask for me." Her eyes grew smoky again. "But I will not have you kissing other girls! Promise that you will have no other wives except me!"

The talk of marriage and wives was beginning to bore David. "You seem to have decided everything else," he said with a shrug. "Why not that?"

"Michal!" Merab's voice called sharply from the hillside. "Where are you?"

"She will be angry if she knows you are here," Michal said to David in a whisper. "Quickly, hide over there!"

David could see no particular reason why he should hide and was not very quick about it, so before he managed to crouch in the underbrush, the bushes above the spring parted and Merab's face appeared.

"What are you doing here with the shepherd boy?" she demanded suspiciously. "If I tell Father, he will have you both beaten."

"We came to the spring to see the doe and fawn," Michal explained. "David almost killed the mother with the sling."

As the two girls climbed the hill, David could hear them talking angrily. "Can you not remember that you are the daughter of a king?" Merab was saying. "The shepherd boy lives with the servants."

"Shepherd boy indeed!" David was tempted to leave Saul's court then and there, but he remembered Michal saying that if he pleased the king with his playing, he would surely be made a prince; the thought of forcing the sulking Merab to bow to him was far too pleasant a prospect to be thrown away. Besides, he reminded himself, as the future king of Israel he was quite as good as anyone in Gibeah, or in the whole nation.

Jethro had not noticed David's absence, so he was able to enter the palace again without arousing comment. The evening meal was quite as meager as it had been the night before, and David found himself regretting that he had let Michal keep him from bringing down the doe. The venison would have done much to give substance and flavor to the stew of lentils and onions forming the main dish.

He still had not seen King Saul, but when he heard the sound of an angry voice shouting in the large room off the courtyard that served as the king's audience and banquet chamber, and the crash of furniture being overturned, he realized that Saul must be in one of this troubled moods again. Shortly Jethro came hurrying into the room where the servants were eating. The old servant's face was troubled and a dark swelling was beginning to form upon the right cheek beneath the eye. "The king is in the grip of the evil spirit again," he panted. "Go in, David, and see if you can quiet him with your singing."

David was staring at the swelling beneath Jethro's right eye; in Jesse's household servants were rarely beaten—and never in anger. "Wh-what if he strikes me?"

"Ignore the blow. When Saul is himself again you will be rewarded with gifts. He is a fine master when his spirit is not troubled."

David picked up his lyre with suddenly trembling fingers, but as he hurried to Saul's audience chamber, he would have much preferred to face a lion in the forests of Judah.

CHAPTER 8

"David took an harp and played with his hand: so Saul was refreshed, and was well, and the evil spirit departed from him." I SAMUEL 16:23

THE SOUND of cursing and shouting, interspersed with the crash of furniture, grew louder as David approached Saul's audience chamber. At the door of the room, Jethro stepped aside and almost shoved David through the door. As the youth's frightened eyes swiftly took in the tableau before him, he realized that here was a challenge such as he had never faced before.

The room was perhaps twice as long as it was wide, the walls made of stone blocks, smoothed and colored a light pink. At one side, a flight of stone steps led to the upper chambers, and at the foot of the stairs were two soldiers, stalwart men from Saul's personal bodyguard, who had been playing *senit*, a game imported from Egypt long ago. In playing this game, a small handful of sticks was tossed from a throwing cup like dice and pieces were moved upon a board marked out in squares according to the pattern formed by the sticks when they fell. The men, however, were motionless now as if Saul's burst of anger had frozen them in the midst of the game, one with the throwing cup still in his hand, ready to toss out the sticks.

A woman sat upon a low bench that was covered by a cushion of goat's hair with a fringed border. She was slender, lovely, and, David decided, much younger than Saul. The fragile beauty of her face seemed vaguely familiar, and he suddenly realized that it was a slightly older copy of Michal's own delicate features. Unlike the soldier, however, the woman did not seem terrified by the ragings David had heard on the way to the room. The amused light in her eyes reminded him very much of her daughter's mischievous expression. She must be Ahinoam, he realized, the youngest wife of the king and his favorite. She did not speak, but David thought he saw a light of encouragement in her eyes, as if she quite understood the difficulty of the task he faced, that of quieting a man who at first glance seemed wholly mad.

King Saul was seated on an elaborately carved throne chair of almug wood set upon a small stone dais. Just as David was entering the room, he stepped down from the dais and seized a slender-necked pottery vase decorated with alternating rings of red and blue. Raising the vase over his head, he sent it crashing against the wall where the fragments rained down upon the two soldiers who had been playing *senit* at the foot of the steps, and as if this were a signal releasing them from their frozen position, one of the men shook the cup holding the sticks and tossed them out upon the floor. Not yet aware of David's presence, Saul stooped to pick up a bowl of glazed pottery containing apples, peaches, grapes, and pomegranates, spilling the fruit out upon the floor as he lifted the container to hurl it, too, against the wall.

The King of Israel was one of the tallest and handsomest men David had ever seen. His hair was jet black and the dark beard growing down his cheeks and along his chin had been trimmed in the Assyrian manner. His long robe of rich cloth dyed with the famous purple of the Phoenicians, a color reserved chiefly for royal garments, had sleeves that came only half-way to his elbows, revealing muscular forearms which were knotted now in the act of lifting the bowl.

David wondered how he could announce his presence without inciting Saul to hurl the bowl at him. His difficulty was resolved by Jethro; from the corridor, well out of range of whatever Saul might decide to throw next, he spoke to David in an urgent whisper.

"Play!" Jethro urged. "In the name of Moses, play!"

David ran his fingers across the strings of the lyre and a burst of music filled the room. At the first notes, Saul stood frozen, with the bowl still raised in mid-air. The two soldiers playing *senit* jerked their heads around in astonishment. Instinctively, David had chosen a melody calculated to appeal to a warrior, the martial music of the most stirring victory chant ever sung in Israel, the *Song of Deborah*. Telling how the hosts of the cruel Captain Sisera of King Jabin's army had been destroyed upon the plains when the Lord had sent an avalanche of rain to mire the iron chariots of the enemy, it was a song of praise for Barak, who had led the armies, and for Deborah, the prophetess who had guided and inspired both him and the fighting men to victory. But most of all, it was a hymn of admiration to God who had given them the victory.

On the second plucking of the strings, David launched into the verses of the song in a clear, effortless voice second only in beauty to the sound produced by the instrument itself:

"Awake, awake, Deborah!
Awake, awake, utter a song!
Arise, Barak and leave thy captivity captive,
Thou son of Abinoam.
Out of Ephraim was there a root of them against Amalek;
After thee, Benjamin, among thy people;
Out of Machir came down governors,
And out of Zebulon they that handle the pen of the writer.
The princes of Issachar were with Deborah;
Even Issachar, and also Barak:
He was sent on foot into the valley.
For the divisions of Reuben
There were great thoughts of heart.

Why abodest thou among the sheepfolds,
To hear the bleating of the flocks?
For the divisions of Reuben
There were great searchings of heart.
Gilead abode beyond Jordan:
And why did Dan remain in ships?
Asher continued on the seashore.
And abode in his beaches.

Zebulon and Naphtali were a people,
That jeopardized their lives unto death,
In the high places of the field.

The kings came out and fought,
Then fought the kings of Canaan
In Taanach by the waters of Megiddo
They took no gain of money.
They fought from the heavens;
The stars in their courses fought against Sisera.
The river of Kishon swept them away,
That ancient river, the River of Kishon.

O my soul, thou hast trodden down strength.
Then were the horsehoofs broken
By means of the prancings,
The prancings of their mighty ones.
'Curse ye Meroz' said the angel of the Lord,
'Curse ye bitterly the inhabitants thereof;
Because they came not to the help of the Lord.
To the help of the Lord against the mighty.'

Blessed above women shall Jael be
The wife of Heber the Kenite,
Blessed shall she be above women in the tent.
He asked water and she gave him milk;
She brought forth butter in a lordly dish.
She put her hand to the nail,
And her right hand to the workman's hammer;
And with the hammer she smote Sisera
She smote off his head.
When she had pierced and stricken through his temples,
At her feet he bowed, he fell, he lay down:
At her feet, he bowed, he fell;
Where he bowed, there he fell down dead.

So let all thy enemies perish, O Lord!
But let them that love him be as the sun when he goeth forth
in his might."

Engrossed in the stirring tale of how Deborah and Barak had led the Israelites to victory and how Jael had destroyed Sisera when he sought refuge in her tent, David did not notice what had been happening while he was singing. When finally his fingers dropped away from the strings, he realized that the room was strangely silent. Saul, he saw, had moved back to the throne chair and sat there now, watching him with brooding eyes from which the fires of anger were already beginning to fade. Ahinoam had not moved from the bench, but she was smiling and, in the corner by the steps, the two soldiers had stopped their game of *senit* to listen. For a long moment after the strains of the thrilling chant died away, no one spoke, then Saul's voice broke the silence.

"Who are you?" The king's voice was almost gentle.

"I am David, the son of Jesse. My lord the king sent for me."

"I remember now," Saul said. "Jethro thought your singing might bring ease to my spirit."

"I pray that it has done so, my lord."

"You are a very skillful musician, David. How long have you been in my household?"

"Since yesterday. Today I polished armor and weapons in the armory."

"You shall perform such menial tasks no more," Saul told him. "So long as I am at Gibeah, you will be my armorbearer and wait upon me to sing and play when it is my desire."

David bowed his head. "The wish of my lord king is my command."

"Do you know other songs?" Ahinoam asked. "Perhaps of a different nature?"

"I know many songs, my lady. In the hills while I watch the sheep, I sing some that no one else has ever heard."

"Would you sing one of them for me?"

David shot a quick glance at Saul, for he doubted that the king would be interested in a song of love such as he knew Ahinoam was asking for. "Let me sing you the fable that Jothan told the men of Shechem, after they had made Abimelech king and he was in danger of his life," he suggested and, without waiting for an answer, began the song:

"The trees went forth on a time
To anoint a king over them;
And they said unto the olive tree,
'Reign thou over us.'
But the olive tree said unto them,
'Should I leave my fatness,
Wherewith by me they honor God and man,
And go to be promoted over the trees?'

"And the trees said unto the fig trees,
'Come thou, and reign over us;'
But the fig tree said unto them,
'Should I forsake my sweetness,
And my fruit,
And go to be promoted over the trees?'

"Then said the trees unto the vine,
'Come thou, and reign over us.'
And the vine said unto them,
'Should I leave my wine,
Which cheereth God and man,
And go to be promoted over the trees?'

"Then said all the trees unto the bramble,
'Come thou, and reign over us.'
And the bramble said unto the trees,
'If in truth ye anoint me king over you,
Come and put your trust in my shadow:
Then if not, let fire come out of the bramble,
And devour the cedars of Lebanon.' "

When David finished the fable, Saul said abruptly, "Sing it again, please, and tell me its meaning."

David sang the old fable once more. "Is my lord familiar with the story behind the fable?" he asked when he had finished.

Saul shook his head impatiently. "I am a soldier, not a scholar."

"I know the story," Ahinoam interposed. "In the time of the judges many years ago, Gideon fought the Midianites in the Vale of Jezreel with only three hundred men. He surrounded the enemy in the darkness, making a great clamor and burning many torches, so that the men of Midian killed each other while desperately seeking to escape. When the people would have made Gideon king, he refused, saying it was not right for him or his sons to rule over them. But after Gideon died, a son of his concubine, named Abimelech, went to the men of Shechem and persuaded them to name him king. They killed all the true sons of Gideon except Jotham, the youngest, who hid on Mount Gerizim, the holy mountain over against Shechem. There he spoke the words of the fable you have just sung."

"You tell the story well," David complimented her.

"But the meaning of the fable," Saul said impatiently. "What is it?"

"It seems to me that the meaning is very simple, my lord king," David said. "The trees are the people who desire a king, as Israel desired you to lead them to victory over the Philistines and rule over them. Having anointed you as king, it is the duty of all people to follow you and obey your commands. If they do not, then it shall be as the song says:

> Let the fire come out of the bramble,
> And devour the cedars of Lebanon."

Saul nodded slowly. "You have spoken well," he agreed. "It must be as you say."

"I still want to hear a love song, David," Ahinoam insisted. "Surely you must have sung at least one."

David was sure that Michal had told her mother about the song he had started to sing for her by the spring. But he had no intention of singing love songs before the king, who might consider him more musician than warrior because of it.

"I will sing in praise of the queen's beauty," he announced as he plucked the strings of the harp again:

> "All thy garments shall smell of myrrh and aloes and cassia,
> Out of the ivory palaces, whereby they have made thee glad.
> King's daughters were among thy honorable women;
> Upon thy right hand did stand the Queen in gold of Ophir.

Hearken, O daughter, consider, and incline thine ear;
Forget also thine own people, and thy father's house;
So shall the king greatly desire thy beauty:
For he is thy lord; and worship thou him.

The daughter of Tyre shall be there with a gift;
Even the rich among the people shall entreat thy favor.
The Queen is all glorious within:
Her clothing is of wrought gold.

She shall be brought unto the king in raiment of needlework:
The virgins, her companions that follow her to him
With gladness and rejoicing shall they be brought;
They shall enter into the king's palace.

Instead of thy fathers shall be thy children,
Whom thou mayest make princes in all the earth.
Thy name shall be remembered in all generations:
And the people praise thee forever and ever."

"Thank you, David." Ahinoam's eyes were shining. "That was very beautiful."

David's status in Saul's household changed considerably after his success in relieving Saul of his melancholy. He no longer slept in the common room with the servants but moved into the quarters of the guards who protected the king's household. Saul ate alone, served by Ahinoam and his daughters, but as armorbearer, a position largely without duties in time of peace, David was only a little lower in status than the members of the king's own family.

Only a few more times in the next several months was David called to play and sing for the king in order to drive away a fit of depression, though he often entertained Ahinoam and the other women of the court. Saul seemed to have thrown off the evil spirit which had troubled him. Alert now and certain of himself, he was busy bringing together as large an army as the tribes would give him from among their young men and training them to use the weapons of battle, particularly those made of iron captured from the Philistines.

For David, the days were rather tedious and, except for daily practice with Saul's guard in using the weapons of war, he was hard put to find a way to spend his time. He was fond of Michal, but she was much too possessive where he was concerned to suit him. More than once he found himself longing for the hills of Judah and the exciting chase after jackal, lion, and bear or even the thrill of hunting the hares that made such savory morsels in the cooking pot.

As the waning of summer promised cooler days and an early resumption of raids by the Philistines, Saul decided to embark upon a tour of the tribes to enlist support for his demand that a sizeable army be kept ready at all times in the neighborhood of Gibeah. Clear-eyed and certain of himself, the king was once again the leader who had excited the loyalty of Israel; it had been weeks since David had been called to sing for him. During the preparations for Saul's departure, David was overlooked. Shortly after Saul departed, he returned to Bethlehem.

Back at home, he felt no particular nostalgia for Gibeah; he was quite happy to resume the task of tending his father's sheep. His stories of Saul's court, embroidered a little, for he possessed the natural instinct of a storyteller, enthralled the boys and girls of Bethlehem, and particularly his cousins, Joab, Abishai, and Asahel. With them he also spent many hours practicing the use of spear, javelin, and bow, and engaging in sham fights with sword and shield.

With the spear and the javelin David soon became quite skillful. Using the bow and arrow he was able to send missiles with great accuracy much farther than he could hope to with the sling. But in handling the two-edged sword, Joab's broad shoulders and powerful body made him by far the most expert fighter of the three. Besides, Joab had a natural aptitude for battle, a love of physical combat, making it inevitable that he would one day become a soldier.

As the months passed, David grew from a stripling into a handsome young man able to hold his own and even excel in physical sports over most of the other youths of Bethlehem—except Joab. And by virtue of his skill with the lyre and his ability to compose beautiful verses, he was a favorite with the girls—and with the mothers whose daughters were approaching the age of marriage.

The brief period when he had lived at Saul's capital was now little more than a faint memory and the night when he and Jonathan had mixed their blood and he had promised never to reveal the facts of his anointing by Samuel was almost forgotten in the busy round of caring for the sheep and playing at war with his cousins. Then something happened that changed David's whole existence as once again the strands of his life were woven with those of Saul and Jonathan, woven this time into a fabric where his threads were soon to become dominant.

It began when the Philistines moved eastward in full force through the passes of Judah and brought up their armies in battle array before the Israelite center of Shochoh in the Valley of Elah west of Bethlehem.

CHAPTER 9

"Saul and the men of Israel were gathered together, and pitched by the valley of Elah, and set the battle in array against the Philistines."

I SAMUEL 17:2

THE COASTAL PLAIN of Canaan, held since the time of Joshua by the "Sea People," later known as Philistines, was about an hour's walk inland from the shore of the sea itself. Toward the beach the dunes piled up by the wind formed a rather gentle slope, but beyond them to the east the ground gradually became more rolling, merging imperceptibly into the range of rough hills that formed the highlands of central Canaan and the territory belonging to the tribe of Judah. In the foothills and wherever the conformation of the shoreline allowed for the building of a port, Philistine cities had risen and thrived. For the most part they stood upon foundations built by earlier Canaanite inhabitants who had been dispossessed from their land by Joshua and the members of the tribes of Dan and Judah. The Hebrews, in turn, had been rudely ejected when the Philistines settled permanently in this area.

From the foothills where their villages were, the Israelite tribes had watched with awe the advance of a horde from the north. No one knew exactly whence these invaders had come, but one thing was certain: they were taller, stronger, and more warlike, for the most part, than the Hebrews and the Canaanites. What was more, they possessed a secret which quickly enabled them to conquer most of that region: the method of smelting and tempering iron to make weapons, implements, and fastenings for the great wooden carts, piled high with belongings, in which their women and children rode as they advanced southward. Of necessity, the Sea People were forced to remain near the coastal plain, where the going was easier for these massive and cumbersome wooden vehicles; but more than that, the love of the sea and its commerce was in their blood.

Some said the Sea People had come originally from the island of Caphtor, as Crete was called in that day, others that they were from the region of the Greeks, although they themselves were not wholly Greek. But the story of their relentless march around the eastern shore of the Mediterranean, or "Great Sea," was told far in advance of their coming, along with descriptions of the fleet of ships which accompanied them. Advancing by land and sea simultaneously, they attacked one coastal center after another, squeezing each city, as by a giant set of pincers. Moving ever eastward and southward toward their goal, the rich and fertile delta lands around the mouth of the Nile River in Egypt, the invaders had plundered Cilicia, gutted the silver mines of Tarsus of all metal which was easily accessible, and used the riches of Cyprus, particularly its copper and other metals, for their own purposes.

At the eastern end of the Great Sea, the Phoenician centers of Ugarit, Byblus, Tyre, and Sidon had fallen in rapid succession, while yet another arm of the invasion had reached as far inland as Carchemish on the Euphrates River, following a path similar to that which had been taken in reverse by Abraham during the journey from Haran to Canaan roughly a thousand years before. With one flank thus protected and the sea on the other side, they were ready to move upon Egypt.

Relentless as the approach of the Sea People had been, however, the seemingly irresistible character of their advance had in the end provided the seed of their own defeat. For the rumors which preceded them caused the energetic Pharaoh, Rameses III, to mobilize a vast army for the defense of the Nile delta. What was more, the Egyptians possessed chariots which were far speedier and more mobile than the heavy vehicles of the invaders, and when the Sea People finally reached the Nile delta, the forces of Pharaoh were ready. Massed ranks of bowmen, keeping far enough away to be out of range of the great spears and broad iron swords, had rained death upon the invaders. At the same time, the ships of the attackers had been driven ashore and smashed by swiftly moving Egyptian war galleys, relying rather upon banks of slaves at the oars for their motive power than upon sails.

In a final battle, one of the greatest that had ever taken place in either Egypt or Canaan, the invasion from the north had finally been halted. Reeling back along the shore of the Nile delta and the coast of Canaan after their defeat in Egypt, the Sea People, already coming to be known as the Philistines, had easily pushed the Canaanites and Israelites out of their coastal cities. Next they had rebuilt and renamed five major centers: Ashkelon, Ashdod, Ekron, Gaza, and Gath. And finally on the southern coast line of Canaan they had set up forges to smelt and work iron, copper, and bronze to replace the weapons which had been destroyed. Quickly recovering from their defeat in Egypt, they had soon become a powerful threat to the Israelites, and particularly to the tribe of Judah whose domain lay just east of the major Philistine cities.

The children of Israel had entered Canaan from the west only a short time, perhaps as little as fifty years, before the Sea People invaded Egypt and were thrown back. During the succeeding years, the Hebrews had been busy with the conquest of Canaan and the Philistines with the task of nursing their wounds and developing, in their confederation of five cities near the seacoast, a nation powerful both in trade and in war. By refusing to share it with those around them, they had managed to keep the secret of smelting and fashioning iron largely to themselves, at least in this area, although it had been known for many years by the Hittites to the north. And with access to Egypt cut off by a succession of strong Pharaohs and a line of fortifications called the Prince's Wall, built just south of the border by the Egyptian kings, the Philistines had no way to expand except eastward. They were lured in that direction by the pleasant valleys lying between the ranges of hills that made up Judah and, particularly, by the broad and fertile lowlands on either side of the Jordan.

At first the Hebrews had been too strong for any major Philistine advance to hope for success. Under Joshua, a succession of triumphs for the fighting men of Israel had resulted in the defeat of the five Canaanite kings before the city of Gideon and their destruction at Makkedah, plus the defeat of King Jabin of Hazor to the north. But following Joshua's death, a period of gradual retreat had set in for Israel, particularly by the southern tribes of Dan and Judah which now found themselves faced on the west by an enemy growing steadily both in numbers and in strength. At various times, large numbers of the Hebrews had been enslaved by the Philistines, yet on each occasion, a great leader of the *shophetim*, or judges, had risen up to emancipate them.

The emergence of Saul as leader of the entire Hebrew federation, hitherto never united completely before, had been recognized by the Philistines as a serious threat to their expansion, even to their existence. And being a naturally warlike and energetic people, they had taken forthright steps to combat that threat. Saul's conquest of the Amalekite kingdom to the south had expanded the domain of the Hebrews and, more important, had brought them alarmingly close to a source of iron and copper which might quickly make them independent of the Philistine smiths. It was inevitable, therefore, that a large-scale invasion of Hebrew territory would be launched by the Philistine confederation. This event took place a few years after David's brief visit to Saul at Gibeah.

The northernmost of the Philistine cities was Ekron, only about an hour's walk from Jamnia, which had been assigned to the tribe of Judah by Joshua at the time of conquest. In this region Samson had carried out his remarkable exploits until, in the nearby valley of Sorek, Delilah trapped him by a subterfuge into revealing that the source of his strength was his hair and finally delivered him to the Philistines as a prisoner. Since it stood in a commanding position among the hills overlooking the plains, Jamnia could have been valuable, but the Hebrews had never tried to hold the immediate region because it was plagued, not only with flies, but also with mice, which sometimes destroyed an entire crop in a matter of a few hours.

Eastward from Ekron and Gath, which lay to the south of Jamnia, the land rose in successive ridges, separated by valleys penetrating deep into the territory of Judah. Many of them contained streams, and along the banks paths had been worn by commercial traffic and sometimes by invasion. Although they ordinarily dwelt in villages among the hills, coming down in the daytime to till the fields and care for the vineyards of the fertile valley regions, the Israelites were often forced to protect themselves against marauding bands of Philistines. The Philistines, on the other hand, had to be in a constant state of readiness lest their nearby city of Gezer, a center for the working of iron, fall into the hands of the Hebrews. As a result, the valleys lying immediately eastward from Ekron and Gath constituted a major source of conflict between the Hebrews and the Philistines. And of these valleys, none offered a more direct route to the heart of Judah and the Jordan Valley, and was therefore the most vital to the defense of Israel, than the one called Elah or, occasionally, "The Valley of the Acacias."

Here, in Ephes-dammim near Shochoh, on one bank of a ravine cut by a brawling stream, the Philistines had marshaled a considerable army with the intention of crossing the stream and taking the main valley road into central Judah. On the other side of the valley, Saul had drawn up his armies in opposition to the enemy and for more than a month the two had faced each other with only the stream between them. Beyond an occasional skirmish between foraying parties, there had been no real action. But, as often happened when armies faced each other, individual champions challenged others from the opposing forces to single combat.

There was considerable precedent for this sort of fighting and on more than one occasion, notably during the tenure of Samson as judge, battles had been decided by individual combat. Now, however, the situation was reversed as far as Israel was concerned, and it was a Philistine who dared to challenge all others, a veritable giant of a man called Goliath of Gath.

Rumors of the impasse in the valley of Elah had been filtering back to the towns of Judah, particularly to Bethlehem which, being less than a day's journey from the battleground, was most concerned. Even worse was the news that King Saul, unable to attack the superior forces of the Philistines and forced to watch them grow daily in strength, had become subject once again to the fits of despair and wild anger from which he had suffered before David's stay at Gibeah. Concerned about his older sons who were with Saul, Jesse loaded a measure of parched corn and some freshly baked loaves for the three brothers, along with ten cheeses for their captain, and instructed David to take them to Shochoh. There he was to observe the situation and bring back a report.

David was overjoyed at the order to visit the battlefield. Being older than he, his cousins Joab, Abishai, and Asahel had gone a few months before to join the soldiers under Saul. And since his father had agreed that he could spend the night in the camp before returning to Bethlehem, he hoped to see his cousins and particularly the giant Philistine who dared to defy the forces of Israel.

As he approached Shochoh, David grew more and more concerned, for he was meeting a steady line of stragglers returning home from the battle front. Finally he stopped one of them and gave the man a drink of wine from a skin tied to the back of the pack mule in the hope of encouraging him to talk.

"Why are you leaving the battleground?" David asked, while the man was drinking. "Surely the fighting is not already over?"

The soldier shrugged. "There will be no fighting; we are beaten before we even cast a spear or loose an arrow."

"Is not King Saul with the army?"

"Saul is there, but not even he can stand against a giant."

"There have been no giants in the land since Joshua killed Og, the King of Bashan," David said. "He was the last of that race."

"I know nothing of Og, or of Bashan," the deserter said. "But I have seen Goliath with my own eyes. He is half again as tall as you are and his shoulders twice as broad. Why, the very sound of his voice shakes the earth and sets ordinary men to trembling!"

"What of King Saul? Or Jonathan? Surely they are not afraid of any Philistine!"

"All I know is that this Goliath, as he calls himself, comes out every day and challenges any man to fight him. And neither Saul, Jonathan, nor anyone else, has gone out to do battle with him."

This was hard for David to believe. He would have wagered that Saul could have stood in combat against any single Philistine, and it was well known that Jonathan had attacked and destroyed an entire garrison of the enemy with only his armorbearer to support him. He was still puzzling over the strange tale told by the deserter, and more than half inclined not to believe it, when he reached the top of the ridge and found himself on the rim of the valley of Elah. Pausing there, he surveyed the situation before him.

What he saw filled him with a premonition of disaster.

CHAPTER 10

"Behold, there came up the champion, the Philistine of Gath, Goliath by name." I SAMUEL 17:23

ON THE FARTHER SIDE of the valley from where David was standing, separated from the Israelite army by a stream, the Philistines were encamped in orderly rows of tents that almost covered the slope. From the camp came the sound of hammers upon anvils, and smoke rose skyward from many bellows as their smiths went about the task of sharpening weapons and fashioning new ones. The whole encampment was a beehive of activity, much of it centered upon a large tent before which five banners were fluttering. These flags, David judged, indicated that all five cities of the Philistine confederation were represented here.

The rumors about the size of the enemy army were only too true, he decided. This could only be a major drive designed to penetrate deep into Judah and cut it off from the other tribes, after which the Hebrews could be pursued eastward toward the land of the Ammonites, across the Jordan and beyond the Salt Sea. There the forces of Saul would be caught between two enemy forces and utterly destroyed.

David was at a loss at first to explain the enemy's delay in attacking, since the Philistines appeared to be about equal in number to the Israelites. But the beehive activity of their smiths seemed to indicate that perhaps all the forces gathered there had not yet been armed with weapons of iron, and that the five kings and their generals had decided to pause in the valley of Elah where there was a plenteous supply of water until that lack could be remedied. The enemy appeared to have few, if any, chariots, but this did not surprise David. The swift-moving vehicles by which the Hyksos people, with whom the Hebrews had first migrated into this land in the time of Abraham, fully a thousand years before, were of little value in the hills and therefore were rarely used in this type of warfare.

Across the valley of Elah from the Philistines, the army of Israel was drawn up in an almost equally formidable array, at least as far as numbers were concerned. But David knew that the iron weapons possessed by the enemy could alone make the difference between victory and defeat. Obviously, too, the sound of the hammers and the roar of the forges must have a dampening effect upon the enthusiasm of the Israelite soldiers, who knew they would shortly have to face formidable weapons.

The tents of the Israelites were arranged by hundreds with fully as much forethought as the Philistines exhibited, indicating that Saul had not lost any of his genius as a military leader. But where the enemy camp hummed with activity, that of Israel was almost oppressingly silent, as if waiting for the inevitable defeat.

David led his mule down the slope and, by asking questions here and there, soon located the camping place of his brothers with the other men from the Bethlehem area. Before he reached them, however, a sudden interruption came from across the valley bringing all activity on the Israelite side to a halt.

"Why have you come out to prepare for battle, O men of Israel?" a stentorian voice shouted in a Philistine dialect which the men of Judah easily understood from having lived so long upon the border between the two nations. David jerked his head around, certain that the man who uttered this voice had used a speaking trumpet to amplify the sound. But he saw at once that he was wrong, as wrong, he realized now, as the deserter had been in his description of the Philistine champion, for Goliath was even larger than he had said. His stocky legs like twin trunks of trees, his body like a massive oak, he towered above his fellows and the Israelite soldiers on the other side of the stream.

"Am I not a Philistine and are you not servants to Saul?" the giant of Gath demanded, deliberately insulting the Hebrews who prided themselves upon being slaves to no man, not even their king. "Choose a man and let him come down to me. If he be able to fight with me and kill me, then we will be your servants. But if I prevail against him and kill him, you shall be our servants and serve us."

From the Israelite side of the valley came only silence, for no man dared cross the stream to what could only be his death.

"I defy the armies of Israel this day." The Philistine flung the challenge at them once more. "Give me a man that we may fight together." When there was still no answer, he spat contemptuously across the brook toward the Israelite camp and, followed by his shield-bearer, stalked back to his own encampment.

David found his brothers and gave them the food he had brought, then went on to give the cheeses to their captain before returning to where the men of Bethlehem sat eating beside their campfires. Hardly anyone went out of his way to speak to him, although many of those camped near his brothers were his own kinsmen. All seemed to have been gripped by depression in the face of the daily challenge and open contempt of Goliath. Finally David sought out Joab and sat down beside him.

"How long has the Philistine defied us?" he asked.

"For forty days," Joab said morosely.

"It is a sad day for Israel when one such as he can curse us for cowards."

Joab only shrugged, for there was nothing to say, but the more David thought of Goliath, the angrier he became. "Who is this uncircumcised Philistine that he should defy the armies of the living God?" he burst out finally, unable to control his indignation. "I wonder what would be done for the man who killed him and took away the reproach from Israel!"

In his anger and frustration, David spoke louder than he intended and a Benjaminite lying nearby heard him.

"The king would enrich him with great riches and give him his daughter in marriage," the man said. "And no doubt his family would be free in Israel."

"Would you claim the reward, stripling?" another man asked,

and a whoop of jeering laughter came from the men around the fire.

Eliab, David's older brother, heard it. "Why did you come here?" he demanded tartly of David. "I know the mischief in your heart. You came hoping to see a battle and now you are trying to provoke one."

David did not relish Eliab's reprimanding him where the men of Benjamin could hear. "If someone does not fight this Philistine and kill him," he retorted, "Israel will be defeated before ever an arrow is loosed or a javelin cast."

"Why not kill him yourself, stripling?" one of the Benjaminites suggested, and, stung by the raillery, David replied, "Perhaps I will."

"A champion!" someone sounded the cry. "A champion to defend us against Goliath!"

David had unwittingly given the men something they badly needed, a release for their futile anger at the insults hurled at them by Goliath.

"A champion!" Taken up by other groups, the shout echoed through the camp. "A champion against Goliath!"

"Now they are making a mockery of you," Eliab said furiously. "Go find your sleeping place somewhere else. Let it not be known that a son of Jesse is a fool."

By now, considerable uproar had arisen in the area assigned to the men from Bethlehem and Benjamin. Crestfallen and still belligerent at the jibes being directed at him, David sought a place with his cousins, but the jeering cry of "A champion!" followed him. Finally he was forced to spread his cloak beside the pack mule at the edge of the camp and there Joab found him sometime later.

"The king has sent for you," Joab told him. "He waits in his tent."

"Do you know what he wants?" David remembered well the first time he had seen Saul in the palace at Gibeah and the thought was not at all reassuring. The king's rage was a frightening thing to behold, and he was not at all surprised that Saul could be angry at him for stirring up the camp.

"Someone told him you volunteered to fight against the Philistine," Joab said. "How could you have been such a fool, David?"

It was on the tip of David's tongue to protest that he had not volunteered at all but had merely been exercising his natural curiosity by inquiring about the reward to anyone lucky enough to kill the enemy champion. But his pride had been deeply wounded by the public tongue-lashing Eliab had given him and the jeers of the men, so he did not answer.

"The Philistine would make two of you," Joab observed as they walked through the camp toward Saul's tent. "The king is much given to anger lately; he may even cut off your head before Goliath can get to you."

David was not at all happy about the situation but his pride would not let him do what, in the circumstances, seemed the only sensible thing; namely, to send Joab back with a message that he had already left the camp and returned to Bethlehem and his father's flocks. Then a thought came to him. If Jonathan interceded with Saul, he might get off with nothing worse than a reprimand. After all, David reminded himself, his only offense was that of stirring up some laughter, and in the men's present mood, that was hardly a crime.

"Where is Jonathan?" he asked. "We were good friends in Gibeah."

Joab shrugged. "I am beginning to think the tales you told about swearing blood brotherhood with Jonathan in Gibeah and cheering Saul out of his melancholy were only idle boasts, but this time you are in no danger of being exposed as a liar. Jonathan led a scouting party eastward yesterday to see whether reinforcements are coming to join the Philistines. He is not expected to return before tomorrow."

With his last hope of escape gone, David would gladly have given up his chances of becoming King of Israel to be back on the hillside before Bethlehem once more, tending the sheep. But there was no way out save to turn tail and run, or prostrate himself before Saul and admit that he had only asked about the reward for killing Goliath out of idle curiosity. And either course would bring upon him once again the jeers and taunts of the camp.

A wiry man wearing the purple-dyed tunic of a high-ranking officer was standing near Saul's tent. When David and Joab approached, he stepped into the light of the torch burning before the tent and David saw that it was Abner, chief captain of the army under Saul. He had seen the older man several times in Gibeah, and knew Abner was highly respected, not only as a brave warrior, but also as an intelligent and able tactician whose clever feats of strategy had more than once saved the less thoughtful king from defeat.

"Is this the boy, Joab?" Abner asked.

"Yes, my lord Abner," Joab said. "But he is only . . ."

"I will take him to the king. You may return to your place."

With Joab gone, David could not help feeling desolate. Abner did not take him to Saul at once, but studied him for a moment without speaking; to David's surprise, no amusement showed in his eyes—only a look of speculation. "So you would fight the Philistine for a reward?" he asked finally.

Here was David's chance to explain how he had become involved in a situation for which he had no appetite, but once again his stubborn pride would not allow him to beg Abner to let him go and pursue the matter of the Philistine champion no further.

"Not for a reward, my lord," he said, "but to avenge the insult to Israel and to the Most High."

Abner's eyebrows lifted and he appeared to debate with himself for a moment. Then he shrugged and turned to the opening of Saul's tent. "Come along," he said. "The king does not like to be kept waiting."

Saul was sitting upon a chest or case to which had been attached carrying handles so it could be used to transport bronze arrowheads and spearpoints on the march. He did not have on the robe of purple he had usually worn in Gibeah, but was dressed now, like the other fighting men of Israel, in a short tunic of rough cloth that came to his knees, with short sleeves covering his shoulders so that the leather straps supporting his breastplate and the similar protection for his back, sometimes called a "target," would not press into his skin. A flagon of wine stood beside him and a half-filled silver cup was in his hand.

David was not surprised that Saul did not recognize him, for he had changed much in the space of two years since leaving Gibeah. For one thing he had grown taller, broader of shoulder and somewhat more sturdy of body, though he was still slender compared to the stockiness of Saul or of Joab. And then his cheeks, upon which there had been only the fuzzy hair of youth when he was in Gibeah, now boasted a curly beard of which he was inordinately proud.

"Who is this?" Saul demanded, lifting brooding eyes to stare at them.

David was shocked by the change in the king since he had last seen him. Then, even in anger, the Son of Kish had possessed the regal bearing of a king and a natural leader of men. But now he appeared to be broken and worn, as if all his strength had been drained out of him. With a shock David realized the cause: Saul was afraid.

David had been quite resigned to confessing to Saul that he had no desire to fight a battle which could only have one ending, his own death. But the realization of Saul's fear did what nothing else could have done; it filled him with a sense of strength he never remembered possessing before. For if the king of Israel was afraid to the point where he seemed no longer fit to be a leader, it could only mean that the time was not far away when David, as Saul's anointed successor, must be strong enough to save his people from destruction. Unconsciously the youth straightened his shoulders, bringing a thoughtful look to the eyes of Abner, who stood beside him.

"Who is this?" Saul repeated, his anger beginning to boil up.

"It is the Judahite who asks a reward for destroying the Philistine giant," the chief captain hastened to explain.

"Has he offered to fight Goliath?"

Abner answered before David could speak. "Yes. Some men of Benjamin heard him. I knew you would want to see such a brave man and ordered him brought directly here to you."

Saul emptied the wine cup in a single gulp and tossed it aside. "You are not old enough or experienced enough to fight the Philistine," he said belligerently.

Saul had just offered David a way out, but a new wisdom had come to the youth during the past few moments. What was happening here, he recognized with an intuition whose source he knew must come from a higher power than himself, was part of a pattern. Just how the pattern would develop as the threads were woven and interwoven, he had as yet no idea. But he did know that he must follow wherever it led, since it was nothing less than the will of God.

"Let no man's heart fail because of the Philistine," David said calmly. "Your servant will go and fight with him."

"But you are little more than a stripling, while he has been a man of war from his youth." Saul's protest was hardly more than perfunctory this time and Abner spoke before the king could say more.

"You have spoken well, young man," the chief captain said hurriedly. "Surely the Lord will be your shield and buckler!"

Somehow the words had a hollow ring. Could it be, David wondered, that all this had been planned by Abner, after his own curiosity concerning Goliath had been jeeringly misconstrued by the men as a challenge to the Philistine? Even a reason for Abner's strategy came to him: perhaps the chief captain had recognized the cancer of fear eating at Saul's vitals and had deliberately brought him to the king's tent tonight, there to be thrust into the challenge whether he willed it or not. For once he was killed—sacrificed would be a better word, David thought wryly—Saul might be convinced that it was useless to consider fighting the Philistine champion himself, and some of the gnawing fear which had attacked the king's soul would be allayed. What was more, Saul's perfunctory protest told David that the king was entirely willing to go along with Abner's scheme, in fact, might even be a partner to it.

In his newfound wisdom, it was easy now for David to understand the cancer that was threatening to destroy Saul's mind. It must be the conviction that God had deserted him because he had failed to be the leader Samuel had anointed him to be. And once God had deserted him, Saul knew that death stood always at his shoulder, whether in the form of Goliath or simply in a pebble underfoot that could trip him and send him crashing headlong down a hillside to be destroyed upon the rocks below. Worst of all, the very fear of death had robbed Saul of the strength to be a man and face it courageously by challenging Goliath and dying, if need be, with the bravery that his people had a right to expect of a king.

A new David was born in that moment. It was a David who could admire Saul and be loyal to him even in his weakness, because God had anointed the Son of Kish to be king of his people, and yet be girded by confidence in his own strength to do what must be done. And feeling compassion for Saul, this new David could even help him carry the burden of his own fear by making it easy for the king to send him to what Saul must expect to be his death.

"Your servant kept his father's sheep," David told the king confidently. "And though a lion came and took a lamb out of the flock, I went after him and struck him and took it out of his mouth and killed him. Your servant killed not only the lion but also a bear, and be sure that this uncircumcised Philistine shall be as one of them, because he has defied the armies of the living God."

"The spear of the Philistine is sharper and longer than the claws of a lion or a bear," Saul warned him.

"The Lord delivered me out of the paw of the lion and out of the paw of the bear," David said quietly. "Be sure he will deliver me out of the hands of this Philistine."

Saul leaned forward and searched David's eyes with his own. In that moment, he seemed to become once again the resolute and determined man for whom David had played the harp at Gibeah, and when he spoke, even his voice seemed to have changed, now containing something that had been absent before, a note of hope.

"Go!" he said. "Go and the Lord be with you."

CHAPTER 11

"And the Philistine came on and drew near unto David; and the man that bare the shield went before him." I SAMUEL 17:41

THE ISRAELITE ARMY was awake with the rising of the sun for word had gone through the camp the night before that a youth from Bethlehem who was not even a soldier had agreed to fight Goliath. Though hardly anyone thought David had a chance of winning, there was still enough drama in the mere fact that someone in Israel had at last found the courage to fight Goliath to insure that no man in either army would miss the spectacle. As always in such a contest, a certain amount of wagering was going on, although in this case it was largely on whether the Philistine would kill the upstart shepherd at the first thrust of the spear or javelin, or allow him to approach near enough to be cut in two with his great sword of iron.

As for David, the new confidence and power he had found in Saul's tent the night before did not desert him and he slept well, wrapped in his cloak beside the campfire of the men from Bethlehem. There had been no more jeering after he had committed himself to fight the Philistine champion; in the early morning, Joab brought him the handful of dates and crust of bread that served as a morning meal for the soldiers in the field.

"I sharpened my javelin last night," Joab said as the two friends ate, squatting beside the fire. "You can take it with you into battle."

David was touched, for he knew how much Joab prized the javelin with its blade and point of iron.

"If you thrust it into Goliath's side between the plates of his body armor, you may find a vital spot," Joab added.

The words were not spoken with much enthusiasm and David knew what Joab was thinking; that long before he got close enough to thrust the javelin into Goliath's side, the Philistine would already have cut him down with the sword or thrust him through with the spear.

"Have you planned your method of fighting him yet?" Joab asked.

David shook his head. "The Lord will guide my hand, just as he sent me here to answer the challenge."

His friend stared at him in astonishment. "Why you when he did not give his own anointed king the courage to overcome Goliath?"

"God has deserted Saul," David explained. "It happened at Mizpeh when he performed the sacrifices without waiting for Samuel to come."

"But Saul still won the battle. Surely that means the Lord relented."

"If that were true, Saul would know it and would not be afraid to fight the Philistine."

Joab frowned; being a man of action, the finer distinctions of thought and logic were generally beyond him. "How is it that you are not afraid, then?" he asked.

It was on the tip of David's tongue to tell Joab that he was the Lord's Anointed now, but he remembered his conversation with Jonathan at Gibeah and his promise never to reveal that truth. "I trust in God," he explained. "He will show me the way."

Joab shook his head slowly. "You have always been a strange one, David. Were anyone else a musician and singer of songs such as you are, I would label him half woman, but I know you are a man for I have wrestled with you and tested my sword against yours. If it would help you, I would go against Goliath in your stead, but I know he would kill me and who would be helped by that?"

David knew Joab meant every word, and he would have told him the truth if he could but he would not go back on his word to Jonathan. "Goliath will come forth soon," he said. "I must go to the king's tent now and meet the trumpeters who will announce that we accept the challenge."

"Then let me fight at your side," Joab begged.

"This must be done alone," David reminded him. "Otherwise the enemy will claim that it was unfair."

As every morning for as long as he could remember, David tucked the sling under his belt. The pouch in which he carried the stones ordinarily used for ammunition was empty but he did not trouble himself about that. If he survived the encounter with the Philistine, it would be easy to pick up stones from the bed of the brook so that he would have the ammunition necessary to protect himself on the homeward journey to Bethlehem.

Then suddenly, with his hand still upon the sling, David understood how he would conquer the Philistine champion. To survive, he must somehow strike the enemy from afar before Goliath could reach him with javelin, spear, or sword, a feat which could only be accomplished by the weapon in which his own skill equaled and perhaps exceeded any warrior in all of Israel: the sling! With that knowledge a weight was suddenly lifted from his mind, for he knew now that God was indeed with him and that he could not fail.

On the way to Saul's tent, David stopped beside the bank of the brook that tumbled through the small gorge separating the two armies, to wash his face in the cool water and clear his head of sleep. There at the bottom of a pool he saw the final proof that the Lord would fight beside him that day. Five stones lay there as if they had been waiting for him, as indeed he was convinced that they had. Their edges had been worn off by the turbulent waters until they were smooth and round, the ideal ammunition for his sling.

Saul was waiting before his tent, the massed ranks of the army of Israel behind him upon the slope. Each man was fully armed, including Saul. The king's spirit seemed to have changed, too, for the brooding light of depression which had filled his eyes last night was gone now. Beside him, Abner, too, was in full armor, as if for a battle.

At David's approach, Saul called to his armorbearer and the youth brought from the tent a second set of the highly polished armor the king usually wore into battle. Taking the brass helmet from the squire, Saul stepped forward and placed it upon David's head.

Saul was a considerably larger man than David, and when the helmet settled about the youth's ears, almost obstructing his vision, a ripple of amusement passed over the massed ranks of men. Ignoring the sound, Saul helped David slide his arms through the straps that supported the breastplate. Designed to protect the chest in battle, it was made of leather, with plates of bronze fastened to the front and back. The chestplate, too, hung loosely upon David, obstructing his movements. And when Saul girded his own sword around the younger man's waist, the murmur of laughter from the troops grew louder, for the shaft of the sword banged against David's knee.

David did not want to hurt the king's feelings, for Saul had been generous in providing him with armor. But he also knew he must somehow rid himself of it before he faced the Philistine as the weight of the breastplate hanging from his shoulders made it difficult to use the sling, and an accurate cast such as he must make would be quite impossible.

"My Lord King," David began, seizing the first idea that came into his mind, "I cannot go with these, for I am not accustomed to them. Let me use my own weapons instead, I pray you."

"That is only fair," Saul agreed. "A man fights best with the weapons he is accustomed to using."

David quickly unbuckled the straps of the breastplate and handed it to the squire along with the brass helmet. Unhampered by the armor, he went to the edge of the stream and selected the five stones he had noticed at the bottom of the pool. Saul seemed on the point of protesting, but just then a shout from the Philistine camp drew the attention of the Israelites to the other side of the stream, where Goliath was coming out for his morning challenge. His shield-bearer, a stripling almost as large as David, went before the Philistine champion, bearing the huge iron shield, the weight of which taxed his strength even to carry it.

Goliath was in full armor, and the morning sun reflected by the brass helmet upon his head almost blinded David, reminding him to approach the enemy in such a way that the sun was not reflected in his eyes when he crossed the stream. The heavy breastplate protecting Goliath's chest was also of iron and a skirt of scale armor hung to his knees, the small sheets of metal sewed to the fabric clashing against each other as he strode to an open space on the opposite side of the stream. Even his legs were protected by greaves, plates of metal molded to the shape of his lower legs from knee to ankle and strapped about his calves.

While Goliath was taking up his usual position preparatory to hurling the challenge, David used the opportunity to study him carefully, searching for a vulnerable spot at which to hurl a stone. He knew he must fell the giant at the first stroke, else spear or javelin could cut him down before he could place another stone in the sling and hurl it. He saw no vital spot not covered by the armor that literally clothed the Philistine from head to foot, until he remembered the jackal he had killed upon the hills above Bethlehem; even at a close range, he had felled the snarling animal by hurling a stone that struck directly between the eyes.

When he studied Goliath again with this in mind, David saw at once the spot where he must place the missile: a small area upon Goliath's forehead, hardly larger than a man's palm, where the edge of his helmet flared out just at the hairline. At that distance it was an impossible target, but David decided that if he got as close to the giant as possible, he would have considerable chance of success. The only drawback was that he would have no opportunity for a second throw, should the first stone miss the target.

"I defy the armies of Israel this day!" Goliath's voice rolled through the valley and echoed from the steep hills forming its sides. "Give me a man that we may fight together!"

Saul hesitated only a moment before his hand went up as a signal to the trumpeters who stood beside the entrance to his tent. The harsh notes of the large trumpets of ram's horn, the *shophar* which always sounded the call of Israel to battle, blasted across the valley. The Israelites saw Goliath stiffen at the brassy note of defiance. From the enemy camp, too, came a sudden clamor as the significance of the *shophar* blast was understood. From all sides men came running to see who had finally dared to challenge their champion, but, in the high drama of the moment, the Philistines overlooked something the significance of which David himself had not noticed; namely, that Saul's men were fully armed, although they seemed to be only standing idly by to watch the uneven contest.

CHAPTER 12

"So David prevailed over the Philistine with a sling and with a stone." I SAMUEL 17:50

AT THE SIGHT of the Israelite champion, a burst of laughter rocketed through the Philistine ranks. David paid no attention, however, but marched resolutely forward across the brook that separated the two armies, stepping nimbly from rock to rock. And as they watched his confident approach, the laughter of the Philistines died away, for it was incredible that a seemingly unarmed man, unarmed, at least, by Philistine standards, should challenge their champion. Most unbelievable of all, he appeared to show no sign of fear.

David's heart was pounding rapidly as he moved forward, never taking his eyes off the small rectangular area of Goliath's skull exposed at the forehead by the flared, lower edge of the helmet. Seen from this distance, the giant was even more overpowering than he had appeared from across the stream, and David could not completely hold back the sudden tide of apprehension that washed at the bastions of his courage and conviction that the Lord would give him the victory. His legs began to tremble; only by leaning slightly upon the staff did he manage to keep the fact hidden from Goliath and the enemy.

As for the giant, he had watched in stunned amazement while David stepped forth from the ranks of the Israelite army and crossed the brook to climb the slope toward him. It was incredible that such a weakling would dare to oppose the mightiest man in Philistia and perhaps in the world. Yet there he was, a mere shepherd, armed only with a staff and sling, advancing upon the Philistine champion as if he were a sheep to be driven back to the flock.

"Am I a dog that you come against me with stones?" Goliath shouted indignantly. "May Dagon curse you this day as I spill your blood upon this ground and give your people into slavery!"

David did not answer, hoping to keep the Philistine busy shouting insults until he could get so close to his target that it would be impossible to miss.

"Come to me!" Goliath taunted. So far he had not even bothered to take the shield from his armorbearer or hurl either spear or javelin, as was customary in the opening stages of a fight. Obviously, as David had hoped, he considered his bare hands weapons enough to handle such a puny opponent. "Come to me and I will give your flesh to the fowls of the air and the beasts of the field!"

David spoke for the first time since he had left the ranks of the Israelite army. "You come at me with a sword and a spear," he said. "But I come to you in the name of the Lord of Hosts, the god of the armies of Israel whom you have defied."

Goliath set himself more firmly upon his broad feet, clenching and unclenching the great hands with which he planned to throttle this upstart who dared to defy him.

"This day the Lord will deliver you into my hands," David said, moving steadily nearer and talking to the giant all the while in the hope of holding his attention. "I will smite you and take your head from you. And I will give the carcasses of the Philistines to the fowl of the air and the wild beasts that all the earth may know there is a god in Israel."

When David paused for breath, Goliath roared his defiance once again and the echo reverberated between the walls of the narrow valley. Almost casually, David put his hand to the pouch at his belt and selected a smooth round stone from those he had taken from the brook. He was near enough now to see the great cords bulging in the massive neck of the Philistine and hear Goliath's knuckles crack as he clenched and unclenched his hands in anticipation. Certain now that the giant would wait to get him within the grasp of those great hands, David dared to go even closer. Only when at last he was certain he could not miss did he drop the staff and let his left hand fall to his waist to fit the stone into the sling.

"All this assembly shall know the Lord does not save with the sword and the spear, for the battle is the Lord's and he will give you into our hands!" David flung the last words veritably into Goliath's teeth, since he was now no more than a dozen paces from him. At the same moment, his right hand seized the strings of the sling as his left hand drew it from his girdle with the stone already well-seated in the pocket. With all the strength of his arm and body, he whirled it twice in a circle about his head. Then, as the cords attached to one side of the center pocket were released, the missile drove straight and true for its target.

The impact of the stone against the giant's forehead was so sharp in the morning air that it could be heard even across the brook on the Israelite side. His eyes still fixed upon the target, David saw the stone sink into Goliath's forehead, crushing bone and brain before it, exactly as the skull of the jackal had been crushed. A horrified look showed momentarily upon Goliath's face before his eyes began to glaze and he stumbled forward. Then his knees buckled and he toppled slowly to the ground.

Four sounds broke the awed silence that followed Goliath's fall. First a moan of fear rose from the ranks of the Philistines massed upon the edge of the small ravine. Second, there was a clash of metal upon stone as Goliath's armorbearer dropped the shield he was carrying and took to his heels toward the Philistine camp. Third was the blast of the *shophar* from the Israelite camp, sounding the call to battle. And finally, there were the exultant shouts of the Israelite warriors charging across the brook to fall upon the enemy, most of whom were totally unarmed, having been too intent upon the strange combat between David and Goliath to pick up their weapons before rushing out of their tents.

As for David, he was concerned with only one thing at the moment, the task of completing his victory over the Philistine champion. Placing his foot upon the chest of the fallen giant, he seized the handle of Goliath's iron sword and drew it from its scabbard. Even though he wielded the blade with both hands, two blows were required to hack off the giant's head. Then, dragging the bloody sword and trophy behind him, for iron weapons were valuable prizes of war, he started across the brook toward the Israelite side. By that time, however, the battle lines were already shifting to the west, as the Israelites pursued the unarmed Philistines, who had been caught unawares when the Israelites attacked them at the moment of David's victory.

After the excitement of the battle with Goliath, whose huge body still lay at the edge of the Philistine encampment across the brook, David could hardly help feeling that he had been ignored. But the battle lines were receding much too rapidly westward for him to catch up and he had no choice except to wait until the army returned. It was the first time he had ever killed a man, and now that the excitement was over, he could not help feeling a little sick. Goliath's head still lay upon the bank of the brook where he had dropped it, but somehow he could not escape the conviction that the sightless eyes continued to follow him about the camp, as if even in death the Philistine were accusing him of having taken an unfair advantage in using the sling.

To escape the seemingly relentless gaze, David finally covered the head with the corselet of armor he had taken from Goliath's body and, since there was nothing else to do until Saul returned and he could start back to Bethlehem, busied himself with caring for the wounded, bandaging them and bringing such surcease as he could to the dying by carrying water to them from the brook. He was still occupied in this manner when Saul and Abner returned to the camp at the head of the main body of the Israelite troops shortly before darkness fell.

Saul went into his tent and, soon after, Abner crossed the brook to where David was giving water to a wounded Israelite. "King Saul wishes to see you," the chief captain said.

By now David had grown accustomed to the stink of the dying upon the hillside and the warm sickly sweet aroma of death. Even Abner blanched a little, however, when he picked up the head of Goliath from beneath the pile of armor and, carrying it in his hand, followed the Israelite captain to the king's tent.

Saul was washing the dirt and grime of battle from his body, using water in a copper basin captured from the Philistines. His armor and weapons lay upon the floor of the tent and David could see from the dents in the breastplate and helmet, as well as the dried blood on sword and spear, that the king had done his own share of fighting that day, as befitted the leader of a people. Only when Saul had dried his face and beard with a towel did he turn to face David and Abner.

"Whose son are you, young man?" he asked.

"I am the son of your servant Jesse, the Bethlehemite," David told him.

"Your skill with the sling saved Israel today."

David shook his head. "The Lord guided my arm, sire. Only he should receive the praise, and you for leading the army to victory when the enemy was caught by surprise."

Saul gave him a startled look. "What were you doing in the camp today? I don't remember seeing you here before."

"My father sent me to bring food to my brothers, Eliab, Abinadab, and Shammah."

Saul nodded. "I know them well; they are excellent fighters."

"My father and all my family are among your most loyal servants," David assured him. "When I tell him how you praised my brothers, it will make him very happy."

"Are you going back to Bethlehem?"

"I am not a soldier," David reminded Saul. "It was only by chance that I happened to come to the camp today."

"By a lucky chance, if it could be called that." Abner spoke beside him. "Unless, as you say, you were sent by the Most High to destroy Goliath."

Again David saw Saul frown as if with displeasure, but the king only shrugged again and pursued the thought no further. "Would you like to remain with the army, if I make a place for you?" he asked.

"My lord king needs only to command and I will obey." David's delight at the idea shone in his face.

"It is settled, then," Saul told him. "You will remain and serve near me always."

"Let your musicians furnish me with a harp," David suggested, "and I will compose a song of victory to be sung around the campfire tonight."

Saul frowned. "There was a boy named David who played and

sang for me in Gibeah years ago. Surely you cannot be the same."

"It was only two years ago, my lord," David told him. "But much has changed since then."

"So it has," Saul agreed. "Your beard makes you look older than I would have expected. And you have filled out into the stature of a man." He turned to Abner. "See that he is given a harp," he directed. "Tonight we will see whether you still sing as sweetly as before, David."

CHAPTER 13

"The soul of Jonathan was knit with the soul of David, and Jonathan loved him as his own soul."
I SAMUEL 18:1

DAVID HAD NOT SEEN Jonathan since he had come to the Israelite camp; when he and Abner came out of Saul's tent, he was overjoyed to find Saul's eldest son waiting outside. The two embraced happily and David followed Jonathan to his own quarters.

"When Abner told me a young man of Bethlehem had killed the Philistine with a stone from a sling, I wondered whether it might be you," Jonathan said. The two had gone inside Jonathan's tent and closed the opening, so they would not be overheard.

"Why would you think that?" David asked, puzzled.

"Do you remember what you told me at Gibeah two years ago? About the time Samuel anointed you with oil?"

"Yes. But what does a lucky throw with the sling have to do with that?"

"Who can say?" Jonathan poured wine from a skin and gave a cup to David before filling one for himself. "Perhaps this is how God's will concerning you is being carried out. Abner tells me you appeared to have no fear of the Philistine."

David smiled. "My knees were knocking so much I had to lean on my staff lest they fail me and I fall to the ground."

"Yet you went on."

"I knew I must get near enough to Goliath to be sure of striking his forehead with the first stone," David explained. "And I was hoping he would be so contemptuous of me that he would wait to tear me apart with his bare hands rather than kill me at a distance with the spear or javelin."

"All that took courage, more courage than any of us possessed."

"Not so much courage as trust in the will of God," David corrected him. "Something told me the Lord would give me the victory. Without that assurance, I could never have crossed the brook."

"The very fact that you felt so confident proves you were doing the Lord's will," Jonathan agreed. "But I wonder how my father would feel if he knew he was honoring the man who will one day replace him as King of Israel."

"Hush!" David cried. "You must not say that."

"It is true, nevertheless; your victory today proves it."

"The men of Benjamin are skilled with the sling," David protested. "Any one of them could have killed Goliath at the distance I was from him when I finally loosed the stone."

"It is true that we have hundreds of men who could have felled the Philistine giant from that range," Jonathan agreed. "But not one of them had confidence enough in God's will that the enemy would be defeated to take the risk." Then his face sobered. "Abner told me something else about this affair as we rode home from Ekron, but I hesitate to tell you now."

David raised his hand with the thumb facing toward Jonathan. "If I searched the skin of my thumb I might find the scar where I pricked it and brought blood to mix with yours long ago. In Gibeah you yourself said there must be no secrets between us."

Jonathan nodded slowly but his face was still grave. "Did you wonder why my father agreed for you, a shepherd from Bethlehem and not even a soldier, to go against this Philistine?"

"Because he hoped I would kill him. Why else?"

Jonathan shook his head. "It was a scheme of Abner's. He told me about it this afternoon on the way back to the camp."

"What sort of scheme?"

"When Abner heard you had inquired concerning a reward for

one able to kill Goliath, he talked my father into persuading you to challenge the champion and fight him."

David remembered the scene last night when Abner had sent Joab to look for him and they had gone to Saul's tent. And the more he thought of it, the more he could see that what had happened there could easily fit in with what Jonathan was saying now.

"Then neither of them expected me to win and I was only a lure to lead the Philistines to destruction?"

Jonathan's pain showed in his face, for in telling David what he had learned from Abner, he was also damning his own father. "Abner was sure the Philistines would be so interested in a fight between you and Goliath that they would forget to protect themselves against attack," he explained. "And that is exactly what happened."

"But those on the losing side were supposed to yield to the winners," David reminded him. "Your father took a great chance in letting me go out against Goliath."

Jonathan shook his head. "You were not even a soldier, David, so neither Abner nor my father considered the conditions of the challenge to hold as far as you were concerned."

"And while Goliath was killing me and the attention of the Philistines was diverted, our army was to fall upon them?"

"That was Abner's plan. You must have noticed that all our men were fully armed and ready for battle."

"I was too intent on killing Goliath to notice anything." David's voice suddenly grew bitter. "And all the time I was only a sacrifice to save your father from defeat!"

"I will not defend him," Jonathan said. "But when I try to put myself in his place, I am sure I would have done the same thing. You have never known what it is to have other people's lives hanging upon your decision, David. It is the heaviest burden a man can be called on to bear; letting one man die to save a nation was a cheap price for today's victory."

"You are right, of course," David admitted, and there was no bitterness in his voice now. In the brief space since the rising of the sun that day, he had matured a great deal. After all, as Jonathan had said, the whole plan had been a brilliant piece of strategy by which almost certain defeat had been turned into victory. The fact that the affair had turned out differently from what Saul and Abner had expected, in that he was alive and Goliath dead, did not really alter the situation at all. Even if he had not won out over Goliath and had fallen victim to the Philistine champion, the Israelite army would still have attacked. And though their chances of overcoming the enemy would have been far less than they had turned out to be when the Philistines took the fall of Goliath as proof that the terrible Israelite god had chosen to give victory to his people, the fact remained that David himself had been only an unsuspecting dupe and completely expendable.

The knowledge of what had really happened, plus his own realization that the brief encounter with Goliath had not actually been a battle at all but merely an exhibition of a skill with the sling that hundreds of men in Israel could easily equal, did nothing to feed David's own self-esteem. And yet the encounter with Goliath had taught him one important lesson; namely, that fear can conquer as quickly as strength, and that the lack of fear is the strongest weapon a man can possess. In years to come, David would hone this knowledge to a new sharpness; it was to be a weapon that would serve again and again.

He did not even realize how much his own situation had changed that day, however, until he stepped out of Jonathan's tent to be greeted by a great roar of acclamation from the soldiers who had witnessed his triumph over Goliath, but had been too occupied the rest of the day to pay homage to him. Now they seized him and, hoisting him to their shoulders, bore him through the camp in triumph to a place of honor, where they had piled the captured spoils, for a great feast of victory.

Flushed and happy, David accepted the homage of his fellows. And when, at the height of the feast that followed, a harp was thrust into his hands and the cry was raised for a song of victory in celebration, his heart filled with melody and he sang what was to be known for centuries afterward as the Victory Hymn of David:

"I will praise thee, O Lord, with my whole heart;
I will show forth all thy marvelous works.
I will be glad to rejoice in thee;
I will sing praise to thy name, O thou most High.

When my enemies are turned back,
They shall fall and perish at thy presence.
For thou hast maintained my right and my cause;
Thou satest on the throne judging right.

Thou hast rebuked the heathen,
Thou hast destroyed the wicked,
Thou hast put out their name forever and ever.
Their memorial perished with them.

But the Lord shall endure forever;
He hath prepared his throne for judgment.
And he shall judge the world in righteousness,
He shall minister judgment to the people in uprightness.

The Lord also will be a refuge for the oppressed,
A refuge in times of trouble.
And they that know thy name will put their trust in thee;
For thou, Lord, hast not forsaken them that seek thee.

Sing praises to the Lord:
Declare among the people his doings.
The heathen are sunk down in the pit they have made:
In the net which they hid is their own foot taken.

The Lord is known by the judgment he executeth;
The wicked is snared in the work of his own hands.
The wicked shall be turned into hell,
And all the nations that forget God.

Arise, O Lord; let not man prevail:
Let the heathen be judged in thy sight.
Put them in fear, O Lord;
That the nations may know themselves to be but men."

Flushed and triumphant, David did not notice that Saul was standing before his own tent at the center of the encampment, watching and listening. Had he seen the king, he might have remembered Jonathan's warning in Gibeah that he must never reveal the fact of his having been anointed by Samuel, for Saul's face was dark with annoyance and with envy. It had been a long time since the voices of the men had been raised to acclaim Saul a hero, as they were acclaiming David tonight. And as the king listened, the fingers of his right hand closed spasmodically upon the shaft of a javelin that stood by the entrance to the tent where a guard had left it when Abner had given him permission to join the merrymakers.

Two people were watching Saul that night, however. One was Abner; as he looked from David, radiant with happiness, to the king, the chief captain's face was thoughtful. The other watcher was Joab who, while rejoicing in the good fortune of his best friend, was also calculating how best to use that good fortune to further certain purposes of his own.

CHAPTER 14

"I the Lord will be their God, and my servant David a prince among them." EZEKIEL 34:24

WHEN FINALLY the clamor died down and David was allowed to go to the special tent Saul had ordered prepared for him, Abner followed. Unnoticed by the Israelite captain, Joab also crept near the tent and remained in the shadows where he could hear all that was said.

"Are your quarters comfortable?" Abner asked, as he closed the flap of the tent with a casual gesture. "I routed out one of the captains of a thousand to make room for you."

"I am flattered that the son of Ner is so concerned for my comfort," David said, somewhat curtly.

The chief captain chose to ignore the frosty note in David's voice. "Today you can have anything Israel possesses," he reminded the younger man. "Even Saul was not acclaimed so highly when he recaptured Jabesh-gilead."

"Yet this morning you were willing to sacrifice me in order to throw the Philistines off their guard."

Abner raised his eyebrows. "So Jonathan told you what I said to him. It might have been better if he had held his tongue."

"And let me think I was a hero?" David demanded tartly.

"Whether you think so or not, you are a hero, David. It took courage to face Goliath and still more to bring him down. Had I possessed such courage, I would have challenged the Philistine myself."

Taken aback by the other's frankness, David had nothing to say. "The task of facing a skilled and well-armed enemy with troops who lack weapons and armor of iron and fight only when they are attacked is no easy one." Abner took a seat upon a box in the corner. "Until our arms and our strength equal or exceed that of the Philistines, we must fight them as best we can by strategy and by whipping up the courage of our men."

"As you whipped up mine to where I would challenge Goliath?"

"I will admit that you were a gift from God, but you have had some reward already. And if you are as intelligent as I think you are, there will be more. How would you like to become one of Saul's captains of a thousand?"

"Captain of a thousand!" David stared at Abner incredulously, certain that he had not heard aright. Not even in his rosiest dreams, save for those in which he was king, had he dared to consider such a possibility. "I am too young," he stammered. "And I have not been tested in battle."

"Who has been tested more?" Abner said dryly. "And who has proved himself more fully?"

"Would King Saul agree?"

"Yesterday you won for Saul a battle that seemed lost. He can hardly fail to give you anything you want."

"I was told that Saul had offered his daughter and great riches to the one who killed Goliath."

"They can be yours—in time," Abner told him. "The position of captain of a thousand would only be the first step toward what I have in mind for you."

"Do you think the men would follow me?"

"A man becomes a leader of others for many reasons, David; most of all, because he has proved his courage and has shown that he can turn defeat into victory. Yesterday you did both." The chief captain got to his feet. "Say nothing of this to Saul or Jonathan; it may take me some time to bring it about."

"And what do you ask of me in return?"

Abner's laughter boomed out. "So you, too, have heard that Abner never gives something for nothing. You have already paid me, David, with a victory over the Philistines. I am still chief captain of Israel, am I not, instead of a slave turning the mills of Gath and Ekron? Why should I ask for more?"

When Abner was gone, David paced the narrow confines of the tent, trying to think. He was far more accustomed to the open hilltops of the Bethlehem area than to the small limits of the tent, however, and decided to go outside. Picking up the harp he had been playing by the campfire, he began to climb the steep side of the hill, pausing only when he came out upon the crest that marked the highest point in that immediate area.

The moon had already risen above the distant range of mountains whose lower slopes were washed by the waters of the Salt Sea. In its soft and almost benevolent light he could see the fertile uplands of Judah to which the valley of Elah was a gateway from the west, stretching out before him. To the south lay the range of hills called Adullam, with its many caves, where the men of Judah had often hidden from pursuit by Philistine marauders. Northward were the central highlands with the ancient shrines of Bethel and Shechem.

For a moment, David felt the same thrill of discovery that he knew Joshua and the children of Israel must have experienced several centuries earlier, when they had viewed this land of verdant slopes and fertile valleys for the first time. In the moonlight, he could see the mathematical arrangement of rows in the cornfields that lined the broader reaches of the valley of Elah and the brown furrows of the fresh and fertile earth between them. To the east, a dark patch that appeared to flow like water before the night breeze could only be a field of ripe yellow grain. The whole area was well known to the men of Judah who for centuries had dwelt in the hills for protection while tilling the valleys below.

The sound of a footstep startled David out of his reverie, and he turned quickly, his hand dropping to the knife at his belt. But when he saw a familiar stocky figure emerge from the darkness, he lifted his hand.

"Does the son of Jesse prefer his own company to that of his kinsmen?" David recognized by the roughness of Joab's tone that his cousin was displeased, though he could not at the moment understand why, unless it were from envy.

"I needed to think," David explained. "So much has happened since yesterday that it is hard to keep it all in order."

"Such as being sought out by Abner and offered the captaincy of a thousand?"

David's voice hardened. "My cousin Joab does not usually go spying on the affairs of his friends."

"Unless he needs to know who is still a friend."

"Why would anything change between us, Joab? I have done nothing to harm you and surely a far better soldier than I could not envy me a lucky throw." He paused, for an explanation of Joab's displeasure had suddenly occurred to him. "Or do you covet the captaincy for yourself?"

"Why should I not covet it?" Joab growled. "I am a soldier; naturally I want to be a leader."

"Has it come to this, then? That you envy me a skill any shepherd possesses? Both of us know you are far more than my equal in battle. In fact, the more I think about it, the more I realize what a fool I must have seemed to all of you when I dared to challenge Goliath."

"Why did you, then?" Joab's tone was less belligerent now, merely puzzled.

David was very fond of Joab and wondered whether he dared to reveal to his cousin what he had thus far spoken of only to Jonathan. "Come sit here on the rocks," he said, having made his decision. "There is much I must tell you."

When David finished telling the story of Samuel's visit to his father's home in Bethlehem, it was a long time before Joab spoke. When he did, his voice was no longer harsh, only thoughtful. "You say you told Jonathan all of this and he believes it to be true?" he asked.

"Yes."

"But why would you be chosen? That is what I cannot understand."

"I have no answer any more than have you," David admitted. "But remember that Gideon was not a soldier when he was selected to deliver the people from the Midianites. In fact, he was threshing grain in the vineyard to hide it from the enemy."

"Are you sure Abner knew nothing of this when he offered to make you one of Saul's captains?"

"How could he? I spoke of it only to Jonathan."

"It is as I thought, then. Abner is trying to win your favor because the men look upon you as a hero. But we cannot let you become indebted to him."

"Then why not let events take their own course, as in the fight with Goliath yesterday?"

"The will of God is still carried out by men," Joab reminded him. "Joshua did not just camp before the walls of Jericho waiting for them to fall. He marched around the city as God directed, blowing the trumpets daily until the day of the city's destruction. And when his men were defeated before Ai, he led a night march across the mountains and lay in wait while a small band of his soldiers lured the defenders of the city outside the walls where he could fall upon them and destroy them."

"I remember those stories. But what do they have to do with me?"

"The Lord has shown you his favor and has anointed you one day to be king of Israel," Joab reminded him. "But if you are to be a worthy king, you must still earn it through your own efforts."

"What comes next, then?"

"You must become captain of a thousand before Abner can carry out his own plans," Joab said briskly, getting to his feet. "We will act first, so Abner cannot say he brought it about himself and thus have a hold over you."

"But how?"

"Nehemiah, one of the chief captains from Judah, was killed in the fighting yesterday," Joab told him. "Tomorrow the men of Judah will select a new captain and who would be a more logical choice than the conqueror of Goliath? Remember, it was Judah who made Saul king in the beginning; without Judah's support, you will never reign over Israel."

"I am willing," David told him. "But how do I go about it?"

"Leave everything to me," Joab said and started down the slope toward the camp. When David did not immediately follow, he paused and turned back. "Aren't you coming?"

"Go on without me," David said. "I need a little while to think."

"Be sure you say nothing of this to anyone," Joab warned. "We must take Abner completely by surprise, else he will forestall us and have Saul appoint a new captain in Nehemiah's place."

The cool of night had already settled upon the ridge, but it was an even deeper chill that made David pull his cloak about him. He was not accustomed to the kind of manipulations Joab had described; he felt, in fact, a strong impulse to flee to Bethlehem, back to the peace he had known watching the sheep grazing upon the hillsides. He reluctantly stifled the impulse, however, for something, perhaps a new wisdom gained since yesterday, told him that in crossing the stream to face Goliath, he had also crossed a boundary from one phase of his life to another.

It was a frightening prospect to one who was, in many ways, still a boy, for he had no way of seeing the dangers and the pitfalls, or even the rewards, that might lie before him. Then, as many times before when troubled by uncertainty and fear, he picked up the harp and ran his fingers across it. And as the notes rippled from the sounding board at its base, a song began to take form deep within his soul, the words flowing with an effortless rhythm that was somehow as reassuring as their content:

> The Lord is my shepherd; I shall not want.
> He maketh me to lie down in green pastures;
> He leadeth me beside the still waters.
> He restoreth my soul;
> He leadeth me in the paths of righteousness for his name's sake.
> Yea, though I walk through the valley of the shadow of death,
> I will fear no evil;
> For thou art with me;
> Thy rod and thy staff they comfort me.
> Thou preparest a table before me in the presence of mine enemies:

Thou anointest my head with oil;
My cup runneth over.
Surely goodness and mercy shall follow me all the days of my
life;
And I will dwell in the house of the Lord for ever.

II. THE CAVE OF ADULLAM

"David therefore departed thence, and escaped to the cave Adullam."

I SAMUEL 22:1

CHAPTER 1

"And the priest said, The sword of Goliath the Philistine, whom thou sleweth in the valley of Elah, behold, it is here." I SAMUEL 21:9

ABOUT A HALF-HOUR'S WALK northwest of Jerusalem, on the regular north-south route from Hebron to Saul's capital at Gibeah, was the priestly center of Nob. Here stood the tabernacle, or tent, in which the Ark of the Covenant was normally housed, and the sacred altar served by a small company of priests and levites under the leadership of Ahimelech. Saul and the army paused at Nob for the night in a service of thanksgiving and sacrifice for their victories. The next day they would move on to Gibeah and make their march into the capital.

Nearly six months had passed since the day of the great victory in the valley of Elah, when David's feat of slaying the giant Goliath had triggered the battle which resulted in a stunning defeat for the Philistines. It had been a busy period spent in driving the enemy back to the area around the five fortified cities of the Philistine confederation, and in securing Judah, for the time being at least, against further depredation. Once again the borders between the enemy and the Israelite tribes were as they had been during Saul's first series of victories, immediately after he was crowned king of the united tribes. In itself this accomplishment was ample reason for rejoicing, but in addition, much valuable booty and many weapons of iron had been taken from the enemy.

On the seacoast, the Philistine domain now stretched from Joppa on the north almost as far south as the River of Egypt. Inland, it curved in an arc to form a rather indefinite and still contested border with Judah, west of both Shochoh and Beer-sheba. The Amalekites, too, had been pushed southward to a point roughly on a line with the southern tip of the Salt Sea. But in spite of the victories of Saul and David, the Philistine domain still encompassed powerful cities, including Gerar, a major smelting and ironworking center. Furthermore, the raw iron ore needed by their smiths could easily be obtained from the Amalekites to the south or the Edomites to the east, who remained more or less in league with the Philistines.

The enemy also retained the lowlands of the rich fertile coastal plain, or *shephelah*. At the moment, however, the men of Judah had no desire to own this region. Accustomed to fighting from caves and steep-sided valleys, they were not anxious to do battle with the enemy upon the plains, where the iron-wheeled chariots of the Philistines put the Hebrews to considerable disadvantage. Only once, in fact, had the Israelites dared to fight against the chariots; that was in the days of the judges, when Deborah and Barak had led them and the Lord had sent an avalanche of rain to mire the chariots of King Hazor on the plains around Jezreel. In this battle, Sisera, the enemy captain, had been slain by a brave woman named Jael when he took refuge in her tent, earning for her a high place among the women in Israel's history.

Those early days of Saul's kingship had been a glorious period, with victory after victory over the enemy that ringed the Hebrew tribes. But the quarrel between Saul and Samuel and the king's illness of the mind had caused the Israelites to lose heart for a time. Now, after David's startling feat of killing the Philistine champion, and the victories which had followed, the tribes were infused with a new spirit. Once again it seemed that there was a chance of holding them together in something resembling a nation, whose strength and fighting ability the other people in the area would respect and fear.

By the time Saul's men had made camp, night had descended upon the hilltop that formed the holy place called Nob. Instead of going directly to his tent, David left the camp and climbed the rocky hillside to its crest. There a group of torches burned before the Tabernacle that was, next to the Ark of the Covenant itself, the most sacred object in Israel.

Like the Tabernacle made by Moses in the wilderness according to God's own instructions, the present symbol of divine presence was a great tent fashioned of luxurious cloth and supported by a framework of acacia—also called shittim wood. From his studies as a boy, David knew by heart the dimensions of the Tabernacle—thirty cubits in length and ten in breadth. The front portion, known as the "Holy Place," was twenty cubits in length; the smaller chamber, the "Most Holy Place," was ten cubits square. The two apartments were separated by a curtain of rich cloth dyed with the purple of the Phoenicians. They were supported by pillars of acacia wood covered with thin plates of beaten gold. In earlier times, the Ark of the Covenant had rested in the "Most Holy Place," but since the Ark was still at Kirjath-jearim, this chamber was now empty.

In the Holy Place stood a table for the shewbread, baked daily and placed fresh upon it as a gift of thanksgiving to God for the manna upon which the children of Israel had subsisted in the wilderness during the long escape from Egypt. Beside the table stood the Golden Candlestick, in which a consecrated candle burned continually, and the Golden Altar of Incense, from which fragrant smoke always curled. The Altar of Sacrifice was not within the Tabernacle but stood to one side in the middle of the rocky hilltop. Made from a slab of stone resting upon four pillars, it was stained by the blood of many sacrifices and blackened by the fires kindled there to consume them.

The flap of the Tabernacle opening had been pulled aside tonight so that the interior of the Holy Place could be seen by the visitors. Attracted by the beautiful symbols of God's presence, David moved closer, and when someone spoke to him from the shadows, he thought for an instant that he was listening to the voice of God himself.

"The son of Jesse need not hesitate to enter the Holy Place," a deep voice said. "The Anointed of the Lord is as one of his priests."

David turned to face the tall man who emerged from the shadows beside the Tabernacle. He was dressed in priestly robes and his beard was trimmed and anointed, not scraggly and stained like that of the prophet Samuel.

"I am Ahimelech, first priest of those who serve the Lord here at Nob and guard his holy Tabernacle," the tall man said. "The prophet Samuel comes here often."

"Did he tell you of me?"

"Yes."

"What about the others? Do they know?"

Ahimelech shook his head. "The time for the truth to be spread abroad has not yet come, but it may not be far away."

"I would gladly make way for Jonathan," David said. "Will you ask the Lord to let him take my place?"

"The will of God is beyond the power of men to change, my son," Ahimelech said. "You must have realized that when you went against Goliath."

"But the enemy has been driven back now. If I return to my father's house, Jonathan can still become king after Saul. "

"Even you must recognize that Bethlehem is behind you," the priest said. "A boy clings to the scenes of his childhood, but when he becomes a man, he must make a new home for himself, even though it be far away."

"And may he never go back?" The words were spoken almost plaintively, for in spite of his high position and the respect the men of Judah paid him for his bravery and his leadership, David had more than once in the past six months found himself yearning for the peaceful days spent upon the hillsides around Bethlehem; he had known no enemies then except the jackals who sought to steal lambs from the flock.

"Not when he has been anointed by the Lord, as you have been, for a special purpose," the priest told him. "Such a one must hold himself ready at all times to do God's will."

"But I no longer know where my path lies. The night before

I went against Goliath, it was as if a voice spoke to me, telling me what I should do. Since then I have heard it no more."

"Something must have brought you here tonight. Surely it was the Lord's work."

David shook his head. "I only came to thank the Most High for the victory over Goliath and for making me captain of a thousand."

"King Saul will make gifts tomorrow from the spoils of war. They are partly the fruits of your own victories."

"But I want to do more."

"Then give the Lord whatever you prize most highly," Ahimelech suggested.

"But I have nothing worthy—" David stopped in mid-sentence, for he had suddenly realized that he did possess something of considerable worth indeed. More than anything he had ever owned, he prized the iron sword he had taken from Goliath; in every village through which they had passed on the way home from the battlefields, crowds had thronged to see it and hear again the story of the great victory. The sword was not only a symbol of that victory, but also a weapon of iron; as such it was extremely valuable to the Israelites.

"Only one thing I possess is worthy as a gift to the Most High," David said slowly. "He let it come into my hands and I will give it to him in return."

When David returned bearing the great two-edged sword of Goliath, Ahimelech was still standing beside the Tabernacle.

"The sword of Goliath!" he exclaimed. "Only one who loves the Lord even more than life itself would give up such a prize. Be sure its value will be returned to you a hundredfold!"

When David returned to his tent, he was not surprised to find Joab waiting there. His cousin had formed the habit of visiting him after most of the camp was asleep. Only then could they discuss the events of the day and their significance without danger of being overheard.

"I came here just now and found you gone," Joab said. "Did Saul or Abner send for you tonight?"

Aware of Joab's distrust of Abner and his consuming desire to occupy the position of chief captain, David had grown accustomed to the fact that his kinsman often read into every action the possibility that he might be influenced by Abner. "I went to the Tabernacle," he explained. "With a thank offering for the Most High."

"Saul is making one for all of us. Why should you give more?"

"This is something personal, a gift I thought I should make beyond what Saul will give."

Joab's voice hardened. "Then Abner allotted you more than the rest when the division was made."

"If you must know," David said somewhat shortly, "I gave the sword of Goliath."

"The sword of Goliath!" Joab stared at him incredulously. "Have you gone mad?"

"Not mad—only grateful. If God had not shown me how to kill the giant, my blood instead of his would now be staining the rocks in the valley of Elah."

"But you have given away your greatest advantage over Saul," Joab protested. "Without the sword to remind him, he will quickly forget that you saved his army."

"I can only obey the will of the Most High," David insisted.

"God favors him who dares when the odds are against him," Joab snapped. "Was it for nothing that I persuaded the men of Judah to choose you as their captain?"

David could hardly deny that Joab had played a considerable part in his being chosen as an officer, when, on the morning after the fight with Goliath, the men of Judah had gathered to select a leader. Everyone in the army had known how important this choice could be, for Saul himself had been selected as the leader of Judah before he became king of the united tribes. It had been Joab who had thrown the Urim and Thummim, as the marked cubes used in casting lots were called, and when David was selected, a mighty shout of approval had gone up from the men of Judah. David knew that Joab had laid the groundwork for their enthusiasm by having his brothers, Abishai and Asahel, spread the word that the conqueror of Goliath was the logical choice.

In only one quarter had his selection that morning been greeted with less than approval. David would never forget the sudden bleak look that had come over Saul's face when the choice was announced, or the thoughtful expression of Abner as the chief captain studied him across the open space where the lots were being cast.

"Did you really control the casting of the Urim and Thummim that day, Joab?" David asked impulsively.

His cousin gave him a quick, appraising look. "Why do you ask? You never have before."

"It has been worrying me," David admitted.

"I *was* prepared to see that the lot fell as we wanted it to fall," Joab answered.

"But did you control it?"

"No. The Urim and the Thummim fell true that morning."

"Doesn't that prove I am acting as the Lord would have me act?"

Joab shrugged. "So long as you act as I would have you act, I have no concern," he said. "Perhaps when we tell it in Gibeah that you gave the sword of Goliath to the Lord, the people will think even more of you because of it."

"Ahimelech says the same," David told him and chuckled. "Besides it was too heavy to carry, even in a victory procession."

Joab took down a wineskin that was hanging on the center pole of the tent and drank, deeply. "What are you going to do after we go to Gibeah?" he asked, wiping his mouth with the back of his hand.

"Return to Bethlehem, I suppose. Saul has already let most of our men go home." Actually, only about two hundred men remained of David's thousand, with Joab as his second in command and Abishai and Asahel as lieutenants.

"Do you want to be forgotten as you were before?"

"What else can I do?"

"Before you came to the valley of Elah, Saul offered his daughter in marriage as a reward to the man who killed Goliath," Joab reminded him. "You could demand that reward."

The thought brought to David's mind once again the memory of Michal's fragile loveliness and the days they had spent together when he had been the king's musician at Gibeah. They had been little more than children then, but Michal had confidently assumed that one day they would be married. And when he remembered how he had almost killed the deer beside the brook and how she had fought him, only to collapse sobbing in his arms, he could not deny that the thought of seeing her again was exciting.

"Will you ask him?" Joab insisted.

"No."

"Why not? He owes you the reward."

"If I am really the Lord's Anointed, why should I ask favors of Saul?"

Joab considered the thought for a moment then nodded. "You may be right at that. When the time comes for you to supplant Saul, it will be just as well if you owe him nothing."

"I will not displace the rightful ruler of Israel," David said firmly.

"Even if it would mean being king of Israel?"

"If the Most High intends me to be king, I will be chosen by the people alone."

Joab flushed. "Is this the thanks you give me for talking the men of Judah into choosing you captain of a thousand? You are not so important yet that you can cast your friends aside, David."

David put his arm across Joab's broad shoulders in a gesture of conciliation. "You and I have been friends since we suckled at our mothers' breasts, Joab," he said. "I will not quarrel with you now, but don't forget you admitted that the lot actually fell true. It was the hand of God that chose me captain of a thousand men of Judah, not the hand of Joab."

CHAPTER 2

"Saul hath slain his thousands, and David his ten thousands." I SAMUEL 18:7

IT WAS MIDDAY before the sacrifices to Yahweh for victory were completed at the sanctuary on the hilltop of Nob. The lambs had been bought by Saul's treasurer with gold and precious jewels captured from Philistine settlements. The animals were slain by Ahimelech and his priests according to the prescribed ritual of Moses, the blood caught in vessels of silver and gold and dashed upon the altar. The flesh was saved to be eaten later but the entrails were burned during the sacrifice. At David's request, his own gift of Goliath's sword had not been announced, and King Saul was in a jovial mood as the military party of perhaps a thousand men crossed the shallow valley separating Nob from Gibeah.

Outside the capital, the procession was met by the major part of the inhabitants of Gibeah who had come out to usher the king and his victorious army into the city. A band of musicians led them, with four men blowing upon trumpets. The trumpeters were followed by others playing upon harps and psalteries, and a group of women, beating timbrels or hand drums, while others shook tambourines. With the women was a group of singers, chanting stories of the great victory as they marched.

David was walking with Joab at the head of his band of some

two hundred fighting men. He was absorbed in listening to the music, when suddenly the sound of his own name caught his attention. Only then did he realize that the women were chanting:

"Saul hath slain his thousands,
And David his ten thousands."

Although he had been acclaimed in the villages through which they had passed on the way from the battleground to Gibeah, David had not fully realized just how much his victory over Goliath had captured the fancy of the people. It was the sort of thing from which great sagas are made, a tale of victory against impossible odds, of personal combat in which courage and skill had won out over strength, like the victories of Deborah and Barak, and of Gideon, which were still sung in Israel centuries after the events themselves.

The road leading to the city gate was lined with people, and, when David appeared behind Saul and Abner, they, too, took up the cry of the women:

"Saul hath slain his thousands,
And David his ten thousands."

As the shouts of the people became a rhythmic chant, Joab moved forward to David's side. "The country could be yours now, if you would but take it," he said in a low voice. "Hear how they acclaim you over Saul!"

David's gaze sought out Saul who, with Abner just behind him, was marching at the head of the procession. He did not need to see the king's face to know how displeased he was, for Saul was marching with his shoulders rigidly held back, his head moving neither to the right nor the left.

At a peremptory gesture from the king, Abner hurried up beside him and David heard Saul say in tones choked with fury, "They have ascribed ten thousands to David but only thousands to me. What else can he have but the kingdom?"

David did not hear Abner's answer but it was obvious that the chief captain was trying to placate the king. Nor was he succeeding very well, for Saul's manner showed no evidence of a change.

"From this day onward, watch yourself every moment, my cousin," Joab said. "Unless you want a kingly dagger thrust between your ribs."

David paid no attention, for he had suddenly caught sight of a familiar face in the crowd. It was Michal. In the two years since he had seen her, she had grown from a fragile, lovely girl into a delicately beautiful woman. She was watching the procession eagerly and when her gaze met his, he was sure her eyes twinkled momentarily in the smile of mischief he remembered so well. The next moment she was looking at him with cool unconcern; then she shifted her gaze to the front of the procession where Saul was marching.

At the gate of the palace stronghold, Saul and Abner went inside, while David led his men to the military campground at the edge of the city. The flesh of the lambs which had been saved from the sacrifices that morning at Nob was soon roasting over the cooking fires, but he did not go over to eat with the others. Expecting a call to celebrate with Saul and the court in the customary feast of triumph, he went to the brook. After scrubbing his body with sand and a handful of twigs gathered from a nearby bush, he put on a fresh tunic he had bought in the city. Then with a small pool as a mirror, he combed his hair with a jeweled ivory comb that had been among the spoils taken from a Philistine town.

When David came back to the camping area, his men were already feasting on the flesh of the lambs and goats sacrificed at Nob, along with some wine and other delicacies he had ordered for them in the city. And since no summons had come for him from Saul's palace, he curbed his disappointment as best he could and sat down with the others. When they finished eating, he tuned the strings of his harp, as he had done hundreds of times in encampments on the battlefield, and was soon leading the men in singing the war chants of Israel.

The next morning, David, along with the other captains, reported to Abner for orders. There were no assigned tasks for the day other than the detail which regularly guarded the palace, and the men were to be allowed a period of rest and an opportunity to visit their homes, if they so desired. As the others were leaving, Abner asked David to remain behind.

"Saul is troubled again by the evil spirit, David," the chief captain said casually.

"I hope it will soon go away."

"Not this one." Abner's tone was dry. "It is envy that troubles him now. Envy of you."

"Surely the king knows he has no more loyal subject in Israel than myself," David protested.

"Saul does not think clearly any more. It might even be best if you return to Bethlehem for a while, but I don't intend to let you go back to the life of a shepherd. You are a natural leader of men, David; I need you near me when the Philistines attack again."

"Do you think we will ever destroy them?"

"Possibly not in my lifetime, but perhaps in yours," Abner said. "But it will not come until all the tribes fight as one nation with weapons of iron such as the Philistines already have."

"Why doesn't Saul go to the people then and tell them it is the will of the Most High that this be done?"

Abner studied the younger man thoughtfully for a moment before he spoke. "Saul was once favored by the Lord of Hosts, as you seem to be favored now. Only if you have known that favor and lose it—something I pray will never happen to you, David—can you understand some of the things that trouble him now."

CHAPTER 3

"A certain man of Bethlehem-Judah went to sojourn in the country of Moab, he, and his wife, and his two sons." RUTH I:1

AFTER HIS TALK with Abner, David was crossing the palace courtyard when he heard a familiar voice speaking his name. He recognized it at once but could not at first locate Michal; finally he caught sight of her standing behind a clump of tamarisk bushes.

"Stop playing games, Michal," he said in mock anger. "You are grown-up now."

She came out and he saw that, though she had grown into a young woman since they had last seen each other, her body was still almost fragile in its slender grace and loveliness.

"So you noticed," she said a little frostily. "I thought the conqueror of Goliath would not even look at a girl any more. No doubt many of them have thrown themselves at you lately."

She was jealous, he realized, jealous of the welcome the women singers and the musicians had given him yesterday. The knowledge brought him a warm sense of pleasure, which he was careful not to reveal to her, for two could play the game she had begun. "At least they appreciated my feat more than you seemed to yesterday," he told her.

"And you loved the flattery, I could see that." He saw her eyes grow smoky with the rising anger he remembered so well. The rich color rose in her cheeks. "Why should you be puffed up over a feat any man of Benjamin could have performed? Father said you were so close to the giant you could not possibly have missed him."

David was hardly surprised to hear that the king had been belittling his victory in the valley of Elah. "Until I went against the Philistine, no man in Israel had been willing to challenge him," he reminded her, and could not help adding somewhat tartly, "not even your father."

She was trying to be angry but the little-girl curiosity that made her so different from her sulky older sister Merab got the better of her temper. "Was he really as tall and as broad as two men?"

"Fully that large."

"Abner said Goliath would have killed you with his bare hands if you had come any closer to him." Her eyes were wide with excitement now. "It must have been thrilling."

"Frightening describes it better."

"But you did march right up to him! Abner told me all about it."

"I had to get near enough to fell him with one throw," David explained. "I would never have had a chance to launch a second stone."

Suddenly David heard loud cries from the palace. A man was shouting in a hoarse voice but the words were run together in an unintelligible jumble.

"Father is raving again," Michal said quickly. "If he sees you here with me, he will be very angry."

Seizing David's hand, she pulled him up a flight of steps that led to a short passageway. This opened upon a flat area atop the palace wall. It was a secluded spot where two sections of the wall came together; when Michal drew him into the small nook, they were as much alone as if they had been a day's journey from the city.

"We will be safe here." Her eyes sparkled with the conspiratorial light that had always enchanted him.

David had almost forgotten how beautiful the view could be from the heights of Gibeah. Sharp, chalk-like ridges stretched away to the north and the slopes were dappled in a shadow pattern made by the morning sunlight. Eastward a succession of ravines marked the drop of the land to the distant bank of the Jordan, a lazy brown ribbon in a bed of green, and further south, the vivid blue of the Salt Sea gleamed at the feet of the pink and yellow hills of Moab.

"Some day I am going to visit Moab," he said. "One of my ancestors came from there."

"How could that be, since you are of the tribe of Judah?"

"It happened during a time of famine in Bethlehem many years ago," he explained. "A man named Elimelech, with his wife, Naomi, and his two sons, Mahlon and Chilion, journeyed to Moab and found work as smiths. The sons married Moabite women named Ruth and Orpah but, after the men died and were buried there, Naomi decided to return to Bethlehem. Ruth insisted on going with her, but the people suspected her of being a spy. They were going to stone her when my ancestor, Boaz, took her under his protection and married her. She was the mother of my grandfather, Obed."

"But the Moabites have been our enemies since the time of Moses."

"Not Ruth. Grandfather said she was so beautiful and so good that everyone in Bethlehem soon came to love her."

"It is a lovely story, David," Michal's eyes were shining. "Almost as beautiful as some of your songs."

"One day I shall put it into verse and sing it to the music of a harp," he said. "Especially Ruth's words when Naomi tried to persuade her to return to Moab because she would be treated as an enemy in Bethlehem."

"Tell them to me."

"Just now you were making light of my victory over Goliath," he reminded her with a smile. "Now you are asking a favor of me."

"I was jealous of the women who sang your praises," she admitted. "And of the way the maidservants in the palace have been prattling about your being so handsome and so brave."

"Once you said I was pretty."

Michal clapped her hands together and laughed. "I remember! And I remember how angry you were then."

"And how angry you were with me the next day, when I would have killed the doe at the spring?"

"Yes. First I tried to beat you, and then I cried until you kissed away my tears."

She was standing close to him now, looking up with eyes warmed by the memory of that day. "Promise that it will always be the same with us, David," she said softly. "Promise that no matter how angry we get at each other, we will let nothing stop us from being friends."

It seemed the most natural thing in the world to kiss her then, as it had seemed beside the brook that day. Her lips were as soft and as sweet as he remembered them and her body in his arms as lovely and as yielding. But there was a difference, too, for since then he had become a man—and she a woman.

It was Michal who finally pushed him away. "You didn't tell me what the Moabite named Ruth said to Naomi," she reminded him a little breathlessly.

"The words are so beautiful," he told her, "that the women of my family have repeated them as part of the marriage ceremony ever since." He went on to recite the immortal words which had become one of the most beautiful traditions among the people of Judah:

> " '*Intreat me not to leave thee, or to return from following after thee. For whither thou goest I will go; and where thou lodgest I shall lodge. Thy people shall be my people and thy god my god. Where thou diest, will I die, and there will I be buried: The Lord do so to me, and more also, if ought but death part thee and me.*' "

"It is lovely, David. I—I am going to cry." Michal buried her face in his tunic while he soothed her in his arms. When she raised tear-wet eyes to look at him, he bent to kiss her again, and he knew he wanted nothing so much in all the world as to have her for his wife.

"Saul offered to give a daughter in marriage to whoever killed Goliath," he told her when finally they broke the embrace. "I am going to claim the reward."

"Was that why you risked your life to kill the giant?"

"Of course." It seemed simpler to maintain the fiction than to take the chance of stirring the rather unpredictable temper that, to him, made her so different from the other girls he had known. "Could anyone want a greater reward?"

It was the right answer, he saw, as her eyes grew soft and warm again. "Let us repeat together the words of the Moabite, Ruth," she said. "Then we will be betrothed and nothing can ever separate us."

A little self-consciously, they spoke the beautiful phrases together. It was a solemn moment that left them both awed and silent in the face of an emotion deeper than either had ever experienced before. Practical Michal broke the spell first.

"Say nothing of this yet to Father," she warned. "Merab has been promised to Adriel, the Meholathite. They have been waiting until Father returned to celebrate the wedding. Once she is married, you can ask him for me." Her eyes twinkled in the familiar smile of mischief. "And don't say you are not being well paid for killing Goliath."

CHAPTER 4

"And Saul was afraid of David, because the Lord was with him, and was departed from Saul."
I SAMUEL 18:12

DAVID WAS hardly prepared for the reception the people of Gibeah gave him when he left the palace and started down to the foot of the hill where his troops were encamped. Crowds thronged about him, begging to hear the story of the fight with Goliath from his own lips, and harps were thrust into his hand with the request that he sing a hymn of victory. Word had spread through the town the night before that Saul was once again in one of the black moods of senseless anger and rage with which the people of Gibeah were already familiar and it almost seemed as if, in honoring David and hearing the story of the great victory, they were seeking assurance that they would not be left leaderless, as had happened before when Saul had been besieged by the evil spirit.

David's progress through the city took on the characteristics of a triumphal procession. Although he would have prevented it if he could have, knowing that word would certainly get back to Saul and make him even more violent, there was nothing to be done. When finally his own men rescued him from the happy crowd and escorted him to his tent, his clothing was almost torn from his body. While he dressed, he told Joab and his brothers about his talk with Abner that morning, but said nothing about his visit with Michal and their private ceremony of betrothal.

"Are you going to Bethlehem?" Joab asked.

"Abner and I think it would be best. When the furor over Goliath subsides, Saul will probably forget his envy of me."

"I was talking this morning with a Benjaminite of Saul's bodyguard," Asahel volunteered. "No one can understand Saul's ravings, so the joke is going around the city that he has become a prophet."

"Before you came to the valley of Elah, there was talk that we of Judah would be fools to keep a coward and a madman king over us much longer," Joab told David. "Perhaps the time has come to speak of it again."

"Saul is no coward," David said sharply. "He killed many Philistines in the valley of Elah while I killed only one."

"The one he was afraid to kill," Joab reminded him. "Still it may be better for you to return to Bethlehem, for a while at least."

David knew what Joab was thinking; that once in Judah, he could begin to develop, as the nucleus of his personal army, his own following among the soldiers who had been under his command. But he had no intention of attempting anything of that sort, for so long as Saul might live, he was the Lord's anointed king of Israel. It was a position David hoped to fill some day, but only when it was the will of God and not the result of destroying the man who filled it now.

"Take Asahel to Bethlehem with you," Joab advised. "He can run to Gibeah in a few hours, should you have need of me there."

David smiled, for he knew Joab well enough by now to read his friend's thoughts. "And also bring you word of what I am doing?"

Joab shrugged. "My life is bound up in yours. Why should I not want to be sure you do what is best for us all?"

"See that you do nothing against Saul," David warned him again.

"Saul is taking care of that himself," Joab said dryly. "In a few more days all of Gibeah will start naming him a madman as they are already naming him a prophet. And who wants either for a king?"

Had Joab been less concerned with David's future, and his own, he might have noticed the presence near the tent of a short, wiry man with the sun-blackened skin and hooked nose of the desert dwellers, sometimes called the *Bedawin*. As Saul's chief herder, Doeg, the Edomite, came and went freely in Gibeah, where he served as his master's body servant. Actually, however, he was a much more sinister figure, a spy willing to sell information, often manufactured in his own cunning and unscrupulous mind, to both sides in a controversy. And even Joab would have been surprised if he had noted that Doeg went immediately to the quarters of Saul's second son, Ishbosheth who, though preferring the pleasures of the table and the harem to the battlefield, still nursed a strong ambition to rule in Israel after his father's death.

David was sitting by the campfire that night with the men of Judah, singing the victory chant of Deborah, when he was told that Jethro, Saul's servant, waited to see him. He stopped playing at once and joined the servant who stood outside the circle of firelight. "What brings you here, my old friend?" he asked. "Has Saul gone completely mad and driven you from the palace?"

Jethro shook his head. "The king is still in the grip of the evil spirit. Will you come and play for him?"

"Did Saul send for me?"

"No. But my lady Ahinoam hopes your playing will free the king from his fit of anger, so that he will be reconciled to you."

"There is no controversy of my making between us."

"Everyone in the palace knows that, except the king. We all hope you and your harp can convince him."

David turned back to the campfire and spoke to Joab. "I am going to play for the king. If anything happens to me, take the men and leave for Judah at once."

"Why not let me come with you?"

"When Saul wants me killed, he can easily hire it done. If I came with a bodyguard, it would only give him reason to destroy me."

Outside Saul's audience chamber they were met by the king's lovely wife, Ahinoam. "He is a little quieter tonight," she told

David. "Your singing did so much for him once before that I am hoping you can bring him back to himself again."

When she opened the door of the audience chamber, David glanced around the room quickly. Saul was seated upon his throne chair on the dais at one end of the room. Michal sat at his feet, while Merab stood at the king's shoulder in the act of filling his wine cup. The two guards near the stairway leading to the upper stories were alert and wary, as if they expected Saul to become violent at any moment. And the chief herder, Doeg, crouched near the door ready to flee at the first outburst of raving from his master.

As she stepped into the room, with David just behind her, Ahinoam spoke. "I brought your favorite musician to entertain you with a song, my lord," she said gaily.

As on his first visit to the throne room, David plucked the strings of the harp and began to sing the song he had chosen while he and Jethro were hurrying to the palace. He had composed it after one of Saul's great victories, long before the king had fallen upon evil times in the controversy with Samuel:

"My heart is inditing a good matter:
I speak of the things which I have made touching the king:
My tongue is the pen of a ready writer.
Thou art fairer than the children of men;
Grace is poured into thy lips:
Therefore God hath blessed thee for ever.

Gird thy sword upon thy thigh, O most mighty,
With thy glory and thy majesty.
And in thy majesty ride prosperously,
Because of truth and meekness and righteousness;
Thy right hand shall teach terrible things.
Thine arrows are sharp,
In the heart of the king's enemies;
Whereby the people fall under thee.

Thy throne, is of God, forever and ever;
The sceptre of thy kingdom is a right sceptre.
Thou lovest righteousness, and hateth wickedness:

Therefore God, thy God, hast anointed thee,
With the oil of gladness above thy fellows.
Thy name shall be remembered in all generations:
And all the people praise thee forever and ever."

Completely absorbed in the music, David had not been watching Saul until a scream from Michal made him suddenly alert. He looked up to see the king, standing on the dais, a javelin poised in his hand. Merab's eyes were wide with horror. Her whole body seemed to go limp, and she dropped the silver wine cup she was holding. It crashed to the floor, and as if the crash were a signal, Saul thrust his right arm forward, hurling the javelin.

David had no time to move, but at the instant of its release a slight shift in the angle at which Saul was holding the weapon told him the king did not intend to kill him. Actually, Saul could hardly have missed at that short a distance unless he had intended to do so. Deflected at the last moment from its original target, David's throat, the javelin ripped through the cloth of his tunic and plunged into a small wooden table beside him.

David did not betray in any way that he realized Saul had deliberately missed him. Getting to his feet, he slowly backed out of the room, controlling rigidly an almost overpowering urge to flee. For at any moment Saul might decide to try again and with the second javelin, he might find his mark.

CHAPTER 5

"And David behaved himself wisely in all his ways; and the Lord was with him."

I SAMUEL 18:14

PREPARING TO DEPART for Bethlehem, David paid little attention the next morning when heralds rode through the city announcing that King Saul had ordered a period of prayer and thanksgiving for victory to be held the following day, culminating at nightfall in a great feast at the palace. He was astonished when a mercenary from Saul's own guard brought an order to the camp of the Judahites that he was to attend with his lieutenants.

Joab was in the city when the messenger came. As soon as he returned to camp, he went to David's tent. "I met one of the king's mercenaries at the edge of the camp," he said. "Is it true that Saul has bidden you to the palace, even though he drove you away last night?"

"It is true."

"Why?"

"As you say, there is no predicting the whims of a madman."

"You don't really think this just one of Saul's whims, do you?"

"No. But he can hardly kill me in the midst of a feast."

"A man can be destroyed in other ways. Since last night, Doeg has been spreading the tale that Saul tried your courage by hurling the javelin and that you fled from the palace in terror."

"He was almost correct," David admitted and touched the slit in his garment where the blade had torn the fabric. "The javelin came that close." His face grew sober. "But what would Doeg have to gain from such a lie?"

"Money, no doubt," said Joab. "Though he serves Saul, it is no secret that he is in the pay of Ishbosheth."

David had never liked Saul's second son, but until now there had been no reason to think Ishbosheth could wish him harm. "Why would he wish to damage me?"

"With Jonathan out of the way, Ishbosheth would succeed his father," Joab said. "Saul was willing to kill Jonathan once, when he broke a rule in battle. And he must have discovered by now that you and Jonathan have sworn blood brotherhood. His mind could easily be poisoned against Jonathan, leaving Ishbosheth the kingdom with Abner to hold it for him."

David rubbed his chin thoughtfully while he considered what Joab had said. "Then you think this affair tomorrow may involve me in some way?"

"To your discredit, you can be sure of that. But there is still time to leave for Bethlehem. I can bribe the mercenary who brought the message to say you had already gone."

David shook his head firmly. "I shall go as if I suspected nothing. But keep Abishai and Asahel near me always in case trouble comes."

David dressed carefully for the affair at the palace; he was determined not to let Saul know he suspected treachery. From a Phoenician merchant who had taken up residence in Gibeah he purchased a tunic-like garment, known in the Phoenician tongue as a *kiton* and made of a fine, soft fabric woven on the looms of the skilled clothmakers of Byblos. The hem, which came to just above his knees, and the cuffs of the short sleeves, were embroidered in colorful scenes depicting tall-masted and long-oared Phoenician galleys in battle. The colors, especially the famous purple obtained from a species of shellfish found along the coast of the Great Sea, were brilliant. And, as with everything done by the skilled artisans from the Phoenician cities, the dyeing was extremely skillful.

Over the kiton, David wore a fringed cloak of a new design

recently become popular with the Israelites. A long strip of a heavier fabric dyed a deep red, it was draped over one shoulder and then wrapped around the upper body with the end hanging on the left side almost to the knee. A soft leather belt or girdle secured it at the waist and sandals of the same finely tooled soft leather were laced about his ankles and calves. His dark hair and beard had been combed and anointed with costly spikenard. His only weapon was a jeweled dagger; worn in a flat scabbard secured to his left upper arm just below the shoulder by a leather strap, it could be drawn with a single motion of the right hand.

For this gala occasion, Saul had thrown open the palace to the public. On tables set up in the courtyard, the flesh of lambs, goats, and oxen, roasted over great beds of coals since early morning, was served with cakes of freshly baked bread, preserved fruits and sweetmeats, pastries and wine in abundance.

Except for rendering the customary obeisance before Saul as a gesture of courtesy upon his arrival, David made no attempt to join those who clustered around the king. With Joab, Abishai, and Asahel, he sampled the food and drink and accepted the plaudits of the people. The feast was at its height when the blare of a trumpet silenced the clamor of voices.

"Where is David, the slayer of Goliath?" Saul inquired loudly. "Let him come before me that I may do him honor."

A roar of acclaim from the people gave evidence of their approval. Beside him, David heard Joab mutter, "Be careful. I fear Saul most when he is affable."

David made his way to a temporary dais which had been erected for the king and his family at the end of the stone-paved courtyard. Something in Saul's manner, particularly the note of smugness and satisfaction in his voice, warned David that his being singled out for an honor was not everything it appeared to be. And when he saw that Ahinoam, too, was frowning, he was sure that she too had detected a false note in her husband's joviality.

"I will not tell again the story of a great victory in the valley of Elah," Saul said. "You all know of it and musicians will sing of it in years to come."

The crowd interrupted with a burst of cheering and for an instant a black frown came and went upon Saul's features. It happened so quickly, however, that David doubted whether anyone else besides himself noticed it.

"Before the battle in the valley, I promised the gift of my daughter in marriage to him who destroyed Goliath," Saul continued. "We have gathered here tonight to carry out that promise."

David heard a gasp from Michal and realized that Saul had given her no warning of what he intended to do.

"My elder daughter Merab, I will give you to wife, David," Saul announced. "Only be valiant for me and fight the Lord's battles."

"No!" It was Merab who had spoken. David saw her looking at him in undisguised dismay, her mouth open, her eyes filled with horror. As for Michal, the color had drained from her face and he feared she would fall in a faint. Even the crowd was silent, recognizing that here was a tense drama whose nature they could not at the moment entirely understand.

Conquering his own dismay at Saul's startling announcement, David spoke quickly, hoping to prevent any further reaction to the king's words. "Who am I?" he said loudly enough for the crowd to hear. "Who am I and my father's family in Israel that I should be the son-in-law of the king?"

He was looking at Michal as he spoke, mutely begging her not to speak out, since something told him Saul expected just that, a resistance to the announcement by those involved which could be turned into an excuse to subject David to public humiliation.

"The son of Jesse is truly humble." Saul's voice was little more than an angry growl. "Does he refuse the honor I choose to do him?"

"Who would refuse so great a gift from the Lord's Anointed?" David answered. "If the king himself considers me worthy to wed his daughter, I need no other testimony of my worth."

The crowd at last found its voice and pressed around David to acclaim him. When finally he managed to break free, he saw that Saul and his family had already left the dais. It was an act of discourtesy that he was sure was deliberate, at least on Saul's part.

"I thought it was the gazelle-limbed Michal you loved," Joab said as David was leaving with his lieutenants.

"It is."

"Surely Saul knew that."

"I am certain he did."

"Then there is more to this than meets the eye," Joab said thoughtfully. "I thought Saul's voice did not ring true when he named you his son-in-law. Obviously he had some other purpose besides making you one of his own family. But just what does he hope to gain?"

"I think he expected Merab to spurn me publicly," David explained. "Or he may have hoped I would refuse her and thus give him affront."

"That may be the answer," Joab agreed. "But someone else must be behind all this. Saul is not clever enough to scheme out such a plot alone."

"Who could it be?"

"Ishbosheth and Doeg, unless I miss my guess," said Joab. "Saul has listened to the herdsman before. No doubt Doeg conspired with Saul to trap you into refusing Merab, so that you could be arrested for giving affront to the king."

"There is reason in what you say," David agreed. "But this attempt failed so the situation is like a game of *senit;* the next throw and shift of the pieces are Saul's to make."

"I wouldn't be too sure of that," Joab told him. "Adriel, the Meholathite, wants Merab for himself." He turned to his brother. "Place a guard at David's tent tonight, Abishai," he ordered. "Lest Adriel slide a knife between the ribs of the son of Jesse."

David was not troubled during the night, however, and in the morning a sensational announcement came from the king's palace. Heralds were sent to proclaim that the king's eldest daughter Merab was betrothed to Adriel, the Meholathite. David understood the act for what Saul intended it to be, a deliberate insult by which the king obviously hoped to provoke him into doing something rash. But angry though he was at the slight, his relief at not having to cope with sulky Merab was sufficient to temper his anger. In the end, he lost nothing in the esteem of the people because of the incident, for by now, most of them considered Saul to be insane.

This was an assumption which the next move by the king tended to confirm. It came about when Jethro, in his capacity as Saul's most trusted servant, visited David in the camp below the city gates.

"Behold, the king has delight in you, and all his servants love you," Jethro announced in the ceremonial language of a public statement. "Now therefore be the king's son-in-law."

David controlled his surprise lest those with Jethro report back to Saul about his reaction. "Does it seem to you a light thing to be the king's son-in-law?" he asked, and could not help adding, somewhat caustically, "seeing that I am a poor man and lightly esteemed?"

"The king does not ask any dowry in money," Jethro assured him.

David's eyes narrowed for it hardly seemed likely that Saul had undergone a true change of heart and was now giving Michal to him in a gesture of apology. "What does he ask, then?"

Jethro hesitated. "I speak only the king's own words," he said with some reluctance.

"A good servant always obeys his master's command," David reminded him, for the old man had ever been kind and friendly.

"The king demands the lives of a hundred Philistines as a dowry, to be avenged of his enemies."

David heard Joab utter a startled curse, but he maintained his self-possession. "Tell the king and his daughter Michal that I will not show my face to them again until I have slain not one but two hundred Philistines," he answered. "Even such a dowry is but small for so fair a bride."

He could be sure Jethro would faithfully repeat his words to Michal and to Saul. And he was equally certain that both would be pleased, though not for the same reason. To Michal, the knowledge that her bethrothed was willing to risk his life in an attack upon the Philistines for her hand in marriage would be assurance of his love for her and his earnest desire to make her his wife. Saul, on the other hand, would be highly pleased at having put him in a position where he must jeopardize his life or be publicly branded as a coward.

The whole plot was worthy of a craftier mind than Saul's, David was sure now. This was no defensive action against Philistine attack. Nor was it a question of men fighting to protect their homes and families, so David could hardly expect large numbers to risk their lives for such a private mission. Instead, the expedition would have to be carried out with only the small number of men who chose to remain under his personal command.

It was a clever plan, and one that could very well result in David's death or a serious defeat that would destroy much of the confidence the people now had for him. To prevent this from happening, as well as to accomplish his aim of providing Saul with the dowry for Michal, David knew he must be even shrewder in planning this campaign than the person who had furnished Saul with a ready-made scheme for his destruction. The whole affair was indeed, as he had said, like a game of *senit*, but this time it was his turn to shake the cup and throw the sticks to determine the next move. And if his hopes were realized, both Saul and Ishbosheth were in for a surprise.

CHAPTER 6

"Saul thought to make David fall by the hand of the Philistines." I SAMUEL 18:25

AN EASY DAY'S MARCH west of Gibeah, and slightly less than that distance east of the Philistine stronghold of Ekron, stood the height called Zorah. From the *shephelah* it was reached by a series of ascents through a valley penetrating the heart of the region made famous by the exploits of Samson.

Though Zorah lay in country claimed by both Judah and the Philistines, it was actually the center point of a border region ruled by neither. For more than a hundred years, small bands of men from both sides had preyed upon villages and settlements in the disputed area, destroying them and capturing the inhabitants. The Hebrews customarily killed their captives on the spot, mindful of Samuel's warning to Saul when he had sought to hold the Amalekite king for ransom and had earned the wrath of the Lord because of it. But the Philistines, canny traders as well as fighters, sold their captives into slavery in Egypt; there young Hebrew women were highly prized because of their beauty and fiery spirit and men because they were usually intelligent and easily trained for skilled occupations.

Since its height formed a vantage point from which the whole of the surrounding region could be kept under surveillance, Zorah had long been the site of a forward observation post. There the men of Judah kept watch to protect themselves against the Philistines, who customarily attacked first in this region. It was to this height that David came with Joab, his brothers, and about a hundred men from their own band.

When word had swept through Gibeah that Saul demanded the lives of a hundred Philistines as a dowry for Michal and that David had promised double the number, almost half of the troops who had gone with him to Gibeah had found need for their presence elsewhere. David did not blame them; neither their homes nor their lives were at stake in this particular venture. Instead, he led the remainder westward to Zorah, planning to launch a swift attack before his presence in the area became known to the enemy. Only through such a tactic could he hope to capture or destroy a large number of Philistines in one operation.

As he surveyed the surrounding country from the hilltop, David could see why it was so important to the men of Judah. From this commanding elevation the eye could range over a broad valley leading westward to the blue waters of the Great Sea. To the south lay several ranges of hills in Philistine territory, with the village of Timnah a little to the east. Beyond them he could see the walls of Beth-shemesh, in which the sacred Ark of the Covenant had once been housed briefly before being taken on to Kirjath-jearim. Farther away, to the northwest, a plume of smoke rose above the outlines of the Philistine center of Gezer, one of the most ancient of the Canaanite settlements. Eastward, the hills of central Judah and Moab were purple in the midday haze.

The leader of the Judahites who were watching at Zorah greeted David with a warm embrace. "The destroyer of Goliath comes at a good time," he said. "A large band of Philistines was seen yesterday by a herder in the valley of Sorek. We have been watching for sight of a fire so that we could tell what village is their goal."

"Then they have not attacked yet?"

"We have seen no smoke. This band was large enough to capture a whole village, so they are probably moving deep into our territory until they come upon a place where they can take many captives."

David had hardly dared hope to come upon a single band of Philistine warriors large enough to provide the full number he had promised in the dowry for Michal. "You bring good news, my kinsman," he told the Judahite joyfully. "If we destroy them, a share of the booty shall go to you and the others here."

"Remember, we number only a hundred men," Joab warned.

"But a hundred of the bravest," David said confidently. "Men skilled in war and not afraid. With only three times that number Gideon destroyed the entire Midianite host in the Vale of Jezreel!"

Joab shrugged. "You will remind me next that Samson slew many Philistines not far from here with the jawbone of an ass. But you are not Samson; don't forget that."

"And don't forget that our weapons are better than an ass's jaw," David retorted with a smile.

"Do you have any idea what town the Philistines might be going to attack?" Joab asked the Judahite sentry.

"They were moving in the direction of Chesalon to the east, but they might have turned south, since you did not see them on the way here."

"We came by way of Kirjath-jearim to the north," Joab explained. "They could easily have been hidden from us by Mount Seir."

"Whatever town they choose, they will no doubt return through the valley below," David said. "We have only to lie in wait and cut them off on the way back to their own territory."

"It is a good plan," Joab agreed. "But first we must know where they are."

"Asahel!" David called to the younger of Joab's brothers who was pouring himself a drink from the water jar filled every morning at the copious spring near the bottom of the hill. "Do you know the country around Chesalon?"

"I have tended sheep within sight of it." Asahel wiped his mouth with his sleeve. "Why?"

"A band of Philistines may be attacking the town. Search out that region and bring us word where they are. We will move eastward along the valley below and meet you as you return."

Asahel picked up a piece of bread and a chunk of meat from some supplies they had brought with them from Kirjath-jearim, and bounded down the hill like a gazelle in flight. He wore no heavy weapons, since his ability to run twice as swiftly and travel farther in a day than anyone in David's band made him far more valuable in that capacity than as a warrior.

"Have the men eat and drink before we start on the march," David instructed Joab. "We may have to lie in wait for the Philistines for some time, and will not be able to prepare food."

While Joab carried out his orders, David munched bread and meat and surveyed once again the view from the height upon which he stood. And as his eyes swept from the blue of the ocean in the west, across the rolling highlands where so much of his people's history had taken place, to the purple haze of Moab far to the east, he felt a new sense of pride and purpose stirring within him and a renewal of the conviction that for him had been set the task of leading his people to a new glory.

It was not simply a feat of arms that awaited him, he was sure, but something far greater. Perhaps—and the magnitude of the possibility set his imagination soaring—perhaps God might even assign him the task of making his people the strongest nation in this part of the world, so strong that even Egypt and Assyria would seek his favor. Then there would be no more war; every man would be left free to work at his tasks, enjoying the fruits of his harvest and watching his children grow up unafraid.

As he stood there, the verses of a song began to form themselves within his soul. It was an experience he had known before, the feeling that another voice besides his own was speaking words to reassure him of the greatness of his own destiny:

They that sow in tears shall reap in joy.
He that goeth forth and weepeth
Bearing seed for sowing,
Shall doubtless come again with joy,
Bringing his sheaves with him.

A rough footpath followed the bank of the stream that tumbled through the valley below the height of Zorah. As David and his men followed this winding path eastward about an hour later, two scouts explored the trail ahead, while others made their way through the underbrush on either side to insure that, should they come upon the Philistines returning from the foray, they would not be caught unaware. In addition, every man in David's command moved with javelin in hand, ready to throw at the first contact with the enemy.

It was late in the afternoon before Asahel appeared on the trail ahead.

"The enemy attacked Chesalon this morning, as you thought they would, David," he reported. "They took most of the people prisoners and are bringing them back in bonds."

"How many fighting men are in the party?"

"Two hundred at least, probably more. I was able to get close to the town without being detected, but I could not count all of them."

"Will they return today or tomorrow?" Joab asked.

"Today. Some were already driving the slaves from the town when I left."

"Then they will be busy driving the prisoners and will not be expecting an attack. We can meet them here in the valley and free the captives."

"If we destroy the Philistines first, the prisoners will be free," David reminded him.

"Our first duty is to help our own kinsmen," Joab said bluntly. "Would you risk a hundred men in one attack to win a dowry and then, if we lose, let our kinsmen go on as slaves?"

"The captives come first, of course," David agreed. "But we may be able to free the sheep and destroy the wolf at the same time. A band of men that large must have come from Ekron or Gath, and it is too near dark now for them to march all the way back to either city by nightfall. They will have to make camp somewhere on the way."

"I saw the spot," Asahel volunteered. "The enemy stopped there on the way eastward and left a supply of food and wine behind, so they must plan to return that way."

"Can we reach it before they do?" David asked.

"By marching swiftly. It is only about an hour away."

"Give the order to march, Joab," David directed. "We will set a trap at the enemy camp and spring it after dark."

The spot chosen by the Philistines was excellent for camping, as it was set on the banks of the stream that flowed through the valley. They had obviously not even considered the possibility of an ambush because the site was surrounded by a heavy growth of underbrush, which suited David's purposes very well. Dividing the hundred men of his party into two companies, he sent one group under Joab's command into hiding on the opposite side of the camping area; the remaining band concealed themselves behind him in the underbrush.

Darkness was already beginning to settle in the glen before the preparations were completed. Not long afterward voices could be heard to the east. Soon a file of Philistine fighting men appeared, guarding a large band of captives. Men, women, and children with their hands bound behind them stumbled along the trail under the prodding spear points of their captors. Many had been wounded and were supported by the others.

The Philistines seemed confident that their raid had gone undetected by the rest of Judah, at least for the moment. Their commander posted no sentries, and while part of the men busied themselves in preparing the evening meal, others herded the prisoners into an open space under the trees. Aside from being allowed to kneel or lie upon the ground to drink from the brook, the captives were shown no consideration.

David had agreed with Joab that a loud blast upon the ram's horn, or *shophar*, which he carried slung across his back, would be the signal for the attack. He wanted to wait, however, until the Philistines had finished eating; an enemy drowsy with food and wine would be slow to fight back.

It was quite dark when the Philistines finally finished their meal. Most of them had stretched out on the ground beside the several campfires; some were already dozing. David lifted the *shophar* to his lips and sent a mighty blast rocketing through the glen. At the signal, his men raised a great shout and launched themselves down the hillside upon the enemy, with Joab's group only seconds behind. In the Philistine camp the surprise was complete and deadly—pandemonium raged as the soldiers scrambled to pick up their weapons and gear.

Even with the advantage of surprise, the large number of the enemy made it impossible for David to win an easy victory. The Philistines fought bravely and, with their superior weapons, might well have won out had they not been caught unawares by the attack from ambush. As it was, the battle raged fiercely for perhaps half an hour, ending finally when some twenty-five of the Philistines managed to retreat westward, leaving their wounded and dying behind them. The captives had not been able to take part in the fighting, since they lacked weapons, but they had shouted encouragement to David and his men. Their cries added to the din of the battle and heightened the illusion that David's forces were far greater in number than they actually were.

While Joab and the men were completing the rout of the Philistines, David busied himself looking after the captives, many of whom were suffering from wounds which badly needed attention. When Joab, panting and smeared with blood from the battle, sought David out, he found him kneeling beside the brook gently washing blood from the face of a boy who whimpered with pain.

"How many?" was David's first question.

Joab grinned. "Enough to win you a bride. My men are busy gathering proof of the victory so that we may take it back to Saul."

"Free the prisoners, then, and give them the food the Philistines did not consume," David directed.

"But the men are hungry. It has been a long day."

"You ate at midday," David reminded him. "And these poor people have been prisoners since morning."

Joab started to protest, for the welfare of his men was always his first concern. But after a second glance at his kinsman's face he shrugged and turned away. For the burning conviction in David's eyes told the stocky lieutenant that still another milestone had been passed in the development of a great leader for his people.

CHAPTER 7

"And Saul gave him Michal his daughter to wife."
I SAMUEL 18:27

EVEN THE MOANS of the wounded and dying that night could not lessen the joy of the Israelite captives at having been freed from slavery. In the morning, David and his band, bearing the grim evidence of their victory and the weapons they had stripped from the dead Philistines, iron being almost as precious to the Israelites as gold, made their way to Chesalon. Here they were forced to pause for a day while the inhabitants of the neighboring villages, to whom word of David's startling victory over the Philistines had spread rapidly, gathered to honor them with a great feast of victory.

When David and his band finally began the return journey to Gibeah, only about a day's march away, word of their exploit had already gone before them; everywhere along their route of march, great crowds turned out to honor them. Thus it came about that David once again entered Gibeah as a conquering hero.

Having publicly announced the conditions of Michal's betrothal to David, the king could not deny him his bride once the evidence was laid before him that two hundred Philistines had been slain. Announcement of the wedding was made by the royal heralds the day following David's triumphal return to Gibeah. His family and kinsmen came from Bethlehem the next day, bearing gifts both for Saul and the prospective bride and groom.

David had not seen Michal alone since his return, as it was customary to shut the bride away from the sight of her betrothed until the last of the seven days of rejoicing and feasting that preceded the final ceremony of marriage. But he was busily occupied, for the people of Gibeah insisted on honoring him again and again. And further, since the family of Jesse was one of the oldest and most honorable in all of Judah, in itself the largest and richest tribe in Israel, there was no end of feasting and celebration by his own kinsmen, who had come from all parts of Judah to attend the wedding of their tribal hero. David was careful to stay out of Saul's way except when courtesy required him to come into his presence. Word from the palace seemed to indicate that for the time being, at least, the uncertain temper of Israel's ruler was under control.

Ordinarily custom dictated that the father return to the bride the major portion of the dowry paid by the bridegroom. This was called the *mohar*, literally the "bride price," and through it she was given assurance of a means of living should the husband divorce her, as he could do merely by making the announcement according to a prescribed ritual. In this instance, of course, such a thing was impossible, since the "bride price" consisted of flesh from the bodies of the slain Philistines; so Saul had announced that he was giving Michal a house in Gibeah as a home for his favorite daughter and her husband, now after Abner and Jonathan, the most important captain in the army.

On the final day of the wedding feast, David, accompanied by Joab, Abishai, and the men of his band, along with a considerable portion of the townspeople, marched through the city to Saul's palace. There David, according to custom, would demand that his bride be delivered to him.

It was a colorful procession, with the groom, his attendants, and many of the townspeople garlanded with bright-colored flowers. Musicians marched before them, playing upon harps and other stringed instruments, trumpets of horn and brass, timbrels and tambourines. A company of virgins, dancing and singing, also accompanied the party; later, at the climax of the wedding ceremony, they would light the way to the nuptial chamber.

The armed men from David's own command who marched on either side of the wedding procession also served an important purpose, for by flourishing their weapons and clashing shield against shield, they sought to drive away any demons that might be present. The music, too, was festive, assuring the ever-present evil spirits that this was a wedding, a time for joy, not a funeral.

Considerable wine had been drunk during the seven days of feasting and many of the wedding party were not very steady upon their feet. But those who could walk straight supported the others and most of them reached the palace without mishap. There David called for his bride in a loud voice and shortly Michal, richly arrayed and with a veil covering her face, was led from the palace by Saul to join her betrothed at the head of the wedding procession.

Michal's appearance was the cue for the young women to begin the traditional wedding chant, a lilting verse which had been sung by the Canaanites long before the Hebrews came into the land:

"Turn, turn, O Michal, the beautiful,
Turn, turn, that we may gaze upon thee.
Ah gaze upon the beautiful one
In the Mahanaim dance.
How beautiful are your steps in sandals,
How beautiful are your feet, O rapturous maiden."

So great was David's joy at the sight of Michal's slender loveliness and the knowledge that at last she was his, that he found himself singing with the others and leaping about in an impromptu dance. His action brought shouts of approval from the onlookers; but when, panting from the effort of the song and the dance, he turned again to his bride, he was startled to see a look of displeasure in her eyes, a look, he realized with a sudden chill of apprehension, strangely like that which he had seen in her father's eyes during one of his rages. But it was gone so quickly that David could assure himself he had only imagined it.

In the palace courtyard David led Michal to a ceremonial

flower-decked threshing sledge upon which they were drawn through the streets of the city to an open field outside. There, enthroned side by side on the sledge, they held court and were honored with dancing, games, music, and feasting throughout the day, while the pile of gifts before them rose higher and higher. With so much going on, the two lovers had little chance to speak more than a few words together before the time approached for the feasting to end. Then once again David and his bride were borne through the city, this time to their new home. In front of it, the ceremonial bridal canopy, or *huppah*, of rich Phoenician fabric, had been raised since morning, marking it as the house of the newly wed couple.

The young women in attendance upon Michal ushered them to the threshold with their burning lamps held high. There, in the presence of witnesses from both families, the two drank the ceremonial wine together and tossed the vessel from which they had drunk, a long-stemmed goblet of exquisite Philistine ware, to break upon the stones. This done, David lifted his bride and carried her across the threshold of their new home, closing the door behind them and shutting out the crowd.

The people did not leave, however, even after the lights in the house had been extinguished. Outside they kept vigil, amidst much merriment and further passing of wineskins from hand to hand, until finally a white sheet was tossed from the window of the nuptial bedchamber. The family representatives then went forward to examine the traditional "tokens of virginity," proving that the bride had indeed come to the nuptial couch undeflowered and therefore undefiled.

CHAPTER 8

"And Saul spake to Jonathan his son, and to all his servants, that they should kill David."

I SAMUEL 19:1

FOR DAVID the first few months of marriage to Michal was a period of unalloyed happiness. In his own home, he was free from the burden of daily contact with the rather unpredictable temper of Saul. And as Merab's husband had taken her to his own city, David was the king's only son-in-law in Gibeah, so that now, having become in addition a hero, he was greatly looked up to here, as well as in his own territory of Judah. From the spring of his happiness, he drew the inspiration for many beautiful songs which he sang in the court of Saul, and which were set down by the scribes for future repetition.

So happy was David in these days that he readily forgave Michal her sharpness of temper, which grew more and more noticeable as time passed. He had known before the wedding that she was of a somewhat unstable temperament, as was her father, given to alternating moods of soaring happiness and periods of anger and black depression. But he had been sure that his love and the happiness of marriage would cure her of those tendencies. Now, as the days passed and she became more and more jealous of his every hour away from her, he could not help being disturbed. Once or twice he tried to talk to her about the difference of their temperaments, but each time she changed the subject as quickly as the mood had come upon her, and he got nowhere. Besides, after each period of depression she was once again the gay and laughing girl who had met him at the spring on his first visit to Gibeah.

As for Saul, David could not fail to know that the king was once more troubled by the evil spirits which were his greatest enemy. And since that same black mood had poisoned the king's feelings toward him on more than one occasion, it was not to be wondered at that such a thing could happen again. David did not realize just how bad the situation had become, however, until Jonathan appeared at his home one afternoon. His steadily ripening friendship with Jonathan had been a source of great happiness to David, and he was distressed to see that Saul's eldest son was deeply troubled.

"My brother Jonathan has the mien of one bringing bad tidings," he said in greeting.

"I could not bring worse," Jonathan agreed. "My father has instructed his whole household to kill you whenever and wherever they find you."

David was thunderstruck. "But surely my friends would not do such a thing!"

"Your friends would guard you with their lives," Jonathan agreed. "But there are always some who would kill for the gold they know my father would give them."

David wasted no moments in futile consideration. "It is time Michal and I visited my own people," he said. "While we are in Bethlehem perhaps the king's temper toward me will cool."

"He has set guards to watch the country around Gibeah lest you leave," Jonathan warned.

"But why? He should know that no one in Israel is more loyal than I!"

"When the evil spirit takes hold of my father he needs no reason to hate you."

"What shall I do, then?"

"Stay in the camp with Joab and your men tonight," Jonathan advised. "I have not yet had a chance to talk to my father about the order for your death. Perhaps I can still make him see reason."

"How shall I know whether or not you succeed?"

"Early in the morning go out with those who till the fields, and hide there," Jonathan instructed him. "My father visits the workers just after sunrise each day. I will accompany him tomorrow morning and try to persuade him that he has treated you ill. If he relents, you can come back to your home. If not, I will help you escape to Bethlehem myself."

"Be sure I will not forget what you are doing, my brother," David said warmly. "But take care lest Saul's temper be turned against you."

Joab was not so hopeful as Jonathan when David told him of Saul's order. "The time has come to break way," he said bluntly. "When we tell the people of Judah that Saul ordered his servants to kill you, they will have him no more as king. Then you can be crowned in his place."

"It will do no good to cause a civil war when we are ringed about with the Philistines," David objected. "So long as Saul is alive, he must still be king of all the tribes."

Joab's hand dropped casually to the long Phoenician dagger at his belt. "It can be easily arranged that he no longer remain alive."

"I forbid you to harm him, Joab," David said firmly. "The Lord has shown me the way before; he will show it to me again."

"I will place a guard here just the same," Joab said. "The mercenaries of Saul's bodyguard would kill their own mothers for a price."

No would-be assassin dared to attack David in the midst of his own men, so the night passed without event. As Jonathan had suggested, he went out early in the morning with the workmen and hid in a clump of underbrush where he could see and hear what happened in the field. Shortly after sunrise Jonathan and Saul appeared; as they walked along between the rows, David could hear Jonathan pleading his cause.

"Let not the king sin against David for he has not sinned against you," Jonathan begged his father. "His works toward you have always been good."

Saul made no answer but Jonathan continued his pleas. "After all, he did put his life in his hand when he killed the Philistine Goliath, and through him the Lord brought a great salvation for Israel. You saw it yourself and rejoiced. Why, then, would you sin against innocent blood and slay David without reason?"

"As the Lord lives, he shall not be killed," Saul said in one of the sudden changes of mood that characterized his malady.

"David!" Jonathan called happily. "Come out now."

Saul looked somewhat startled when David appeared, but he put on a smile of welcome and embraced his son-in-law with some evidence of affection. "Come back to the palace and play for me," he begged. "The house is not the same without your music."

For a period of several weeks, there was no sign that David was not welcome at Saul's palace. Michal especially was happy at this turn of events for she had missed the comparative luxury of the palace and the companionship of her sisters and brothers. For a while the coolness which had crept between her and David even seemed to have disappeared.

Then the Philistines attacked again, and through a clever piece of strategy on David's part, the Israelite troops under his command were able to drive the enemy back and capture a fair amount of booty. The people of Gibeah and the surrounding towns welcomed him to the capital with great enthusiasm. Once again the cry of "Saul has slain his thousands and David his ten thousands!" was heard in Gibeah; inevitably it came to the ears of Saul.

Upon his return, David had resumed his regular visits to the palace to play for Saul, but when the king once again hurled a javelin so close to him that it barely missed, he realized that the break between the two was now final. It was already dark when the disturbing incident took place. David lost no time in seeking out Michal where she was chatting with her mother and sisters and taking her to their home in Gibeah. There, she faced him angrily across the second-floor bedroom of their home.

"Why did we have to leave in the night?" she demanded, for he had half dragged her through the streets from the palace with no time for an explanation. "It is not right for me to flee my father's house like a thief!"

"Not even when he cast a javelin at your husband?" David demanded curtly. The sudden change in his relationship with Saul had disturbed him deeply and Michal's petulance was only a further irritation.

"He missed as he did before, didn't he? No doubt he was only testing your courage."

"My courage needs no testing. Who should know that better than Saul?"

"What are you going to do?"

"We will leave Gibeah tomorrow with Joab and my men to guard us."

"Does the mighty David flee like a criminal caught stealing?" she demanded tartly.

David shrugged. "It is better than being murdered in your bed by a hired assassin."

"My father would not stoop to such a thing," she flared. "If he wants you killed, he will do it himself in a fair fight."

"Was it fair to instruct his servant to kill me on sight?" David demanded. "But for your brother Jonathan, I would be dead now."

David had bolted the door downstairs but he had not expected Saul to molest him further that night. When he heard the rattle of metal on metal outside, a sound not ordinarily heard in a peaceful city at night, he realized that he had underestimated his father-in-law, an oversight that could easily cost him his life. Obviously Saul had sent men to follow him, rightly surmising that, since Michal was with him, he had gone to his own home.

Michal stiffened at the sound and moved to the window. Drawing back the rich draperies of Egyptian linen given to the bride and groom by the people of Gibeah as a wedding present, she looked out. When she turned to face David, her eyes were wide. "There are armed men outside. I recognized Doeg, the herdsman."

David had blown out the oil lamp that burned in a bracket upon the wall. He went to the window and looked through the curtain. For a moment he could see nothing; then a short, bandy-legged figure darted from one shadow to another and he recognized Saul's herdsman and private spy, Doeg, the Edomite.

"They have come to take me by stealth and kill me," he said in a whisper.

Michal clung to him, her former petulance gone in the face of the grave danger. "What can we do?"

"If I could get word to Joab, he would bring men and drive the mercenaries away, but it would mean fighting in Gibeah and the tribes would have to take sides between us. I don't want that to happen—at least not yet."

"I am afraid," Michal wailed. "They might even kill me if I flee with you!"

David felt a stab of pain at the realization that she had considered her own safety before her desire to be with him. "You will be in no danger if you stay here," he told her. "Get word to Joab in the morning that he and the men must not follow me or give battle to Saul's supporters. Tell them to return to Judah quietly as soon as they can. I will not be responsible for a civil war in Israel."

"What will you do?" She was regaining her self-control, now that she knew she would not have to flee with him.

"I don't know yet," he admitted. "But Doeg and the mercenaries cannot make an outcry either. The people of Gibeah would kill them if they realized what was happening."

From downstairs came the sound of a sharp rapping upon the door. "Quick," David told her. "Answer and tell them I am sick."

Michal opened the window while David busied himself tearing down the linen draperies from a window on the other side of the room. This window gave access to the rooftop of an adjoining house, a route of escape that had just occurred to him.

"What do you want?" he heard Michal ask the men outside.

"The king desires your husband's presence at the palace." David recognized the voice of a mercenary in Saul's personal guard, and knew he could expect no mercy from that source. As Joab had said, any one of them would murder his own mother for a high enough price.

"He is sick and cannot come," Michal answered. "Go back and tell my father."

There was a low-voiced colloquy below, after which they heard departing footsteps. From the window, Michal could see that several men remained behind to guard the house. Letting the hangings fall back in place across the window, she went to where David was tying the linen draperies together to make a stout rope.

"Doeg went back to the palace," she reported. "But others are still watching outside."

"We have gained a little time, at least. Help me let this rope out the window. I will tie it to a chair and, if you steady it against the wall, I can climb down and escape by the 'Road of the Roofs.' "

"They will surely look for you in Bethlehem," she warned, while they worked together tying the strips of linen into an improvised rope.

"Your father fears Samuel; I will try to join him at Ramah until all this blows over. Then I can send for you to join me there."

"If all this had not happened, you might one day have been king and I a queen!" she cried. "Now everything is lost!"

"Nothing is lost as long as we are both alive and have each other," he told her, but she only wept the harder and refused to be consoled.

"I cannot live the life of an outlaw to be hunted and sleep in caves," she protested. "I was born a king's daughter and I have lived in the palace all my life. You cannot ask me to do it!"

"Remain behind where you will be safe, then," he said. "But I swear by the Most High that I shall one day claim you again as my wife." Kissing her quickly in farewell, he stepped through the window, straddling the sill for a moment to give her further instructions. "When I have gone, pretend I forced you to help me escape. That way your father will not hold it against you that I got away."

Now that she was in no danger herself, Michal worked willingly enough to help him escape. She held the chair against the window ledge in order to secure the upper end of the rope, and watched while he let himself down the brief height separating the window of his own bedchamber from the roof of the house next to it. When his feet struck the tiles of the roof, he released the rope and she drew it up into the chamber.

David's last sight of Michal was the glow of her white face at the window, but had he known how many years would elapse before he saw her again, the wrench of parting might have been far greater. As it was, his pain was sharp enough; he was losing the girl he had known and loved at the foot of the hill at Gibeah, where they had watched the doe and her fawn drinking at the spring—a girl who, he knew now, had never really existed except in his dream.

CHAPTER 9

"David fled, and escaped, and came to Samuel to Ramah." I SAMUEL 19:18

IN CHOOSING RAMAH as his place of hiding, David had acted with some forethought. The village lay almost directly north of Gibeah, while Bethlehem, where Saul would be sure to look for him first, was more than twice as far to the south. Ramah was not one of the traditional cities of refuge like Kedesh, Chefrin, Hebron, Bezer, and Ramoth where hunted men had always been able to find shelter when their lives were in danger. A religious center by virtue of Samuel's presence there, Ramah was a haven where David could hope to find freedom from Saul's persecution.

An olive grove lay along the southwest slope of the ridge upon which Ramah was built. There David, wrapped in the heavy cloak of the Israelite fighting man, spent the remainder of that first night. As yet, the realization that he was a fugitive with a price upon his head did not weigh heavily on him. He was much more concerned with what Joab might do when he heard of the present crisis, for in the king's attempt to assassinate him, Joab might see his chance to rally Judah for a break with Saul, and might then disobey the instructions David had asked Michal to relay to him.

David was awakened from a light sleep by the voices of people going to work on the small farms that dotted the hillsides of this region. He rose and started walking along the roadway leading into

Ramah, but he was careful to keep to the road so that he would appear like any ordinary wayfarer and not attract attention. Although he was very hungry, he knew he must refrain from asking anyone for food, lest he be recognized. News of his break with the king could have reached the area already, and the farmers might consider it their duty to report his whereabouts to the king. He had to content himself, therefore, with a few handfuls of olives gathered along the way, the right of any traveler who found himself faint with hunger while on a journey.

The route between Gibeah and Ramah marked the very backbone of the central highlands of Canaan. To the east, a succession of valleys led downward toward the Jordan, lying far below the heights where David was traveling. The rich valley land beside the river made an inspiring prospect in the distance, and from the ridge it was easy to see why the Philistines continually sought to break through the mountain passes of central Canaan and gain control of the fertile lowlands. Since Judah lay squarely across the paths by which the enemy must reach this rich prize, there could be no peace of any duration between Philistia and Judah until one or the other had been destroyed.

Just *when* Samuel's prophecy that he would one day rule in Israel would be accomplished, David had no idea. His fortunes were at a lower ebb now, it seemed, than they had been at any time since his anointing by Samuel at Bethlehem; but that the Lord had indeed singled him out for the task, he still did not doubt for a moment. And the strength of that conviction gave him the courage to go on, even though he knew that probably Saul had already sent out mercenaries to search for him and destroy him.

In Samuel's modest home at Ramah, the old prophet listened intently to the story of his relationship with Saul and the attempt at assassination in his own home the night before. "The Son of Kish knows the Lord has withdrawn his favor from him," Samuel said when David had finished the account. "Only the evil spirit drives him now."

"Will it ever loose its hold?"

"I cannot tell what Saul's fate will be," Samuel said. "But be sure the will of the Lord will be done and you will one day rule in Israel."

"What shall I do in the meantime?"

Samuel had aged considerably since that day long ago when he had anointed David at Bethlehem. His hand trembled now as he stroked his beard, and the tortuous pattern of the veins showed against the alabaster pallor of his skin. "Let it not be said that the Lord was unmerciful and gave the Son of Kish no chance to redeem himself," he said finally. "You must go back to Gibeah."

"Suppose Saul tries to kill me another time?"

"You will have done all you can. After that you will be free to seek your own future."

"I will not make war against Saul in order to become king," David insisted.

"The Lord does not ask that of you," Samuel told him. "Journey with me to Naioth and stay with me a little while before you return to Gibeah. Perhaps the Most High will reveal some other truth to me."

"If you are sure it is safe."

"Whom the Lord hath anointed he does not desert," Samuel assured him.

In the tiny village of Naioth, David spent several pleasant days talking to the old prophet about the glorious past since Abraham had first come into this land from the northwest, and the future which God had promised to his people here if they would worship only him and obey his laws. David did not fully realize it at the time, but Samuel was preparing him for the day when he would become Israel's king and assume an intimate and responsible relationship with God and with the people he would rule. A peaceful interlude, and an enjoyable one, it lasted until word came that Saul had sent men to arrest David and bring him to Gibeah. He would have left at once to seek refuge in the hill country, where only the shepherds knew the paths, but Samuel would not let him flee.

When the messengers of Saul came to Naioth, they found Samuel standing among the priests who served him; the messengers were so intimidated by the authority of the old prophet's manner that they turned away without trying to carry out their orders. A second group arrived a few days later and were likewise sent away by Samuel, but David knew now that he could not remain at Naioth any longer. For if Saul dared to send mercenaries to the old prophet the next time, a bloody slaughter of the priests could well occur.

"I will go to Gibeah and seek out Jonathan," David told Samuel. "He can be trusted to make a final effort for a reconciliation with Saul."

"Go, then," the old prophet said. "And whatever you do, know that the blessing of the Lord is with you."

David did not enter the capital city itself on his return, but hid in the dense underbrush that grew along the brook at the base of the hill. He had been fortunate in coming upon one of his own men on the road and had sent him for Jonathan, with instructions also to Joab that he should not come to him for fear that Saul might learn his whereabouts. When shortly the king's son appeared, the two embraced warmly.

"What is my iniquity that your father seeks my life?" David asked.

"God forbid that you should die at his hand," Jonathan protested. "Whatever you desire, I will do it for you."

"Tomorrow is the new moon," David said. "As the son-in-law of the king, I should sit at his table, but I will hide here instead. If Saul misses me, tell him I have gone to Bethlehem for a yearly sacrifice made there for all of my family. If he says it is well, there will be peace between us. But if he is angry, you will know he intends evil toward me."

"It is a good plan," Jonathan agreed. "I will do as you say."

"You and I have made a covenant together," David reminded him. "If you find any iniquity in me now, I beg you to slay me with your own hands."

Jonathan held up his thumb so that David could see the tiny scar where he had pricked the skin with a dagger and they had mixed their blood. "If it pleases my father to do evil to you, I will reveal it to you and send you away that you may go in peace," he promised. "Only while I live, show me the kindness of the Lord and also do not cut off your kindness from my house; not even when the Lord has cut off the enemies of David from the face of the earth."

"I swear it," David gripped the other's forearm in the traditional gesture of friendship. "But who shall tell me if your father answers you roughly and intends evil toward me?"

"On the third day go to the field where you hid before," Jonathan instructed him. "I will come to the field and shoot three arrows as if I were shooting at a mark, and send a boy to find them. If I say, 'Look, the arrows are on this side of you,' then come out, for there is peace toward you in my father's household."

"And if there is no peace?"

"Then I will say to the boy, 'Look, the arrows are beyond you.' "

"I will watch by the field on the third morning," David agreed. "But take care lest harm come to you because you helped me."

The days were long but David spent them resting in the little glen through which the stream flowed. He hid himself in the morning, when the people who worked in the fields filled their water bottles at the spring, and in the afternoons, when the workers returned to Gibeah for the night. On the third morning he awoke early and made his way to the field where Jonathan was to shoot his arrows.

On any other occasion, David's poetic instinct would have been aroused by the many sights and sounds that marked the beginning of a new day. Above him, the city of Gibeah was just beginning to come to life, while across the descending series of slopes and valleys to the east the red streamers of dawn were already appearing around the peaks of Moab.

From the houses clustered around the fortress at the top of the hill he could hear a woman trying to rouse her child from bed, then the bleat of a goat being milked, and the clank of metal against metal as guards detailed for the day made ready to relieve those who had been on duty during the night. From the fortress itself, David could hear the voices of the officers giving commands, as preparations were made for opening the gate to allow the detail from the camp below to march inside. He had commanded this detail himself on many occasions, and the thought that he was now a fugitive, waiting to learn whether or not he would still be hunted like an animal, depressed him profoundly. In his own house, or at Saul's palace, if her father had believed the story of David's forcing her to help him escape, Michal would be awakening just now. A stab of pain went through his heart as he remembered how lovely she was, and for a moment he knew such an acute longing for those early days when they had watched the doe and her fawn drinking at the spring, that it was like a knife thrust into his very heart.

The sun was stronger now, and David pictured the streets of Gibeah as the brightening city came to life. He heard the men, yawning and stretching as they went to raise the shutters and move aside the screens which had protected the shop fronts. Women spoke softly to each other as they set out the dates, crusts of bread, and jars of milk cooled by the night air that formed the morning meal. Their soft voices floated down, mixed now and then with the sound of a street peddler as he cried his wares of olive oil, bread, and packages of figs and dates.

Gibeah was not a manufacturing city, as were most of the Philistine centers to the west, but it did contain a few shops where artisans plied their trade. In these, David knew, the proprietors would already be setting out their hammers and punches for shaping metal, or the awls and needles used for working leather. Potters would be working the clay, dug from pits in the hillsides the day before. On another street, a yawning scribe would be setting out his tablets of clay, along with parchment, papyrus sheets, and tiny cups of ink. The moneylenders, too, would be setting up their little cabinets on which to display their coins, ready to lend to any and all who were willing to pay the exact amount of usury allowed by law, but no more, on pain of punishment by God.

The wakening of the city was a warm and pleasant blending of small sounds. It had been music to David's ears during the months he had lived in Gibeah in a fine house, enjoying the high position and the luxury that went with being the king's son-in-law. But now, unless Jonathan called out this morning that the arrows had fallen near him, he was going to have to give up all this and flee from the wrath of Saul into the hill country of the disputed land between Judah and Philistia. And even there he could hope for nothing better than a cave as his habitation and such food as he would be able to scavenge for himself.

The voices of people going to work in the fields reached David's ears as he secreted himself in the underbrush. Soon he saw Jonathan approaching from the city; his bow was in his hand and a quiver of arrows hung from his shoulder. Behind him trotted the boy who was his armorbearer. "Run," David heard him tell the boy. "Run and find the arrows I shoot."

As the boy started across the field, Jonathan took an arrow from the quiver and fitted it into the bow. David was watching intently. When he saw his friend draw the string well back, his heart was suddenly heavy, for it could only mean that the arrow would be shot well ahead of the boy scurrying across the plowed field.

The bowstring twanged noisily as the arrow was released. David watched the missile fly in a long trajectory above the boy's head and fall to the earth well ahead of him. Two other arrows in rapid succession sped from the bow, each falling to the earth a little beyond the other; when the boy paused to look at them, Jonathan called loudly, "Is not the arrow beyond you?"

It was the signal that Saul had not relented and that David must flee for his life.

CHAPTER 10

"And David arose, and fled that day for fear of Saul." I SAMUEL 21:10

IT TOOK THE BOY only a few moments to gather up the arrows Jonathan had shot. When he returned with them, Jonathan gave him the bow and quiver and told him to carry them back to the city. The boy took off up the path leading to the gate; when he was out of sight, Jonathan approached the clump of bushes where David was hiding.

"Go in peace," he said. "And remember we have sworn both of us in the name of the Lord that he will be between us and between your seed and my seed forever."

"Your father will not be reconciled?"

Jonathan shook his head sadly. "When I mentioned your name to him, he went into a frenzy of raving and gave orders to the mercenaries to kill you on sight. You must leave here at once before anyone sees you."

"I must see Joab first."

"Give me a message and I will deliver it to him. You will be taking your life in your hand if you try to go into the camp of the Judahites."

"Tell Joab I am safe and well and that I will send for him later when I know what I am going to do."

"The message shall be delivered," Jonathan promised. "But go now before the mercenaries start searching for you."

Knowing that Saul would send men to Samuel at Ramah and Naioth to seek him, David took another route on his second flight from Gibeah. This road led to Judah but long before nightfall of the first day's journey, he was famished. When he found himself near the priestly center at Nob, he turned aside and approached the low hill upon which stood the Tabernacle and the Altar of Sacrifice that formed the most sacred spot in all of Israel. Ahimelech, the priest with whom David had talked on a former occasion, came out to meet him when he approached the Tabernacle. "Why are you alone?" he asked somewhat warily.

David was sure from the priest's manner that word of his difficulties with Saul had already spread here, but he was not ready as yet to announce a complete break with the king. Since he had not been able to take his own weapons with him in his flight from Gibeah, he must first obtain food and arms.

"The king has sent me on a mission," he explained. "I have no food, so please give me some bread or whatever else you may have."

"I have only the hallowed bread," Ahimelech said doubtfully. This was baked each morning and placed upon the altar, lest the Lord visit the Holy Place and be hungry, for it had been plainly stated in the instructions to Moses: "Thou shalt set upon the table shewbread before me always."

"Please give that to me for I am faint with hunger," David said.

Ahimelech took a loaf of the bread which had been saved from the altar the day before for the use of the priests, and gave it to him, along with some olive oil and a handful of dates. David had not noticed a flock of sheep grazing on the hillside, or the bandy-legged little man who had followed him to the shrine and was now standing behind a tree, listening avidly to what was said. The eyes of Doeg, the Edomite, gleamed when he saw that the traveler had no weapons, and his hand loosened the long dagger he wore at his belt. He could not attack David in the Holy Place lest he defile it and thereby earn the anger of both the priests and Saul. But there were many places along the road where one could lie in wait for an unarmed man, knowing that Saul would reward him well for bringing proof of David's death.

David finished eating and looked around the knoll. "Do you have a spear or a sword?" he asked.

The priest's face was pale with fear. He had caught sight of Doeg and, knowing the Edomite, fully realized that word of everything that happened here would quickly get back to Saul. He did not reveal the herdsman's presence to David, however, lest blood be shed at the sacred shrine.

"You brought here the sword of Goliath, the Philistine, after you slew him in the valley of Elah," Ahimelech said. "It is wrapped in a cloth behind the ephod. Take it if you will."

David hesitated to accept the priest's offer for two reasons. Having been forged of iron and designed for Goliath's great strength, the sword was so heavy that it would at best be an unwieldy weapon. But since he planned to carry it only to Bethlehem, where he could obtain more suitable weapons, this was not particularly important. What did trouble him was the fact that in getting the sword he might have to touch the sacred ephod.

An upper garment worn by the chief priest while carrying out the rituals of sacrifice and worship, the ephod had been prepared originally according to the instructions of Moses and ornamented with rings, earrings, armlets and jewels of gold. The present ephod, woven from fine linen in blue, purple, and other rich colors, was, according to the directions in the ancient books of record, as nearly like the original as it had been possible to make it. These specified that the ephod should be square, with four rows of three stones, symbolizing each of the twelve tribes of Israel, set cleverly in jeweled mountings sewn to the cloth of the sacred garment itself. It was also considered to have more than simply a symbolic value because of the widespread belief that, when touched by a priest, it would enable him to foretell the will of God and the events of the future.

No other weapon except the sword was available, however, and since it would be folly to travel far without some means of protecting himself, David entered the Tabernacle. Taking great care not to disturb the richly ornamented ephod, he carefully lifted up the great weapon. He had forgotten how heavy it was, and the burden of its weight almost staggered him. For a moment he considered putting it back and risking the journey to Bethlehem without a weapon; but deep inside him the warning voice which had never advised him wrongly spoke against such a course. Finally he slung the leather belt from which the sword was suspended across his shoulder, as it would have dragged on the ground had he buckled the harness about his waist, and left the Tabernacle.

Doeg was still watching when David came out of the sacred tent. When he saw the weapon, his face clouded, for he was of no great courage, and except in the darkness and by stealth would not dare to attack an armed man. He did not follow David, but instead took the road for Gibeah, leaving the sheep to graze unattended in his haste to tell Saul that the man he hated had visited the priestly center and no doubt could be followed from there and destroyed.

David paused at Bethlehem only long enough to leave the sword of Goliath at his father's house and obtain food and weapons before traveling westward toward the disputed land between Judah and Philistia. Not even there could he be sure of safety against Saul, however; so with a price upon his head, he decided upon a rather daring move, a visit to Philistine territory.

David's purpose in going to the enemy for refuge from his own people was twofold. For one thing, he was not well known to the Philistines, having remained behind during the major part of the battle in the valley of Elah. He doubted that even the enemy soldiers who had witnessed his destruction of Goliath would recognize in the skilled fighting man of today that same youth who had felled their champion with a stone. For another thing, he hoped to scout the Philistines' territory against the time when, as king of Israel, he must carry the battle to them by invading the very heartland of the enemy confederation. The place he chose for a temporary haven was the frontier city of Gath, ruled over by King Achish.

In times of peace the Hebrews often came down to Gath to have their tools sharpened by Philistine smiths and to sell the hides and cheeses which were this pastoral people's chief export and source of income. In turn, the Israelites bought tools of iron and the marvelous leather-colored, highly ornamented pottery for which the Philistines were famous throughout that part of the world, just as their ancestors, the Mycenae, had been famous for their exquisite earthenware.

Built upon a huge white cliff of chalk, Gath was truly an impressive city. David had brought a hoe and an axe from Bethlehem on the pretext of having them sharpened by a smith, so he had no trouble in entering the city with a group of workers coming in from the fields at nightfall. And once inside, he could not help but be impressed by the strong walls and heavily fortified gates of the Philistine center.

From the hill upon which Gath stood, the view was awe-inspiring, with the mountains of Judah rising in step-like order in a broad sweep to the east. Directly north lay a broad expanse of fertile plain, with a lofty fortified tower, which he learned later was called Ramleh, overlooking it. To the south stretched another plain, while the west was filled with the deep blue of the Great Sea. Perhaps twenty smaller settlements were visible from the height of Gath, proof of the steadily increasing population of Philistia which kept the five kings so well supplied with fighting men.

Another thing that startled David was the tallness of the men of Gath; though he himself was above medium height, many of them towered over him. He was reminded that Goliath had come from this city and the magnitude of the task which would face him, as king, of conquering these people and bringing peace to Judah and all of Israel, appalled him. Turning away from the wall which he had climbed for a look at the countryside, he sought a drinking house, where sleeping pads were customarily rented to travelers. Before he could find a bed for the night, however, he had the misfortune to stumble into a Philistine soldier in the rapidly deepening twilight.

"Stupid one!" the man growled, pushing him away. "Look where you are going."

When David's hand dropped to the hilt of his dagger with the instinctive reaction of a fighting man, the soldier saw the movement and drew his own sword. As he stepped back to leave room for the fight, if it should develop, he got a better view of David's face and spat out a startled curse.

"By the golden beard of Dagon himself! It is David, the son-in-law of Saul! Defend yourself, Hebrew!"

David let his hand slip across the hilt of the dagger and fall to his side, for the Philistine had already unsheathed his sword and a fight here could only end in one way. "You have put the wineskin to your lips too often, my friend," he said with a shrug. "How can I be myself and the son-in-law of the hated Saul at the same time?"

The Philistine soldier studied him suspiciously. "If you are not David, then you are his twin," he said, but doubt was already beginning to show in his voice. "I saw this David in the valley of Elah when Goliath was killed, and again on the road when our party was attacked on the return from Chesalon."

"I never heard that the Hebrew had a twin brother," David kept his voice light so that the other could not detect the tension under which he was laboring.

"Nor I," the Philistine admitted. "Which is all the more reason why you and he are one. Come. I will take you before King Achish."

David had no choice except to obey the prodding of his captor's swordpoint; to resist would have labeled him guilty and earned him a thrust through the body.

Soon he found himself entering a large chamber, walled with giant blocks of stone, where a tall man with a hawk-proud face and deep-set intelligent eyes occupied a throne chair set upon a dais. David had been casting about desperately in his mind during the march through the city for some way to effect an escape from what, as he realized now, had been a foolish venture in the first place. Between the ruthless Philistine king and the madman who ruled Israel, what chance was there of surviving? But suddenly an idea came to him. It was a desperately simple ruse and to carry it off would require all his powers of deception.

The Philistines had adopted the old Canaanite gods as their own, adding them to the particular deities which they had brought with them from their ancient homeland. Like the Hebrews, they saw the world as a place filled with spirits, both good and bad, upon whose whims a man's fate could hang. As an Israelite, David knew he could expect short shrift at the hands of the king of Gath, but as a madman, might he not be able to excite so much fear lest the spirits inhabiting his body escape to others that he would be thrust from the city? Fortunately he'd had much contact with a prime example of a madman, King Saul. And it was the irony of fate that his own life, which Saul was so eager to take, should now depend upon his ability to imitate the Hebrew king.

As they were crossing the throne room, David began to shout and swear, throwing himself about and falling to the floor. There he kicked and jerked in spasms so convincing that Achish would not let him be brought nearer to the throne than twenty paces.

"The man is mad!" the Philistine king snapped to the soldier who had brought David to the palace. "Why have you brought him to me?"

"It is David, the son-in-law of Saul, my lord king," the man protested. "I recognized him outside."

"He is as mad as his father-in-law, then," Achish said. "Do I have need of madmen that you bring this fellow into my presence? Take him away."

"But my lord king—"

"Away with him before the evil spirits that inhabit his body are loosened among us!" Achish ordered. "Drive him through the city gates and close them after him."

David understood the words of Achish, for the Judahites and the Philistines of this border region were familiar with each other's speech, but he was careful not to let up in the part that he was playing. Still cursing and shouting, throwing himself upon the ground every fifty paces or so, he allowed himself to be driven through the gate by the Philistine soldier, who was now as anxious as Achish had been lest the evil spirits be loosed from his body.

Only when he was outside the gate and safely in the wood, did David drop the pretense. Nor did he pause for the night in Philistine territory, but made his way as best he could in the moonlight along the roadway toward Judah. Finally he came to the height of Adullam which lay on the south side of the valley in the disputed area between Judah and Philistia. There he hid among the trees until morning came and he could make his way up the slope to one of the many caves which pocked the hillside. And when, about a week later, he saw Joab and nearly a hundred loyal members of his own band marching through the valley, he ran down to hail them and guide them to his hiding place.

Only when he had finished telling of his adventures in the Philistine city of Gath, did David notice the presence of a stranger, a slender man in the garb of a priest, who was carrying a package wrapped in rich cloth.

"This is Abiathar, the son of Ahimelech," Joab said.

"You are welcome, Abiathar," David said warmly, "although I have only the shelter of a cave and food from the hillside to offer you, in return for the shewbread your father gave me. I hope Ahimelech is well."

A spasm of pain passed over the face of the priest and he looked away quickly, but not before David saw his eyes film with tears.

"Ahimelech is dead, David," Joab said. "He and all the priests at Nob were massacred. Only Abiathar escaped."

"Who dared to desecrate the holy place of God?" David demanded angrily. "Surely not Saul!"

"The order was Saul's, so it must rest upon his soul." Abiathar had found his voice now. "But the hands that wielded the swords were those of Doeg, the Edomite, and the mercenaries of Saul's bodyguard."

It was apparent what had happened at Nob—apparent, too, what the reason was. "Then your father was killed because he sought to help me?"

Abiathar shook his head. "The Lord's Anointed can only do the will of the Most High. When my father saw Doeg and the mercenaries coming, he took the ephod from the Tabernacle and told me to bring it to you." Unfolding the wrappings of the package he carried, the priest held the ephod in his hand for David to see. As he did so the jewels embroidered with their settings into the fine linen of the priestly garment caught fire in the sunlight and glowed with a brightness almost rivaling that of the sun itself.

"A sign!" Joab shouted. "A sign of God's favor for the Son of Jesse!"

David himself could not help being startled by the beauty of the gems adorning the ephod and the way they glowed in the rays of the sun. And even if the occurrence were not the sign Joab had said it was, he recognized that the others needed the encouragement which came from believing it to be God's way of showing approval.

"You shall be my priest, Abiathar," he said. "Whoever seeks your life seeks mine, and with me you shall be safe. Guard well the ephod, too, for I swear one day to bring it and the Ark of the Covenant and the Tabernacle together again in a Holy Place of their own."

To a casual listener the oath might have appeared merely an idle boast, for the only men on whom David could really depend were gathered around him now. They numbered but a few more than a hundred, while Saul opposed him with the armies of Israel. But then, he reminded himself, the odds had been far greater in the valley of Elah, when he had crossed the brook to face Goliath.

III. THE FALL OF THE MIGHTY

"How are the mighty fallen in the midst of the battle!" II SAMUEL 1:25

CHAPTER 1

"For by thee I have run through a troop; and by my God have I leaped over a wall." PSALMS 18:29

THE MONTHS David spent in the region of Adullam and the nearby wood of Hareth were busy ones. He had taken his family to Moab, where they had kinsmen and would be safe. When he launched a series of lightning-swift attacks upon roving Philistine bands in the area, his fame as a leader of men grew rapidly; the original nucleus of about a hundred men, brought to him by Joab and his brothers, increased to about six hundred. Many of these were homeless men who inhabited the borderland between Judah and Philistia and were welcome in neither; though their presence swelled David's forces to a very respectable figure, it also posed problems of supply.

It was the season of the harvest, a period when the Philistines always increased the frequency of their raids upon the towns of Judah. They would carry off the freshly threshed grain and sell into slavery any of the people they could capture in the fields. When the depredations of the enemy threatened the inhabitants of the nearby town of Keilah with loss of their entire harvest, David launched a swift attack upon the Philistines and drove them off. In gratitude, and with the hope of warding off future enemy attack, the elders of the city invited David and his band to quarter themselves there.

Keilah was situated at the crown of a cone-shaped hill, surrounded by a stepped succession of walled terraces largely covered with fields of grain and a few vineyards. A big spring gushed from the hillside not far below the top, with a brook flowing from it in a succession of shallow pools. Still another spring at the foot of the hill drained into a wide, twisting stream. It was a pleasant area and very fertile. The workmen went out in the morning to till the fields or reap the grain, and returned in the evening to the protection of the city wall.

So long as the danger from the Philistines remained, the quartering of David's troops in Keilah was a satisfactory arrangement for all concerned: David and his men furnished protection, while the town supplied them with food and other necessities. In fact, when David seriously considered making the arrangement a permanent one, he sent for Abiathar to bring the sacred ephod from the caves of Adullam where the priest had been living since his escape from the massacre at Nob.

Abiathar was ushered into Keilah with great ceremony and rejoicing, though some of the inhabitants grumbled that Saul would be sure to seek the return of the sacred symbol of Israel's faith. David himself led the procession through the city gates to the small building where Abiathar and the ephod were to be housed. As he was leaving after the ceremony, the priest called to him.

"A messenger came to Adullam while you were away," he said. "Saul has given your wife to another."

David was stunned. Although he had good reason to know that Saul was implacable where his former son-in-law was concerned, it had never occurred to him that he would deprive him of Michal.

"Who is the man?" he managed to ask.

"Phalti, the son of Laish."

With his family forced to flee to Moab, his wife given to another, and all his possessions seized, David could hardly be blamed if even the victory over the Philistines at Keilah turned now to ashes in his mouth. Fortunately, he had little time to be despondent, for the town, and his band, were busy with a great celebration called the Festival of the Harvest, or the First Fruits.

The festivities opened in the afternoon, when the people began pouring from the city to a shady grove where an altar had been set up. A group of singers chanted a hymn of thanksgiving while others accompanied them on pipes, timbrels, psalters, and the *shophar*. In the heart of the grove where the altar of sacrifice had been set up, the people gathered before Abiathar who presided at the ceremony because of his former residence at the priestly center of Nob, and of the fact that he was the son of Ahimelech, chief of the priestly company there. It was the custom to select one from among the people as chief singer. By common consent this honor was given to David, already known far and wide as the sweetest singer in all of Israel, and one highly favored by the Lord. As the two men stood beside the altar, the people filed by, bearing the traditional gifts of first fruits. These were offered to the Lord in thanks for their good harvest and for the defeat of the enemy. Soon the altar was piled high with bundles of barley and wheat, grapes, dates, and figs, along with a young fowl, a kid, and a baby lamb.

Actually, the Festival of the First Fruits had sprung from an even older custom, the sacrifice of the first-born, which had been widely practiced in Canaan when the Hebrews had come into the land. In obedience to God's order and as a proof of his faith, Abraham, the father of the Hebrews, had placed his only son, Isaac, upon an altar on the hill of Moriah in the neighborhood of Jerusalem. As Abraham had lifted the ritual bronze knife to slash the boy's throat and pour out the blood of the sacrifice upon the stones, God had stayed his hand; ever since, the sacrifice of the first fruits and the ritual payment to a priest of a ransom for the first-born had taken the place of human sacrifice.

When the placing of the sacrifices had been completed, the priests who were assisting Abiathar quickly slashed the throats of the animals. As the blood poured out upon the stones, the dry wood was set afire by a torch, and the flames leaped up to consume the offerings. While the smoke curled skyward from the grove, David struck the strings of the harp given him by the people of Keilah in place of the one he had left behind in the precipitous flight from Gibeah, and began to chant a poem of thanks to God for the gift of an abundant harvest and the assurance of life for another year:

"Our hearts rejoice in the Lord;
He quickeneth the dry seed in the soft earth.
He refresheth the land with rain;
He maketh grow the spreading olives.

The warm wind of the east is the breath of his nostrils;
He bringeth to full ripeness the seed of grass and vine and trees;
He spreadeth before man a feast in the land.
Blessed be the Lord, blessed be his name."

When the song was finished, the musicians began to play another tune, and the people, in their exuberance, started to dance. Soon, the men and women formed two lines facing each other and, as the music took on a more compelling beat in a lower key, began the traditional dance of mating. In the figures of the dance, the men pursued the women while the latter retreated in mock refusal, only to yield finally in the last bars of the music. The re-enactment of the drama of pursuit, yielding, and conquest was only symbolic tonight. But a week later, at the end of the festival, the men would lie down to sleep upon the threshing floor. By lying beneath the cloak of her beloved then, a maid could choose without shame the man whom she wished to be her husband.

His duties as the singer, or cantor, finished, David left the others and went to sit upon a rock farther down the slope, beside the spring that gushed from the earth there. The rush of the water brought back the memory of another such spring, and the girl he had held in his arms beside it. He had been happy then, happy as only a young man with his life before him and his love in his arms can be. But now Michal, who had been so briefly his, was lost to another, though he intended to fulfill the vow he had made to reclaim her one day as his wife. And although she was far away, perhaps even then in the arms of another, something about the soft rush of the water seemed to allay at least a small part of the pain.

The rattle of a stone just above the spring brought David to his feet, dagger in hand. But when he recognized the tall figure of Abiathar, still wearing his robes of office and with the sacred jeweled ephod about his neck, he slid the weapon back into its sheath.

"Why does the Son of Jesse hide himself while others celebrate?" Abiathar asked. "The people are asking for you to do you further honor."

"I was oppressed by a deep melancholy," David admitted. "The sight of others in their happiness only made it hurt the more."

"You have lost much, as have I," Abiathar agreed soberly.

"But you have found a welcome here, while I must go on. When Saul learns that we are in Keilah, he is certain to pursue us."

"He already knows."

David turned startled eyes upon the priest. "Surely the people of Keilah did not betray us?"

"Not the people, but a few among them who are greedy. Several of the Council of Elders sent a message to Saul, telling him you are here."

"How did word of this come to you?"

"Many things are told to a priest that might not come to the ears of others. The Elders fear lest you and your men decide to quarter yourselves in the city for a long time."

"And perhaps take control of it entirely?" David's voice was harsh.

"That, too, was in their minds. But do not think too ill of them. They have known as brigands many who are with you now; in fact, some were driven out of Keilah for crimes they committed."

"It is true that I have not asked questions of any who offered to fight with us against the Philistines," David admitted. "When was this messenger dispatched to Saul?"

"Three days ago."

"Then he will return soon."

"He came this very evening while the festival was in progress. I heard him reporting to the Chief Elder and I have sought you out to warn you."

"You must not take such a chance again," David warned. "Here in Keilah you have found refuge and a position of honor at the head of the priests. All that will be lost if it becomes known that you warned me."

"It will be lost in any event," Abiathar said calmly. "When you leave here, I intend to go with you. And take the ephod."

"But that is madness! Why put your own life in jeopardy for one who caused the death of your father and the other priests at Nob?"

"Those who serve the Most High must always be ready to help the Lord's Anointed," Abiathar said simply. "My father was obeying that law when he gave you the shewbread at Nob. The ephod carries with it the power to divine the will of God. If you are to defend yourself against the superior numbers possessed by Saul, you will have need of it."

For a moment David's throat was so filled by emotion that he could not speak. Finally he reached out and gripped the forearm of the priest. "Tell me what word the messenger brought from Saul," he said.

"The king was pleased to hear that you are in Keilah. The messenger repeated his very words to the Elders: 'God has delivered him into my hands for he has shut himself in by entering into a town that has gates and bars.' "

"There is plenty of water outside the gates, and enough grain in the villages nearby to feed an army, so Saul could put Keilah under siege if he so desired," David agreed. "But we have a weapon he does not know of. Perhaps the ephod will tell us whether or not the people of Keilah will betray us?"

"We can only ask and see," Abiathar said. "Let us pray for God's will to be revealed."

Standing beside the stream, David spoke to the God whose presence near him he had never doubted for a moment, even as a boy herding sheep on the hillsides of Judah. "O Lord of Israel," he prayed. "Your servant has heard that Saul seeks to come to Keilah to destroy the city because of me. Will the men of Keilah deliver me into his hands, and will Saul come down, as thy servant has heard?"

For a moment there was silence, then Abiathar spoke quietly. "Saul will come and the men of Keilah will give you up."

David got to his feet. There was no lack of resolution in his manner now. "We will leave the city tomorrow, before Saul has a chance to trap us here."

"Where will you go?"

"The forest of Hareth will not be safe for us, nor will the caves of Adullam, since both are nearby. This time we must go into the wilderness of Ziph." He put his hand once again upon the priest's arm. "It is not too late for you to remain behind, Abiathar. The blood of your father is a heavy enough burden upon my soul; I would not have yours added to it."

Abiathar smiled. "You forget that I, too, am of Judah. And though I do not belong to the family of Jesse, I have heard many times the words of your ancestor Ruth, '*Intreat me not to leave thee, or to return from following after thee.*' "

"May God always show us his will through you and the ephod as he has this night," David said gratefully. "I will not disturb the men at their revels; they have earned the pleasure they are having tonight. But tomorrow we will begin the journey into the wilderness."

For once, however, the ephod did not reveal the whole truth. Shortly after sunrise the next morning, while most of David's men, as well as the people of Keilah, were still asleep, sentries on the wall shouted down the news that a great army was approaching to surround the city. David himself hurried to the tower while Joab and Abishai routed out the men; he needed no second glance to recognize the tall man in splendidly polished armor who led the soldiers now deploying skillfully around the base of the hill upon which Keilah stood.

It was Saul. And his army, David estimated, could hardly number less than three thousand men.

CHAPTER 2

"And David abode in the wilderness in strong holds." I SAMUEL 23:14

DAVID CAME DOWN from the tower to find Joab and Abishai at the head of their men, holding back an angry and clamorous population.

"These fools want us to open the gate and surrender the town to Saul," Joab reported. "They do not care that all of us would be destroyed."

The Chief Elder, a corpulent man whom David knew to be the wealthiest merchant in the town and one of those who had sent for Saul, stood in the front rank of the crowd. "We have no quarrel with Saul, the rightful king of our people," he said pompously. "It is not our responsibility that he seeks to trap rebels and destroy them."

"So we are rebels now," Joab snapped. "A few weeks ago you were happy enough to welcome us into the city as heroes."

"He is right, Joab," David said quietly. "These people have no quarrel with Saul."

"Leave the city now and we will make no move to keep you from departing," the Elder promised.

"Hah!" It was a snort of contempt from Joab. "But you will not mourn if Saul sweeps over us as a flame would sweep the stubble of the harvest in the field."

A great light suddenly shone in David's mind. "Say no more, Joab," he murmured in a voice that only his lieutenant could hear. "I know how we can escape from the city."

"People of Keilah, you need have no fear!" David spoke loudly now, for the benefit of the Chief Elder and the crowd. "As we saved you from the Philistines who were destroying the harvest and carrying off your cattle and your young men and women, so will we secure you from the threat of Saul."

"We have nothing to fear from Saul," the Chief Elder spluttered. "It is you and your men from whom we need to be rescued."

An angry growl came from Joab at the words, but David answered before he could speak. "The word of the Son of Jesse has never been broken," he told the crowd. "You have my promise, at the price of my losing the favor of the Most High if I break it, that we will leave Keilah by tomorrow. You can see for yourself that Saul is letting his men rest after the journey from Gibeah. There will be no attack today."

"You will leave tomorrow?" the Elder asked doubtfully.

"You have my word," David assured him. "Before noon tomorrow, you can open the gates to your king."

With that assurance the crowd dispersed; but David had trouble keeping Joab quiet until they were safely inside the tower overlooking the hill before the city.

"What foolishness is this?" the chief lieutenant demanded. "Have you lost your wits as you pretended to do in the palace of Achish?"

"Look down the slope toward Saul's camp and tell me what you see," David said.

"I see the stubble of the grain stalks, the two springs, and the brooks that drain them. And I see three thousand well-armed men, holding our six hundred prisoner."

"Surely you see more, Joab," David said with a smile. "It was you who told me just now how we shall escape from Keilah."

"Make me no riddles! We cannot throw stones at Saul as you did at Goliath."

"Not stones, but something even better. Torches."

"The stubble!" Joab was quick to catch on. "Not even Saul could fight against the fire that will sweep down that hillside once the stubble is put to the torch." Then he shook his head. "But neither can we walk through flames, nor on ground so thick with burning embers that a man's feet would be blistered before he took ten paces."

"We will run, not walk," David explained. "And in water, not on embers. The fire will be set on the other side of the hill, so that Saul will think we are escaping in that direction. Actually, we will wade the brook, hidden by the rushes and the underbrush that grow along its banks."

Joab studied the scene below, the spring high up on the slope, and the stream that flowed to join a second spring near the bottom. "It is possible," he admitted. "But it would have to be done exactly right, or else the flames will sweep back up the hill and trap us before we can make our way to the brook."

"I think the wall there will protect us." David pointed to the wall supporting the topmost terrace. It was made of stone and provided a level area outside the city gates, with the higher of the two springs only a few steps below it. "We will set fire to the slope tonight, before Saul can attack. The wind usually dies down around midnight, and with the air quiet, the flames will flow down the hill like water, instead of being blown across toward the brook where we will be moving. Say nothing of this in the city, but lay in a supply of torches. And at midnight, when the town is asleep, gather the men around the gate opposite Saul's encampment. That way it will be too late for any traitor to give the alarm."

"We are lucky the harvest is already in," Joab said. "Otherwise we could all be condemned to death for firing the fields." So had it been written in the laws Moses received from God during the long sojourn of the Hebrews in the wilderness after the flight from Egypt: "If a fire break out and catch in farms so that the stalks of corn or the standing corn in the field be consumed therewith, he that kindled the fire shall surely make restitution."

It was the custom of the Israelites, as it had been that of the Canaanites before them, to encompass their fields with hedges of thorn, planted close together to keep out animals which might eat the grain, or men who might accidentally set the fields afire. In addition, during the latter months of the growing period when the grain was tall in the fields, watchmen were kept constantly on duty to guard against the possibility of fire, which could sweep through the whole countryside, destroying the food of the people for an entire year and causing a severe famine. Once the harvest was gathered in, however, the situation was different, and farmers often burned off the stubble to destroy weeds.

In order to be sure that the proper area would be fired, David himself had chosen to lead the fifty men whose task it would be to set fire to the north side of the hill. Shortly after midnight, they filed silently through the gate of Keilah, carrying torches which had been soaked in melted tallow so that they would ignite easily. Once they had taken up their positions, David gave the order, and a half-dozen men bearing flaming torches rushed through the gate. It took only a few moments to light the torches of the fifty men who waited. As soon as his brand was aflame, each man ran about a dozen steps through the dry stubble in the fields, laying down a line of flame before he hurled his torch far down the hill to start a second row of fires. This task accomplished, David and his men raced around the terrace just outside the main wall of the city to join Joab and the others, who were already pouring through in a single file, keeping as quiet as they could while they made their way to the brook and waded into the cold water tumbling down the hillside.

From the camp of the Israelites below, a great clamor had arisen. As David and his men silently began to descend the hill, they saw torches and heard the sound of men moving rapidly toward the northern area, where a wall of flame was now racing through the dry stubble down the hillside. Judging from the clamor, Saul had decided, as David had hoped, that his intended prey was fleeing with the flames as a shield. He never dreamed that the fire itself was only a diversionary tactic in order to allow David and his men to make their escape in the protection of the screen of underbrush growing beside the brook that tumbled down the hill.

It was rough going for David's men, forced to leap from terrace to terrace and wade pools where the water was often up to their knees. Every now and then, a soldier would tumble into the water in the darkness, and the crash of metal against stone would ring out loudly in the stillness of the night. Fortunately, the clamor from below was great enough to hide even that sound.

In the confusion resulting from the fire and the danger that the flames sweeping through the stubble would destroy his supplies, it was almost an hour before Saul discovered the trick that David had used to make his escape. By then, the prey was well away from Keilah and moving toward their old haunts in the forest of Hareth. There they rested during the day, and that night continued the retreat before the superior numbers of Saul into the wilderness of Ziph. Moving by way of trails that were well known to them, they traversed the mountainous country west of the southern terminus of the Great Sea, working toward the stronghold of Engedi upon its western shore.

Situated roughly halfway along the length of the Salt Sea, Engedi was a fertile oasis fed by a great spring known as the Fountain of the Kid. David had often gone there with caravans from Bethlehem to get salt from the briny lake. Now he hoped to find a refuge for his band in the maze of caves that riddled the hills above the town. The inhabitants of Engedi, however, were not happy to have quartered in their city six hundred men, many of them wanted for crimes in their own towns and villages, and they sent word to Saul of David's presence.

Moving along the ancient caravan trail that followed the shore of the Salt Sea, Saul came very near to trapping David at Engedi. In fact, only David's precaution in having thoroughly explored the caves above the town and located routes of escape through subterranean passages saved him from destruction.

In coming to Engedi, Saul had taken little risk, since he was following so well established a route of march. Abraham had taken this same caravan trail northward nearly a thousand years before, when he had gone to rescue his nephew Lot from King Chedorlaomer. But Saul dared not pursue David and his band deeper into the wild mountain fastnesses called the Wilderness of Judah, lying south of the Judahite center of Hebron. Therefore, he prudently withdrew his forces to Gibeah. Meanwhile, after a few weeks in the wilderness, David moved his people into the hills near the towns of Ziph, Maon, and Carmel, lying a short distance south of Hebron.

The section around Hebron was famous for its vineyards and olive groves. This fertile district had only one drawback: its nearness to the Philistine centers of Lachish, Eglon, and particularly Gath, to the west, and the town of Ziklag, some distance to the south. These strong centers, guarded by powerful garrisons, were a constant threat to the Israelite inhabitants of Judah who were constantly being harassed by raids in which their crops were carried off as the enemy had carried off part of the produce of Keilah to the north, and their young men and women sold into slavery.

David could not dwell with his band in the population centers of this region for fear that Saul would once again try to bottle him up in one of the towns, where the tremendous difference in the strength of their forces would work to the king's benefit. But to the southeast, in the wild mountainous region of Ziph, Maon, and Carmel, there were plenty of caves to shelter his forces; there, too, he could count on a welcome from the populace, who were badly in need of the protection he could give them against the enemy.

A great basin stretched from the nearby town of Juttah southward as far as Carmel. It was almost free from stones for these had been gathered long before and used to dam the gulleys and small valleys with the barriers called "gadairs," which held back the floods of the rainy season and eventually caused the formation of small fields of rich topsoil where further grain patches could be sown. A beautiful and prosperous region, save for the ever-present dangers of Philistine attack, it formed an ideal home for a large band of roving warriors such as David now headed. There was ample shelter for them among the hills, and when too hard pursued, they needed only to retreat southward into the vast desert reaches of the Negeb. At the same time, they could defend against enemy attack the prosperous area south of Hebron and westward along the *shephelah*, to the borders of Philistia. In return, the people were for the most part quite willing to pay a tribute in grain and other produce for the protection David was affording them.

For a while David settled here and was as content as a man could be who knew his destiny lay in far wider spheres, yet could not see any evidence that this destiny was being worked out. Then an event occurred which was calculated to lessen whatever confidence he still had in this destiny. Word came to him that Samuel, the old prophet who had anointed him to be king in Israel, and had been his guide and mentor in times of trouble, was dead.

CHAPTER 3

"And David arose, and went down to the wilderness of Paran." I SAMUEL 25:1

WITH THE DEATH of Samuel, David could hardly be blamed for feeling that his last tie with Israel had been severed, and all hope lost of the glorious future promised him by the old prophet of Ramah. He dared not attend the funeral of Samuel alone, less Saul seize him and have him put to death. Nor could he take his band of six hundred fighting men, for if Saul chose to seize him, civil war would break out in Israel and Judah would be pitted against the other tribes; then the whole nation, joined together for the first time under Saul, would be torn apart, leaving it an easy prey for the Philistines who devoutly hoped for just such an eventuality.

Depressed and unsure of himself and his future, David took a course which many another man had followed before him and would follow again. Alone, with only his weapons and his harp upon his back, he turned his face southward toward the vast and lonely area known as the Wilderness of Paran; there he would seek, as had Moses after his flight from Egypt, some revelation of God's purpose for him.

South of Hebron, the hills of Judah gradually flattened out until finally the landscape spread into a vast plain, extending toward a watercourse. Often dry in the season of no rain, this was turned into a veritable torrent during the recurrent downpours of the wet season. Known as the River of Egypt, this usually dry river bed had been the traditional border between Egypt and Canaan for more than a thousand years; the real border, however, was the famous Princes' Wall, a fortified line in the south guarding the entrance to the amazingly fertile delta region of the Nile mouth. There Abraham had gone to pasture his flocks in a time of famine, and there Jacob and his sons had journeyed to join Joseph in Egypt. Also in the delta, a Pharaoh had subjected the Israelites to a bondage which had lasted for several centuries. They were finally led out of Egypt by Moses, formerly a prince in the house of Pharaoh, to begin the long journey that was to bring them once more into Canaan.

As they traveled through the Negeb, or "Land of the South," to reach the Promised Land, the wanderers came upon a number of fertile oases. One of the largest of these was near Kadesh. Here the children of Israel had paused to enjoy the pleasures of the rich oasis, with its luscious grapes, figs, pomegranates, and other fruits. The fertile grasslands for pasturing flocks and herds along the watercourse had truly seemed like the Promised Land itself. Eager to seize the territory for themselves, the wanderers from Egypt had sent out spying parties to determine the strength of the people who must be conquered if they were to make this land their own.

A few, such as Joshua and Caleb, had returned with glowing tales of the country around Hebron, a land even more fertile than the area near Kadesh. But many of the others, faint-hearted souls who saw only the thick walls of the Canaanite cities and the iron weapons of the inhabitants, were certain that the enemy was too strong to be defeated. Convinced that this enemy was invincible, the Israelites were easily defeated in a brief foray. They had then turned east to follow a route which, after a whole generation of travel and fighting, had finally brought them into Canaan, under the leadership of Joshua.

David did not pause to enjoy the pleasures of the oasis at Kadesh, however, but stayed in the hills. Bearing southward through the country of the Kenites, he came at last into one of the wildest and most formidable regions in the whole area. This was the Wilderness of Paran, not much more than a day's journey from the Red Sea.

It was not a land calculated to raise the spirits of a weary and depressed traveler, uncertain of his purpose and his future. Neither was this a land where David, were his identity known, could hope to find a friendly reception, for the Edomites, who occupied the region, were traditional enemies of Israel, and particularly of Judah, with whom they shared a common, though not well-defined, border. Long ago, Ishmael, driven from the home of his father Abraham by the hatred of Sarah for his mother, Hagar, had pitched his tent in this same wild land, as had many another homeless wanderer. Here, traveling by day and sleeping by night in caves, David sought an answer to his own future.

The weeks spent in the wilderness marked one of the lowest points in David's career, a time in which even his faith in God's purpose for him was strongly attacked by doubt. He could not have told just what it was he was seeking; perhaps he hoped that God would speak to him in a dramatic way, as from a burning bush, and shore up his weakened bastions of self-assurance. Whatever David might have expected to hear, no such assurance reached his ears. But he would not have been the resourceful youth who had struck down Goliath if he had spent his time despairing about the insufficiency of his own faith in God's purpose for him.

As he traveled, he looked about him and saw things he had never seen before, things which, as the future leader of a nation destined to become great, he was storing in his mind against the time when they might help him to rule his people well. From a hill in Paran, he watched caravans pass along the great King's Highway, a trail by which travelers from the lands east of the Jordan, and even from Assyria and far-off Mesopotamia, had carried goods to and from Egypt for more than a thousand years. He saw pack animals laden with weapons of the Hittite metal produced in Damascus; fine jewelry of silver and gold; and copper utensils from the shops of the Kenites, through whose country he had passed. He saw turquoises and other fine jewels from the mines of Sinai on the way to the palaces of Assyria, and whole pieces of furniture carved from ivory by artisans in Egypt for rich buyers in the land of Mesopotamia. He saw pottery, though none more exquisite than that fashioned by the skilled artisans in the cities of Philistia. And he saw rich fabrics, though not so fine as those from the looms of Byblos where cloth was also dyed with a purple tint derived from shellfish gathered on the shores of the Great Sea.

Sometimes, when he dared to go down into a town along the King's Highway, David talked to caravan drivers and merchants as they rested in the caravansaries outside every village for the convenience of travelers. There he heard tales of the magnificence of the Pharaohs and the luxury of oriental monarchs in the "Land Between the Rivers" from which his ancestors had come. As he listened, David's world began to widen; his mind adjusted itself to the concepts of a nation greater than Israel had been even at the height of Saul's conquest, a nation which one day might take its place in equality of strength with Egypt, Assyria, and Phoenicia.

If these were dreams, David could be forgiven them, for he was not wasting his time in idle fancy. His questioning gaze was discovering other things about this land to the south, things of immediate importance to his particular destiny as a ruler of his people if that destiny were still to be fulfilled.

Along a caravan trail leading from Edom to the city of Gerar, one of the major smelting centers in the southern part of Philistia, he saw great loads of iron and copper ore being carried from mines in the Wilderness of Paran. And in the villages of the Kenites, he saw double bellows, made from skins inflated by pumps operated with the feet, fanning the coals underneath kettles containing molten copper. He watched the smiths add precious tin to harden copper into bronze and fashion it into arrowheads, spearpoints, javelins, swords, and implements for farming and threshing. And he saw them form molds in sand and clay, into which the copper was poured to form tools such as giant saws for splitting out boards to be used in building, or for cutting blocks of stones used in the construction of fortifications. And although he learned little of the techniques of iron-making, for this was a jealously guarded secret of the Philistine smiths, he did learn that Gerar and the area around it was a region whose control would furnish Israel with the weapons of iron it so badly needed.

These were activities of which David had possessed little knowledge before. As he traveled, storing up everything in his eager and questioning mind, a new concept of what could be God's purpose for Israel was beginning to take form in his mind. It was a grandiose concept for a young man who must live like a fugitive. But then he was one of the few in any generation who possess the imagination to dream such dreams and the courage and energy to carry them out. Fortunately, the Edomites, the Kenites, the Kenizzites, and the Amalekites, through whose country he was traveling, did not know his identity or guess what lay before him. If they had, they would have seized him and executed him forthwith.

Busy as he was, observing and traveling from place to place, David was still deeply troubled because he had not yet experienced the revelation of God's will which he had sought in this journey far from the borders of his own tribe and his own people. Finally, saddened that God had not once again shown the trust which had inspired him to fight Goliath, he turned his steps northward toward the area around Carmel where Joab and his men awaited his return, and his decision as to their future course.

Somehow, on the return journey even the going seemed easier, perhaps because his body had been toughened and strengthened by his long and arduous traveling through a wild and forbidding country. His steps were not eager, however, as God had said the steps should be of those who loved him when, upon the sabbath, they went to join their fellows in worship, for he could bring the men who trusted him no answer to the question of their future. And so one day, when he came at nightfall to a nearly dry stream in a small, narrow valley not far from the oasis of Kadesh, he was too weary and dispirited to eat his evening meal, or even to seek out a cave for shelter. Instead he wrapped himself in his heavy cloak against the chill of the night and lay down beside the stream. In his exhaustion, he fell asleep almost immediately.

Tired and depressed, David had not noticed the thunderheads massing above the mountains to the east of his impromptu camp. Nor was he awakened by the fury of the storm gathering over the hills, where the headwaters were of the almost dry stream beside which he lay. Even the thunder and lightning did not disturb him until the rain began to drum down and the almost dry bed of the stream suddenly became a small torrent. When he stumbled to his feet in the pitch blackness, the water was swirling around his ankles.

David was familiar enough with the awful force of these sudden downpours to realize the danger in which he found himself, trapped by darkness in a narrow valley with the swiftly rising water all about him. During the few moments he wasted in trying to decide the best course of action, the water had already reached his knees. The black of the night was illuminated only fitfully by the darting flashes of lightning, but in one of these he saw that it would be futile to try to climb the side of the narrow glen in which he had taken refuge. If escape were possible, it must be downstream in the hope of reaching a point where the narrow valley widened out and he would be able to climb to higher ground and safety.

Stumbling in the darkness, with only the lightning as illumination, he started making his way down the banks of the stream. The water was deepening rapidly as the torrent poured down from the hills beyond; he had gone barely a hundred steps before it was swirling about his waist; in another fifty, he was swept off his feet and tumbled upon the crest of a raging wave. For the first time in his life, David knew the imminence of death, but he had no time to do more than cry out to the Lord to look down upon him and save him, for all his energies were needed to stay afloat. Time and again the fury of the torrent sent him plunging beneath the surface of the water, where his body was battered by the stones of the stream bed until he was only half-conscious.

Somewhere along the way, he instinctively managed to seize hold of the trunk of a dead tree and hang on to it as it turned and thrashed upon the current. Only its buoyancy kept him afloat; one more battering upon the stones of the stream bed would have left him unconscious. Dazed and only half-alive, he did not realize that the rain had finally stopped, and that the waters of the stream had begun to subside. Only the branches of the dead tree that had embraced his body had kept him from drowning in the first place; now the tree held him in that embrace still when it came to rest, high up on the valley wall where the crest of the flood had deposited it.

The sun awakened David. Its warmth caressed his bruised and battered body, and for a long moment he lay there, scarcely able to believe he was still alive. Finally he extricated himself from the branches and, though every movement was an agony of bruised flesh and sore muscles, he managed to climb the rest of the way up the wall of the ravine in which he found himself. His weapons were gone, as well as his waterskin and the food he had carried. Of all his possessions only one thing had been saved: the harp. Suspended by a tough cord around his neck, it had somehow not been torn from him in the wild battle with the torrent.

Painfully he climbed the last jutting outcrop and pulled himself up to stand upon it. And as he stood there, with the warm sun like a protecting mantle about his body, a great joy filled his soul. With a conviction born from the dreadful agony of the flood and the sight of a green oasis shining in the sunlight before him, he knew now that God had not deserted him, and never would, so long as he might live. Moved by an impulse to thank the Most High for the miracle of the waters, he took the harp from his back and tightened the strings, until once again they sang with melody when he touched them with his bruised fingers.

The song was one of gratitude, trust, and confidence in the future. He had begun it long ago on the banks of a brook in sight of Saul's fortress at Gibeah; now, on a peak in the wilderness, he sang the rest:

"Why art thou cast down O my soul?
And why art thou disquieted in me?
Hope thou in God; for I shall yet praise him.
For the help of his countenance.

I will remember thee from the land of Jordan,
And of the Hermonites, from the hill Mizar.
Deep calleth unto deep at the noise of thy waterspouts:
All thy waves and thy billows are gone over me.

The Lord will command his loving kindness in the daytime,
In the night his song shall be with me.
And my prayer to the God of my life.
Why art thou cast down O my soul?
And why art thou disquieted within me?
Hope thou in God, for I shall yet praise him,
Who is the health of my countenance and of my God."

CHAPTER 4

"And Nabal answered David's servants, and said, Who is David? and who is the son of Jesse?"

I SAMUEL 25:10

DAVID FOUND JOAB and his band in the hills back of Carmel, the area known as the Wilderness of Ziph. He was greeted with wild acclaim. While he ate roasted goat flesh and freshly baked bread, he conferred with Joab and his brothers about the events which had taken place since his departure several weeks before.

"From the way you look, we need not go farther south," Joab observed. "You have barely enough flesh on your bones to hide them."

"The Negeb has nothing for us," David agreed. "At least, not yet."

"What do you mean?" Abishai asked.

David's eyes took fire as he told of the mines, the workers in metal, and the caravans of ore being shipped from the Arabah and the Wilderness of Paran. "One day, Israel must control that region," he said. "Then we shall not lack for iron tools and weapons and for chariots to use in defending ourselves against the enemy."

"That is brave talk for a fugitive," Joab scoffed. "But how do you know Saul is not moving against us even now?"

"I know it because you have spies posted to the north to warn us," David retorted. "Unless you were content to sit and wait to be destroyed while I was away."

"Am I a fool that I would leave us unprotected?" Joab growled. "Saul has not moved yet from Gibeah, but some people of this region are saying they do not need us any more, and there was grumbling when Asahel went to gather in our share of the crops. Yesterday I heard that Nabal has sworn not to pay it this year."

"Nabal?"

"The largest landowner in the region around Carmel. He dwells in Maon."

"Is he a Judahite?"

"No, he is from the house of Caleb."

"That means his people have been here since Joshua divided Canaan among the twelve tribes," David said. "Nevertheless, he must pay like the others."

"Now that you are back, I will send men to him at once," Joah said. "Our sentries report that he is in Carmel, shearing sheep."

"Is it a large flock?"

"Three thousand sheep and a thousand goats."

David's lips pursed in a soundless whistle. "That would be more than even Saul possesses. I will send Nabal greetings by the messengers; a man of such importance deserves a personal invitation to pay for the protection we have been giving him."

Ten men were selected to call upon Nabal, with Asahel in command. "This is the message you will give him," David told the youngest of Joab's brothers. "Say, 'May peace be upon you and all your house and all that you possess. Your shepherds will tell you that since we have been in this region, we have not troubled them, and that nothing of theirs has been missing during the whole time they were in Carmel. We have protected your fields and your flocks against Philistine attack. We have brought peace to all who dwell here.' "

He paused and looked questioningly at Asahel, who nodded to show that he was committing the message to memory.

"Say to Nabal further, 'Therefore, let my men find favor in your eyes, for we come on a good day. I pray you give whatsoever comes into your hands to your servants and to your son David.' "

"I will tell him your exact words," Asahel promised.

"Take carts with you to bring back the gifts," David directed. "After the way we have protected Nabal's flocks, he will surely not be ungenerous."

It was mid-afternoon before the sentries, watching from the heights above the camp, sent word that Asahel and his men were returning. In anticipation of a feast, cooking fires had been burning for several hours to provide beds of coals over which to roast the meat Asahel would bring; the women had also readied the mills to grind the grain. Made from two stones, one hollowed out to form the base into which the grain was poured and the other rounded to move within it, each mill was turned by means of a peg driven into a hole in the upper stone. Two women were required for the grinding: one to turn the moving stone; the other to pour in the grain and gather the flour.

By now, David's band included many women and children, so there were plenty of eager hands to supply wood for the fires and grind the grain from which cakes would be baked for the coming feast. But a cry of disappointment went up when Asahel and his band rounded the hill near the campsite; for the carts were empty and the men bore no burdens.

David was dozing inside his tent. The outcry of disappointment in the camp awakened him and he rushed to the tent flap to meet Asahel and Joab. Asahel's face was red with embarrassment, but Joab's was dark with anger.

"Where are the gifts you were sent to bring from Nabal?" David asked the younger brother.

Asahel raised his hands and let them fall in an eloquent gesture. "Our hands are empty," he admitted.

"You did not see Nabal, then?"

"We found him with the shearers and gave him the message in your very own words."

"What did he say?"

"This Nabal is a man of a very churlish manner," Asahel said. "When I gave him your message, he answered, 'Who is David? And who is the Son of Jesse? Many a servant nowadays breaks away from his master; why should I take bread and water, and meat that I have killed for my shearers and give it to men about whom I know nothing?' "

"You are sure he said just that?"

"I have told you his very words," Asahel affirmed.

David felt a deep surge of anger. He had brought order and peace into this land where none had been known for centuries; because of it the landowners of the area had prospered as they had never prospered before. No Philistine had dared to raid here for many months and no Israelite feared to till his field lest he and his children be carried off into slavery. In return, nothing had been asked of the landowner except food and clothing for himself and his band; yet the richest man in the area, and therefore the one who had profited most by David's presence here, refused to pay a rightful tribute.

Until now David had managed to avoid fighting with his own people; even when he and his men had been surrounded at Keilah, he had managed to extricate his band without bloodshed between brother Israelites. Now, however, he must punish Nabal, otherwise, he would lose face before his own people and give them, for the first time, a legitimate reason to doubt his qualities of leadership. But to punish Nabal, the hand of brother must be raised against brother. David did not try to evade the decision, now that he was faced with it.

"Separate four hundred men and leave two hundred here to guard the camp," he directed Joab. "We will visit this churlish fellow in the morning and teach him a lesson he will never forget."

With David's first words Joab had begun to smile. "You heard the command of the Son of Jesse," he told his brothers joyfully. "By this time tomorrow, the possessions of Nabal will be in our hands."

Nabal's refusal to pay the tribute had indeed placed David in a bitter quandary. He wrestled with it throughout the night, but found no answer except to lead the four hundred men to Nabal's camp and make an example of the churlish landowner. He fully realized that Saul would seize upon this action as an excuse to name him a complete brigand now, one who did not hesitate to attack his own people. Yet he could not see an alternative. If he let Nabal evade paying the tribute, other landlords would follow his lead.

When at sunrise David came out of his tent after a sleepless night, Joab was beside the brook, splashing his face and torso. David knelt beside him. His slender frame seemed oddly fragile next to Joab's massive strength.

"I was afraid you might change your mind about punishing Nabal," Joab said, as he dried his face and hands and put on the tunic of heavy cloth that he wore beneath his harness and armor in battle.

"Why?"

"Any fool can see you do not have an easy choice. The tribe of Caleb is a small one, but they have always been doughty fighters. If they decide to turn this lesson to Nabal into a blood feud, many heads will fall before it is finished."

"I am glad to see you appreciate some of the burdens of leadership," David said. "Would you have me let Nabal go unpunished?"

"I will not let you do that, even if I have to march you to his camp at sword's point," Joab told him. "Just now, the Philistines are busy fighting Saul in the north, while we grow steadily in strength. But if the enemy ever heard that you had let a mere landowner browbeat you, they would decide you do not have all of Judah behind you, and would move south again. Then we should once again be caught between Saul and the enemy."

"You don't paint a very rosy picture."

Joab was not listening, however; his eyes were fixed on the slope leading to the glen. A large caravan with pack animals heavily laden with grain, fruit, and freshly killed meat was approaching. But it was not the caravan that held David's attention when he followed Joab's gaze. Riding the lead mule was one of the most beautiful women he had ever seen; at the sight of her, something began to stir within him that had lain dormant, it seemed, since the day when he had last held Michal in the embrace of love.

"By the beard of Moses!" Joab exclaimed. "Nabal has sent us a real tribute this time, a real tribute, indeed!"

CHAPTER 5

"And David said to Abigail, Blessed be the Lord God of Israel, which sent thee this day to meet me."
I SAMUEL 25:32

THE CARAVAN CAME to a halt at the edge of the camp, and the woman who was riding the lead mule dismounted. Even in that ordinary movement there was an extraordinary gracefulness that stirred David's soul.

"I seek David, the Son of Jesse." Her voice was low and throaty like, David thought, the deep strains of a harp. As she stood beside the mule, she was completely serene although the eyes of more than six hundred people were upon her. At closer range she was even more beautiful than she had appeared when riding upon the animal. Her hair was black, and her eyes were dark but lit with a lambent fire which, David knew instinctively, could burn with a consuming flame of passion. She was tall and molded on classic lines; in fact, she reminded him of a statue he had seen at Gath in the palace of Achish during his brief visit to that monarch's court. There was the same symmetry of form, the same unstudied grace and loveliness imparted to the marble by the loving hands of the sculptor. And yet, as he could plainly see, she was living flesh, and he felt a sudden surge of desire for her that left him trembling.

"Is the Son of Jesse among you?" The voice of the visitor

brought David's thoughts back to the present, and he stepped forward to meet her.

"I am David," he said.

The woman glanced at him quickly. In the warm brightness of her eyes he could see that she, too, felt the spark of attraction between them. Then her gaze dropped modestly, and she knelt to prostrate herself at his feet.

"Let this iniquity be upon me, my lord," she begged. "And let thy handmaiden Abigail, I pray you, speak that you may hear."

David stepped forward to lift her to her feet, but her next words stopped him with his hand half extended.

"My lord, I pray you, do not consider seriously this man of Belial, Nabal my husband, for folly is within him." She rose gracefully and raised her eyes to meet his. "I, who am your handmaiden, did not see the young men you sent to Nabal my husband. I was not with him when he refused to pay tribute to you for the peace you have brought to him and his flocks. Nabal is greedy and foolish, but he is not evil. As the Lord lives and has withheld you from coming to shed blood and from avenging yourself with your own hand, let your enemies and they that seek evil to you be as Nabal."

It was a clever plea, implying that David had not planned to attack Nabal, although it must have been apparent to her that at least two-thirds of the camp were preparing to march.

"Let this blessing which your handmaiden has brought to my lord be given to the young men that follow you." Her gesture indicated the small caravan that waited behind her. "And I pray you, forgive the trespass of Nabal, my husband. The Lord will certainly make you a sure house because you fight the battles of the Lord, and evil has not been found in you all your days."

"Is she a prophetess that she can foretell the future?" Joab grumbled beside David. He had been looking forward to the raid upon Nabal, but now that the landowner's wife had brought a far more generous tribute than Asahel had been instructed to collect, there would be no need for the action.

If Abigail heard Joab's comment, she gave no hint of it, for her eyes were upon David's face alone. In fact, it was as if the others did not exist and only the two of them were there, a man and woman meeting for the first time and instinctively knowing that it would not be the last.

David had no reason to punish Nabal now, for everything he had intended to ask of the churlish landowner had been given to him, plus a gift beyond price which he sensed was also his for the taking—Nabal's beautiful wife. But overcome as he was with an almost overpowering surge of desire for her, he could not forget that to take her would set the whole tribe of Caleb against him in a bitter blood feud.

"Blessed be the Lord of Israel who sent you to me this day, and blessed are you for keeping me from avenging myself with my own hands." He turned to his band who had been watching the little drama being played out in front of the caravan. "We were making ready for a feast and now the wherewithal has been brought to us. Let there be rejoicing that she who favored us this day may know we are grateful."

A cheer broke from the crowd at his words, and the people moved to unload the pack animals and carry into the camp the meat, the grain already ground and ready for making into cakes, and the leather and cloth which had made up their burden. David held out his hand to Abigail and, placing hers within it, she allowed him to lead her to a bench that had been placed in front of his tent. Joab gave him a keen glance, then turned toward the cooking fires where the people of the camp were busy preparing for a feast. The two were left alone.

"You will surely incur the rage of your husband by what you have done," David suggested.

Abigail shrugged. "It was not to save him that I came, but to save you."

"Why would you do that when we have never seen each other before?"

"The people of this region knew no peace until you came," she explained. "The Philistines are afraid to attack us now. If you had punished Nabal and forced him to pay the tribute, a blood feud between Judah and the tribe of Caleb would have resulted. With so many hands raised against you, you would have been forced to move on; then peace would once again have left the land."

"Is it peace you want to preserve or the life of your husband?"

She gave him a level glance. "Those who spoke to me of you did not lie. You are not one to be taken in, even by a woman. I spoke the truth when I said he is the son of Belial. Nabal thinks only of money."

"Yet you married him."

"My family was poor and he offered a large dowry. In this region, a woman is sold like a cow or pig."

"Would Nabal divorce you—for a price?" He felt a stab of conscience at the thought of Michal, but she seemed so far away now, the memory of her almost totally obscured by the reality of this slender graceful woman who carried herself like a queen.

"He would sell anything he possesses for a price," she said. "But you are a hunted man. Where would you find the money?"

"Suppose I took you by force?"

Her gaze did not falter, and his heart leaped at what he saw revealed there. "Were I the one to be considered, or even you, I would follow you this moment," she said. "But Israel needs such a king as you will be, David, and I will not endanger your life or your future by causing bloodshed between my tribe and yours."

"By this time, your husband may know that you came here," he warned.

"He is already drunk at a feast he is giving to boast of not paying the tribute," she said contemptuously. "When he is sober, I will tell him what I have done; then it will be too late for him to do harm."

"What about us? Is it to end—like this?"

"The Lord is with you," she reminded him. "If I were not certain of that, I would have let you kill Nabal and take me as a prize. Be sure the Lord's will is to be done with both of us." They had been sitting on the bench; now Abigail arose. "I must return with the servants and the pack animals before my husband becomes sober again."

"Are you sure he will not harm you?"

"Nabal is a coward," she told him. "He knows the men of my family would punish him if he harmed me."

"Go home in peace, then. I have listened to you and have

accepted your tribute." The words were for any of his men who might be listening; the meaning was for her alone.

As David stood in front of the tent and watched the erect, graceful figure of Abigail as she rode away from his stronghold, a voice within him argued that he was a fool to let her go. He should have taken her and pretended that the tribute had not been given. Then he could have led his men down to destroy her husband and seize the rest of Nabal's possessions.

Abiathar, the priest, came around the corner of the tent and paused beside David. "A beautiful woman and a desirable one." Then he added pointedly, "And another man's wife."

"You need not remind me. I know the penalty for adultery in Israel." As a boy in Bethlehem, David had seen a man and woman taken in adultery condemned by the Council of Elders, and executed by the traditional Hebrew method of stoning. He had been too young to understand fully the nature of the crime, but he had never forgotten the screams of the victims as the hail of stones had fallen upon them, or the hate-contorted faces of the accusers, who, according to tradition, had been given the right to cast the first stone.

"Had she been free, she would have come to me," David said, making way for Abiathar to join him upon the bench. "But since she is married, she would not let me embroil myself any more than I am now."

"Then she is as wise as she is beautiful."

"And capable of building a consuming fire within a man's loins," David agreed broodingly. "Have you consulted the ephod lately, Abiathar? Is there any word of what lies ahead of me?"

"When I seek the help of the sacred vestment, I see only the need to keep away from the hands of Saul," the priest admitted. "Yet I am sure a far brighter future awaits you."

"Would that I too could see it, then," David said despondently. "Abigail's visit kept me from turning into a brigand today. But what of tomorrow, when someone else decides not to pay the tribute? If I let the six hundred become separated, the Philistines will hear of it and attack the disputed land once more. Yet only by providing for them can I hold them together."

"The Lord has favored you in all your ventures before," Abiathar reminded him. "And today he saved you from grave danger, when it seemed that there was no possible way to escape it."

"But only by confronting me with a temptation that has not troubled me before—the longing for a woman's embrace."

"You could take a wife. It is not good for a young man to contain his seed when there are vessels eager and willing to receive it."

"Before I escaped from Gibeah, I swore I would one day take Michal back."

"What if she is satisfied with Phalti?"

"That milksop? How could she be?"

Abiathar shrugged. "Women value many things in a man besides courage and comeliness of person."

"Are you saying she might choose Phalti before me?"

"I am only warning you," the priest said. "You have been hurt many times, David, but you have not become hard and resentful, as Saul did after his quarrel with Samuel. Take a wife from among the women of your own tribe, and forget your worries in her embrace. Then, when you are king, you can—if you wish—still take Michal back."

"Since I cannot have Abigail or Michal, I will put off taking a wife for a little while," David told him. "In the desert I had a vision, Abiathar, a vision of Israel as a nation so great that the Philistines would not attack us. We would build great cities with smelters for working iron, and seaports from which ships could sail to all parts of the world to make our merchants rich and our people skilled artisans. If I become involved with other men's wives, the people would turn against me, and it would take longer than my lifetime to build that dream." He rose to his feet. "Guard the ephod well and seek answers from it when you can. Soon Saul will defeat the Philistines or be defeated; either way, the will of the Lord must guide me."

To one of his problems, the flame of desire aroused within him by Abigail's beauty, the answer came when Asahel returned several weeks later from a trip to Carmel.

"The Lord has brought down yet another of your enemies, David," Asahel cried jubilantly. "Nabal is dead!"

CHAPTER 6

"And Saul knew David's voice, and said, Is this thy voice, my son David?" I SAMUEL 26:17

DAVID STARED AT ASAHEL incredulously. "By whose hand?" he asked finally.

"His own, or the Lord's. Who can tell?"

"How did it come about?"

"I had the story from Nabal's own steward," Asahel said. "When you did not come down to attack him, Nabal gave a great feast, like a king celebrating a victory."

"Abigail spoke of it. She said he was already drunk when she left."

"He knew nothing of her coming here until he awakened from a drunken stupor the next morning," Asahel confirmed. "The steward said he is a vain man, and when he learned how his wife had saved him from destruction at your hand, he was so mortified that he became as one under a spell. He lay like a stone for ten days before the spirit gave him up. Now he is in the grave and his widow wears mourning; but there is little sorrow in Carmel for Nabal."

Nor could David find sorrow in his heart for the dead man. If Nabal had not been grasping and greedy, he could have yielded the modest tribute asked for protection of his fields and flocks, and would still be alive. But then, David reminded himself, he would not have met Abigail and would not now be in a position to ask her to become his wife.

With considerable impatience, David waited through the prescribed period of mourning before sending Abiathar as his agent to arrange the marriage. The priest returned, followed by Abigail riding upon a mule and accompanied by five handmaidens, along with considerable goods; for in leaving her a rich widow, Nabal had performed, however unwillingly, at least one charitable act during his life. The marriage was celebrated with due ceremony, and in Abigail's arms, David found a peace he had not known for many months.

With his wife's considerable resources at his command, David was able to purchase additional weapons and continue training his men. His band had now grown so large that even Achish of Gath was afraid to hunt him down. Meanwhile, his spies reported that Saul had returned to Gibeah after a skirmish in the north. The situation was thus left at something of a stalemate. The Philistines were unable to throw all their forces against Saul, for fear that David would attack in the south; while Saul could not win any considerable victory over the enemy in the occasional engagements that were fought from time to time among the hills and valleys of central Canaan.

Abigail was everything David had hoped she would be—lovely, intelligent, concerned for his welfare, and always ready to solace him with her embrace. But as the months passed and she failed to become pregnant with his child, he could not hide his disappointment. He was now the strongest man in Israel after Saul himself. And even though he was still hunted by the legal government of the nation, the people of Judah looked to him for leadership. It was generally understood that at Saul's death, David would become king of that tribe and probably of Israel. Under such conditions, and with his growing maturity, it was only natural that he should desire an heir.

Sensitive to David's moods, Abigail realized what was troubling him and brought up the subject herself. "My lord is displeased that I have not conceived," she said one evening, as they sat before the campfire.

"How could I be displeased with you when you mean so much

to me?" David said. "But I should like to have a son, even though I have no kingdom to give him."

"I bore no child to Nabal, but that might have been because I did not love him."

"At least I could never doubt your love after the bliss I have known in your arms." He picked up the harp that had been lying beside him and ran his fingers over the strings. A soft melody filled the glen. "Before you came I had almost stopped playing; now the songs come welling up like the waters of a sweet spring, released from bondage within my soul by the touch of your hands."

She lifted his hand and kissed it, holding the palm against her cheek. "Truly I have been favored above all women," she said softly. "And because I have been favored, it is not right for me to deny you the child every man should expect of his wife."

"But I—"

She put his own fingers against his lips to stop the words. "Please, David. It is not easy for me to say what I have to say; let me do it in my own way." She took a deep breath. "Since your seed has not kindled life in my womb, you must seek more fertile soil in another."

"I will not put you aside," he protested. "Not even if I never have a son."

"You are a man of importance and entitled to several wives," she reminded him. "Among the young women I brought with me when I came to you is a daughter of Jezreel called Ahinoam. Take her as your second wife; I know she would never try to supplant me in your heart."

David remembered the girl. She was slender and dark-haired, slight of step and quick to laugh, as had been another Ahinoam who had been kind to him. It did not occur to him that he might have noticed the young Ahinoam because she reminded him of the older Ahinoam's daughter, the girl who for a very brief time had been his wife.

"I will take her," he told Abigail. "But only because I hope for a child by her."

The daughter of Jezreel proved to be sweet and gentle, although in his arms she had none of the fire of Abigail. Nevertheless, his seed failed to kindle life in her womb immediately. By this time, however, David had other things to concern him, for the spies he paid to watch Saul had reported that the king was moving southward with three thousand men. Apparently, Saul hoped to trap him in the forest stronghold.

David and Joab, with the latter's brothers and a Hittite named Ahimelech, leader of a company of about a hundred mercenaries, listened as the spy gave his report.

"Did you learn how Saul found out where we were?" David asked.

"The men of Ziph sent word to him that you were dwelling here in the wilderness," the spy reported.

Lying about two hours' march south of Hebron, Ziph was a fairly large town, located on the crest of an elevation in the midst of a wild country of hills and steep-sided glens. To the east lay Jeshimon, as the wilderness country toward the Salt Sea was called. Jeshimon was a region of bare hills, sometimes known to the people of that area as the Valley of the Shadow of Death because, even at noonday, the sun did not always reach into the tortured depths that turned the area into a wild pattern of crests and chasms.

Almost a year earlier, David and his band had settled near Khoresh—a word meaning "wood"—about a half-hour's march from Ziph. Khoresh was a particularly good vantage point, since from its height, only a little lower than that of Ziph itself, they could survey a broad, turbulent sea of white peaks and winding paths. The wilds of Jeshimon abounded with caves which would make excellent hiding places so, even though the traitorous men of Ziph who had betrayed their presence there would no doubt continue to inform Saul of their whereabouts, David had little fear that the Israelite king would be able to trap him in a country such as this.

"Is it thus that they repay us for saving their crops and herds from the Philistines, and their sons and daughters from slavery in Egypt?" Joab demanded angrily. "Give me a hundred men, David, and I will make the men of Ziph wish they had never spoken."

"You know that would only force us to seek refuge even deeper in the wilderness."

"But the men are tired of always fleeing. If you do not lead them in a victory soon, they will rebel against you."

David's eyes narrowed. "And you, Joab? What would you do?"

The stocky lieutenant's face turned a deep red. "My brothers and I swore to support you in the valley of Elah, and we will not desert you, though ten thousand were brought against you. But it is unnatural to let Saul have his way and not fight back."

"This time we will fight back, Joab," David promised, "but in a way that Saul will understand without our having to pit six hundred men against three thousand. You will take the bulk of our band and hide on the far side of the chasm of Jeshimon. Even Saul cannot follow you there."

"And you?"

"I may be able to teach Saul a lesson, but at least I hope to teach Abner one."

"Abner is no fool," Joab warned. "Even though I hate him, I would be the first to name him a brave fighter and a skilled leader."

"I will take no risk," David assured him. "This time only one other will go with me when I visit the camp of Saul."

"I will be proud to go with you," Joab's brother, Abishai, offered. "Ahimelech and his men can guard the families of our band, and Asahel will be needed as a messenger."

"I could not want a braver man at my side," David told Abishai warmly. "Send the women and children into the Wilderness of Maon tomorrow, Joab, and assign Ahimelech and his hundred to guard them. Then, when Saul's army is sighted, make certain that they see you. As soon as you are sure that they have sighted you and your men, fall back into the chasm under the ridge of Hammahlekoth. If I know Saul, he will follow."

"By the tents of Israel!" Joab exclaimed admiringly, all his peevishness gone now. "When Abner discovers the trap we have led him into, he will sweat blood!" Then his face grew sober. "But you are foolish to let them go unscathed, David. My men know every nook and cranny of that chasm; we could cut Saul's army to pieces there with less than half the six hundred."

"Better still, we could march around Saul's forces while they are trying to find their way out of the chasm, and perhaps take Gibeah itself," Asahel suggested.

Joab's eyes took fire. "Then the people would certainly rise up and deprive Saul of his kingship."

"Right now Israel needs all of us," David told them. "I have a plan, and I will tell it to you after all this is over. If it works out, we shall never need to hide from Saul again."

The movement of the band southward into hiding places among the crags and in the caverns, with which they were already familiar, began at once. By the time Saul's army was sighted two days later, Joab and the main party were ready. When trumpets began to blare excitedly from the ranks of the Israelite army, Joab was sure that they had been seen. He gave the order to fall back to a point about a two-hours' march from Ziph. There a great cleft divided the land, a chasm with almost perpendicular sides and narrow points of entrance and egress.

David and Abishai were already in position on the crest of a ridge overlooking the chasm. Watching from the protection of a cave, they saw Joab lead his men into the narrow valley and disappear among the shadowed crevices. David had scouted this region many times, and knew that Joab would shortly lead his band out of the trap by way of a secret passage which would carry them to the other side of the chasm and to safety. To Saul, however, pursuing eagerly and certain that he was about to trap and destroy David and his men, it would appear that they were retreating into an indefensible situation from which there was no escape.

"Saul is even now panting upon your trail," Abishai reported happily. "But he will sing another tune when he realizes you have led him on a fool's errand."

"By then, I hope he will be more afraid than he was of Goliath," David agreed. "Unless you and I fail in our mission this night."

As he watched the brave array of fighting men, with their weapons and armor shining in the afternoon sunlight and the tall, handsome figure of Saul himself marching at their head, David found himself thinking of another time when he, too, had been a leader of this very troop, honored by all for killing Goliath and for his subsequent victories over the Philistines. Now, several years after he had been forced to flee from Gibeah, he was still a hunted man. But if his new plan worked, the situation would soon be drastically changed.

"Joab is out of the chasm now," Abishai reported. "I caught the gleam of the sun from a shield on the other wall a few moments ago."

"Then Saul must be wondering how the hare has escaped the hunter," David said. "Any moment now, Abner should be able to persuade him not to risk the coming of darkness before making camp for the night."

The sound of a trumpet blast floated up from the chasm a few moments later and David's assumption was confirmed. From their vantage point upon the height, he and Abishai watched as darkness began to fill the depths of the gorge, although it was still daylight where they were standing. Soon points of light winked below as campfires were lighted, but across the gorge there was still no sign of Joab, for David had instructed him not to reveal his presence before morning.

"We had best sleep awhile," David told Abishai when they had finished eating some bread and cold meat. "We shall need to be wide awake when we go into the camp; one false step and Saul will be upon us."

They were not wearing the sandals with wooden or hard-finished leather soles that were the common footgear of soldiers on long marches; they had put on boots of soft leather, more often worn inside the house, in order to avoid awakening the camp by the sound of their footsteps or the clatter of a stone sent bouncing down the hillside. It was shortly after midnight when David awakened Abishai. They began the tedious job of descending the steep slope of the chasm wall in the darkness, following a path used by hunters in pursuing the agile wild goats that lived among the crags.

David was sure that Abner had prudently posted men at vantage points both above and below the camp, which had been made part-way up the wall of the narrow gorge. But he did not think sentries would have been posted along the sides of the gorge, since it would have been impossible for a large attacking party to descend the steep slope without being detected. This fact he utilized now to make his way into the center of the camp. There, from long acquaintance with the way Saul and Abner reasoned, he knew exactly where to look.

The snores of sleeping men were all around them as Abishai and David made their way through the Israelite encampment. Saul, they saw, was lying upon a narrow shelf on the side of the gorge. His heavy cloak was wrapped about him, and a second cloak was folded up beneath his head as a pillow. His spear, a long-handled and iron-pointed weapon with which the king was very expert, was stuck into the grassy turf beside his head. Near it stood an earthenware bottle of water, at hand in case he should awake and want a drink during the night.

"God has delivered your enemy into your hands," Abishai whispered, as he looked down upon Saul's sleeping form. "Let me use my spear and you can be sure I will need no second stroke."

It was a tempting prospect, for if Abishai killed Saul, no guilt would fall upon David. In fact, he had only to move up the hill-side and leave Abishai behind to avoid even witnessing the deed when it was done. But David shook his head.

"No one can raise his hand against the Lord's Anointed and be without guilt," he said firmly. "The Lord will smite him, or his day will come to die in battle. I will not lift my hand against him, but I will take the spear at his head and the cruse of water."

Only a moment was needed for David to pluck the spear from the ground beside Saul's head and hang the bottle at his leather belt. Picking their way back up the side of the gorge along the narrow path, the two left the Israelite camp as they had come, undetected. Only when they were high above the sleeping army atop the ridge did David take the curved ram's-horn trumpet that was always slung over his shoulder and blow a giant blast upon it.

The sound echoed and re-echoed from the steep walls. To Saul and his army encamped there, it no doubt seemed as if a great army was upon them. A clamor of voices arose from the gorge, mixed with the clatter of metal upon rock and the cursing of soldiers as they hurried to pick up their weapons and form a defense against the force which they fully expected to be upon them at any moment. In the darkness and confusion, comrade could easily have started fighting with comrade, and a bloody melee would have followed. But such was not David's intention.

Lowering the ram's horn, he made a trumpet of his cupped hands and shouted down into the glen: "Abner, son of Ner! Why do you not answer?"

"Who are you that cries to the king?" Abner shouted from below.

"You are worthy to die because you did not guard the Lord's Anointed!" David told him. "See where the king's spear is and the cruse of water that was beside his pillow."

A sudden babble of voices from below indicated that they now knew David had stolen into the camp unmolested, and for a brief time, had Saul at his mercy. It was Saul who spoke now, and the voices of the others quickly died away. "Is this your voice, my son David?" he asked.

"It is my voice, O king," David replied. "Why do you pursue me when no evil is in my hand? If the Lord has stirred you up against me, let him accept an offering. But if it is the children of men, cursed be they before the Lord, for they have driven me out from my inheritance."

For a moment there was no answer. Then Saul spoke again. "I have sinned," he admitted. "Return, my son David. I will do you no more harm, because my soul was precious in your eyes this day."

David lifted Saul's spear with the handle pointing forward and hurled it far out over the gorge. "Here is the king's spear," he called down when he heard it strike on the rocky path far below. "This day the Lord delivered you into my hands, but I would not lift my hands against the Lord's Anointed. As your life was much set by this day in my eyes, so let my life be much set by in the eyes of the Lord, and let him deliver me from all tribulation."

"Blessed be you, my son David. You shall do great things," Saul answered. But David did not hear. He was already making his way toward the opposite side of the deep chasm, where Joab and the men of his own band had been listening to the interchange between him and Saul. He and Abishai reached the camp just as the sun was rising over the distant hills of Moab and the Salt Sea.

"You have made a fool of Saul once again," Joab said as they ate their morning meal. "Why are you downcast?"

"Would you risk your life on Saul's promise to leave me alone?" David asked.

"Not even on his oath," Joab admitted. "But at least nothing has changed."

"Much has been changed," David corrected him. "Once the people of this region were happy to give us shelter in exchange for our protecting them against the enemy. But since the Philistines no longer attack, they fancy themselves free of danger, and we are not welcome any more. If we continue here, we will one day be caught between Saul and the Philistines, with no more places to hide."

"It was you who decided not to fight back," Joab reminded him bluntly. "If you had let Abishai kill Saul last night, you could be on your way to Hebron now to be crowned king of Judah."

"Saul will not die by my hand or with my permission," David said firmly.

"Then how are we to live? You know he will soon forget you spared him and come seeking you again."

"I can see that there is no making peace with Saul," David agreed. "Our only course, then, is to pretend to make peace with our other enemy, the King of Gath."

Joab dropped the water cruse from which he had been about to drink. It struck a rock and shattered. "Is this the change you spoke about before we set out to trap Saul in the gorge?" he demanded.

"Yes. I have been considering it ever since word came that Saul was moving against us once again."

"But will the Philistines believe we are loyal to them?"

"I saw Achish once and I believe we can come to terms with him."

"Don't forget you had to pretend madness to get away that time," Joab warned. "What if Achish recognizes you as the madman?"

"By coming to him for safety, I will prove that I am mad no longer."

"The plan is daring enough to succeed," Joab agreed. "And it would certainly give us what we badly need: a place to live unmolested by Saul until he is dead, and you can be proclaimed king."

"Meanwhile we can learn much from the Philistines," David pointed out. "And lay up a supply of iron weapons against the day when we need them."

"But won't Achish suspect trickery?"

"He is no fool, but the benefits of peace with Judah will be obvious to him. And he will see the advantage of having a strong fighting force in the south to hold back the Amalekites and the Edomites when he moves northward again, with the other kings, against Saul. If he agrees to take us as allies, I intend to ask him for a city in the south where we will not be directly under his thumb."

"And where we can forage for ourselves against our old enemies," Joab agreed with enthusiasm. "It is a good scheme, David. My brothers and I will support you in it."

"Tomorrow we will send emissaries to Achish," David said briskly. "They will tell him that Saul has driven us into becoming mercenaries, and that we seek safety with him. Achish will be flattered that we think him strong enough to be our protector."

As it turned out, David had correctly estimated the reaction of Achish of Gath to his suggestion that the band become his vassals. And since the Philistine chief could also see the advantage of locating such a large force of trained fighting men elsewhere than in his own capital, he quickly agreed to David's suggestion that they be quartered in the south. The town of Ziklag was assigned to them. There, a few weeks after his last meeting with Saul in the wilderness, David and his band settled themselves in the first real home they had known since the beginning of their association.

When word came to Saul that his former son-in-law was now a vassal of the Philistines, no more attempts were made to destroy David, since, in making such a drastic move, David had apparently cut himself off from his own tribe of Judah.

But there, as David had shrewdly planned, Saul was wrong.

CHAPTER 7

"And David smote the land."
I SAMUEL 27:9

THE PHILISTINE CITY of Ziklag was no more than a day's march to the west of David's old haunts in Maon, Carmel, and Ziph and only a little farther than that from Hebron, the traditional capital of the tribe of Judah. Directly south of Ziklag was the Judahite town of Beersheba, a thriving oasis on the main trade routes through that region. And only a short distance to the west, through the plains and rolling hills of the *shephelah*, lay the city of Gerar, one of the great iron-working centers among the Philistines.

Life was far easier for David and his people in Ziklag than it had been in the wilderness. The land around the town was black and fertile, capable of producing fine crops and rich pastures. In nearby Gerar, there were four furnaces for smelting iron ore brought in from the mines of the Negeb, including one for swords alone, so that vital metal was plentiful. Particularly satisfying was the fact that they no longer needed to bring their tools and weapons to Philistine smiths for sharpening. The Judahites had been forced to do this for many years, and paid exorbitant fees for the service. As a result, David and his men were able to lay up an ample supply of metallic implements, such as axes, saws, hoes, and harrows, in addition to their weapons, and to smuggle many of these articles to friends and relatives in Judah.

David and his people, now numbering considerably more than six hundred, were living an almost pastoral life as opposed to their previous existence as hunted men, but he did not allow them to become overly complacent in their new-found prosperity. Atop one of three low hills, Ziklag had few natural fortifications, but by posting watchmen on the other two elevations and sending spies out into the surrounding countryside, he could be sure of ample warning in case of attack.

David did not content himself with these preventive measures, however. He took more direct steps to make certain that the neighboring Amalekites and other tribes of the Negeb did not try to destroy him. The six hundred still formed a compact band of trained fighting men. Placing them under the leadership of Joab and his brothers, David used them somewhat like a spear, driving deeply into the territory of the roving Bedawin tribes to the south.

In the swift raids, the Hebrews obeyed strictly the rules Samuel had laid down for Saul: that every enemy with whom they came in contact should be destroyed and his possessions seized. Thus, by striking out from Ziklag in a series of lightning raids, David was able to take a great toll among the Amalekites and the Edomites. In the process, he captured much booty and built up considerable wealth for himself and his followers, yet with little risk of his activities being reported in detail to Achish, to whom he gave at least a nominal fealty.

Shortly after coming to Ziklag, David let it be known secretly in Judah that his real loyalty still lay with his own tribe. And to the elders of the neighboring Hebrew villages—such towns as Jattir, Hormah, Aroer, Beersheba, and even Hebron—he was always careful to send part of the spoils from his raids upon their ancient enemies.

So long as David ruled well as the king's deputy in Ziklag and paid the required tribute, his overlord, Achish, had no reason to trouble him. Besides, the Philistines were busy building up strength for another attack upon Saul through the northern mountain passes, so the ruler of Gath was glad to be free from the task of guarding a sometimes troublesome southern frontier, as well as of maintaining a state of armed truce with the Judahites to the east. David was careful to send back regular reports of military actions to Achish, along with part of the spoils. But in each case, he claimed that the tribes attacked were in the southern part of Judah—such people as the Kenites and the Jerahmeelites—with whom the kingdom of Gath had been having trouble for many years.

Had Achish been less preoccupied with the affairs of the Philistine confederation, David might not have been able to keep up this deception as long as he did. But as it was, it lasted a year and four months. Finally the day came which he had realized all along was inevitable, and he was faced with a difficult dilemma. It came in the form of an order for him and his fighting men to meet Achish in Gath and march northward for a major campaign against Saul and the army of Israel.

David had no alternative. If he were not to destroy everything he had built up during his stay in Ziklag, he would have to obey the summons of his Philistine overlord. He led his men northward to Gath. Finding that Achish had already left that city, they moved on toward Shunem, the rallying point of the Philistine forces on the heights overlooking the Vale of Jezreel in northern Canaan.

David did not want to enter the Philistine camp until he had had an opportunity to study the situation secretly and plan a course of action, although, as yet, he could see no possible answer to his dilemma. He halted his band for the night at the ancient city of Dothan. David's forces were no less than a day's march from the rallying point at Shunem. As he was resting and seeking in his mind for some way to avoid joining Achish in the actual battle against Saul's forces, Joab and his brother, Asahel, approached.

"Asahel was in the town buying supplies," Joab said. "He learned something interesting."

David had become very fond of the slender, rangy Asahel, who served as custodian of the supplies as well as courier. "Speak, O swift-footed one," he said with a smile. "What did you discover?"

"The merchants in the village are saying that Saul consulted a witch to determine the future of the battle," Asahel told him.

"But Saul himself drove all witches and wizards out of Israel long ago, at the behest of Samuel."

"The woman practices witchcraft in Endor. They say the king went to her of his own accord."

"Even Saul should have known better than that," David said. "It is well-known that witches tell you only what you wish to hear."

"You forget that Saul, too, is possessed by an evil spirit," Joab said. "Perhaps the one called out to the other."

"Did you learn what the woman told him?" David asked.

"According to the story, Saul forced her to call up the spirit of Samuel and ask the prophet what he should do to keep from being destroyed by the Philistines. Samuel is said to have told him that he would not only lose the battle but that both he and Jonathan would be killed."

"You say the spirit of Samuel told this to Saul?"

"So the story goes," Asahel said. "I heard it in several places and it was always the same."

"If Saul is going to die, you cannot help him, David," Joab said. "Why not delay joining Achish until it is over? Then your hands, at least, will not be stained with blood."

If the tale were true, there was wisdom in Joab's advice, for if the Philistines won easily over the Israelites in the coming battle, Achish might be so overjoyed that he would forgive David's tardiness in arriving upon the field of battle. But to take such a chance, based on what was almost certainly a rumor, meant risking his own life, plus those of the people who depended upon him—the men of his band and their families back in Ziklag.

"We cannot be guided by such things as spirits summoned by witches," David decided. "But if I can find a way to delay, I will try to do it."

"Meanwhile, pray that the witch was telling the truth about Saul," Joab said. "It could be the beginning of something important for you."

David and his men joined Achish the next morning in Shunem, where the Philistines were readying a major thrust through the

Vale of Jezreel and the passes leading to an important crossing of the Jordan near Beth-shan. Once in their possession, Beth-shan would serve as the key to unlock the treasures of the fertile valley lands on the other side of the Jordan, for there lay the fabulous region called Gilead and the ancient trade route on the east bank known as the King's Highway.

Saul certainly must have been wasting his time with witches, David decided, as he surveyed the position of the two opposing forces. As the headquarters of the Philistine army, Shunem, which overlooked the plain, had been turned from a small village into a large and busy military center, dominated by the tents of the five kings who made up the Philistine confederation. Opposing this impressive array, Saul's army stood with its back to Mount Gilboa. There was no apparent way of escape for Saul's men, since the gently sloping eastern side of the mountain afforded little protection against the chariots, which David saw being used here for the first time.

In the steep-sided valleys and rock-littered stream beds of Judah there had been no maneuvering room for the wheeled vehicles, some with murderously sharp iron scythe blades anchored to the wheels which could cut a terrible swath through the ranks of men on foot. But here on the plains the situation was quite different. There was ample room here for the chariots, a factor which had led the Philistines, after their campaigns through the valleys of Judah had failed, to turn their activities northward.

Achish greeted David warmly. "You and your men shall assuredly go out to battle with us," he promised.

"You shall see then what your servant can do," David said. But as he spoke, he was casting about desperately for a way to avoid direct participation in the debacle which, judging from the miserable leadership evident in the Israelite position, now seemed certain.

"You will march at once to help cut off a retreat by the enemy southeastward, by way of Aphek," Achish confided further.

David's hopes suddenly soared, for everything that took them away from the immediate scene of battle might also relieve him of the necessity of fighting against Saul. He saw Joab's eyes brighten, too, and knew that the lieutenant realized the flanking movement southeastward toward Aphek could be a way out of their dilemma. But when about an hour later he saw the size of the Philistine flank encamped at Aphek, his hopes began to sink. Nearly half of the great army was spread out across one of Saul's possible routes of retreat; even without David's men, this was a sufficient force in itself to defeat the Israelites.

"Saul must have indeed been listening to witches instead of his own generals, to let himself be caught here between the jaws of a trap," Joab said in disgust. "This is a black day for Israel."

"And for us," David agreed somberly. "I can see no way out except to fight against our own people."

The column had come to a halt at the edge of the bivouac area. There, a tall Philistine, a prince, judging by the magnificence of his trappings, joined Achish. They parleyed a few moments, and then the Philistine general began to inspect the men of Gath. He noted their size and the ready state of their weapons and gear with approving eyes. But when he came to where David and Joab stood at the head of their troops, he stiffened.

"Hebrews!" He spat the word out as if it were a curse. "What are they doing here?"

"This is David, who has been with me for some time," Achish explained. "I have found no fault with him."

"Is this not the David of whom they sang, 'Saul slew his thousands and David his ten thousands'?"

"It is the same," Achish admitted.

"How could he better reconcile himself with his old master," the Philistine demanded, "than by bringing him the heads of our own men? Send him back, lest in the battle he turn on us as an adversary."

The two Philistines had moved aside during the angry discussion, but David could still hear them. For a moment it seemed that Achish would defy the Philistine general; yet finally he shrugged and called David over to him.

"You have been upright and your comings and goings have been good in my sight," he said. "Nor have I found any evil in you since the day you came to me. Nevertheless, the lords of our army do not favor you, so you must leave before you displease them further."

David could hardly contain his joy, though he was careful not to let Achish see his elation. "What have I done that I may not fight against the enemies of my lord the king?" he asked in a token protest.

Behind him, he heard Joab grunt with surprise, but the stocky lieutenant did not interfere.

"As for me, I know you are good," Achish said. "But the princes of my people have said, 'He shall not go up with us to battle.' So rise early in the morning and depart with all who accompanied you here."

"It shall be as you wish," David promised. "We will leave with the rising of the sun."

By the light of dawn the following morning, David and his men were moving southward from Aphek along the caravan trail that crossed the Jordan near Beth-shan. From a peak overlooking the Vale of Jezreel, they paused to look back upon the battleground where Saul's forces would soon be pitted against a far more powerful enemy. Gravely disturbed, David drew away from the others. He could find no pleasure in the fact that Israel, as a nation, might well be destroyed before sunset tomorrow. He did not notice Joab's presence behind him until the stocky lieutenant's hand dropped upon his shoulder in a reassuring gesture.

"It pains me as much as it does you that we cannot help our brothers under Saul, but they are the victims of his folly," Joab said. "If he had not wasted his time seeking to learn the future from witches, he would not have let himself be trapped there on the slopes of Gilboa."

"We still might make a forced march around the northern flank and divide the Philistine attack."

"And be cut off when Saul's men are driven back by the enemy chariots? You know better than to consider such a foolhardy move, David."

"But Israel will be cut to pieces there in the foothills."

"Perhaps, but I think that if the battle starts to go against him, Abner will have the good sense to withdraw and take his army across the Jordan at the fords near Beth-shan. They will be safe on the eastern side, but Judah and all of our people west of the Jordan will be at the mercy of the Philistines. Then there will be only one man strong enough to lead them, David. I will not let you throw away your life, and mine, in an attempt to save a cause that was lost years ago."

"Joab is right." Abiathar had come up from behind while Joab was speaking. The priest and the ephod traveled everywhere with David now so that the sacred oracle could be consulted whenever its help was needed. "The days of Saul are drawing to a close," Abiathar continued. "When he is cut down, you must be ready to take up the mantle of the Lord's Anointed. By pretending to become a vassal of Achish, you saved us all—and Judah. You must not let your concern for Saul endanger the only people who can keep Israel alive."

"As a boy, Saul was my hero and Jonathan my sworn blood brother," David said. "I cannot help feeling sorrow because I am not able to come to their aid now."

"I will consult the ephod, if you desire, and see what is the will of the Lord," Abiathar offered.

David shook his head. "Who can doubt that we are obeying the will of the Lord, since he sent the Philistine prince to save us from having to fight against our own people? Give the order to march, Joab; we will return to Ziklag and our families."

But when they topped the first of the three hills overlooking Ziklag, it seemed that David might have been wrong in assuming that God was looking after them. For before them lay a smoking ruin with only a few old people who were too weak to walk any distance, poking about in the rubble.

CHAPTER 8

"But David pursued, he and four hundred men."
I SAMUEL 30:10

THE STENCH OF THE TOWN assailed their nostrils as they drew closer; what had been the city gates was now a pile of rubble. David called a halt beside the well, from which, not more than two days ago, he judged, the women of the town had paused to talk and laugh together as they filled their water jars. Now an old man so feeble that he was forced to support himself with a crooked stick was trying unsuccessfully to draw water from the well. David took the pitcher and drew water for him.

"What happened here, my father?" he asked.

"Is it David?" the old man quavered, looking up at him with rheumy eyes.

"Yes. We have just returned from the north where the Philistines are preparing for battle."

"Two days after you departed with the young men, the enemy came. They must have had spies watching, for they joked among themselves about how you were helping to fight their enemies while they seized all our possessions."

"Who were they?"

"Amalekites. The first to come were young men riding on camels. With no walls and only women and children to defend it, the town fell even before the other Amalekites arrived on foot."

"Did you say they had camels?"

"Yes. Great, rangy beasts that can run much faster than a man and travel a long distance without water."

"That explains why they were able to attack so swiftly, once we were on the way north," David said to Joab. "The Bedawin tribes among the Amalekites use camels, and their young men are eager warriors. But what did they do with the women and children? I see only a few bodies."

"They drove them away, like cattle, to become slaves," the old man explained. "Even your wives, Ahinoam and Abigail."

As he was talking with the old man, David had been half-conscious of a deep-throated muttering from the massed ranks of the men. Fully half of them had lost loved ones, and all had lost possessions in the swift raid by the desert dwellers from the south. The muttering became a threat when a man shouted from the ranks, "Let David be stoned for leading us on a fool's errand while our wives and children were being driven off into slavery!"

Joab whirled, his javelin drawn back to throw. "Whoever speaks such words again will feel my blade in his heart!" he challenged. "David has lost more than any of us. Does any fool think he is not as concerned as we are?"

The muttering stopped in the face of Joab's forthright words, but David paid no attention to it. " Abiathar," he called. "Bring out the ephod."

The priest stepped forward. Opening the package that contained the brilliantly colored sacred vestment with its sparkling jewels, he held it out so that David could touch it. With his fingers resting lightly upon the fabric, David lifted his eyes to the sky, where the sun was not yet at its midday height.

"O Lord, my God," he prayed. "Shall I pursue this troop and overtake them?"

He had turned instinctively to the one who had guided him in all his endeavors, hoping desperately for some answering assurance in his soul, such as had come to him that night after he had killed Goliath. And, as on these other occasions, it seemed now as if the same voice did speak within his soul, telling him to pursue the vandals and regain what had been lost.

David wasted no time. "God has spoken to me through the

ephod," he announced. "We will pursue the Amalekites. Everything that has been taken from us will be regained."

A mighty shout went up from the men at this decision.

"Find what food you can here and fill the water bottles at the well," David ordered. "We will march southward as soon as the slain have been buried."

While some of the men filled the water bottles and gathered what food they could forage, others dug shallow graves for the bodies of the few who had been killed in the raid. As he waited for them to complete these tasks, David wandered through the remains of what had been his home. Here a woman's jeweled trinket, overlooked by the attackers in their haste, winked in the bright noonday sunlight. There a toy of one of the servants' children lay broken and crushed by a heavy sandal. As he studied these few reminders of everything he had loved most, a deep rage against the enemy who had done this filled David's soul. When God delivered the attackers into his hands, he vowed, he would wipe them from the face of the earth in retribution for this deed of violence.

The track of the retreating Amalekites across the shifting sands of the desert country south of Ziklag had long since been erased. This did not trouble David, however, for from previous campaigns in the area, he already knew the location of the Amalekite centers to which the attackers would most likely take such valuable prizes before dividing them and selling the women and children to the ever-present Egyptian slave dealers.

He could be fairly sure that the enemy would not travel as far east as the city of Beersheba, for there they could expect to meet a fairly strong defense by the men of Judah to whom it belonged. Their logical route of retreat, then, lay almost directly southward, across the caravan trail east of Beersheba. There they would reach the larger road from Jerusalem to Egypt, where they might come upon slave traders at any moment.

South of the caravan trail lay the brook called Besor. It was toward this that David directed his course. He made no attempt to pick up the trail that was lost in the sands south of Ziklag; instead, he led his men in a swift march southward. The realization of what might be happening even then to Abigail, Ahinoam, and the others drew him on. He marched at the head of his men and gave them no rest until darkness fell.

David would have continued on when they reached the brook, but Joab called a halt. "Fully a third of the men are too footsore and weary to go on, even tomorrow," he protested. "If you force the others to go further now, they will rebel."

"Make camp, then," David agreed. "But send Asahel southward with some scouts, lest the Amalekites use their camels for a swift foray against us in the night."

"The men cannot continue tomorrow as they have today," Joab warned. "The weight of the food and water we must carry already bears heavily upon them."

"With the women and children holding the Amalekites back, they cannot be very far ahead of us," David said. "In the morning, have every man who can march take only his weapons and a bottle of water. The third of our forces you spoke of can stay here and guard our supplies."

"What if we do not catch up with the enemy tomorrow?"

"It will not be the first time I have been hungry," David said grimly. "The Amalekite town of Rehoboth lies a little over a half-day's march to the south. We can get supplies there and push on even to Kadesh, if necessary. The enemy must be taught a lesson he will never forget, else he will be forever snapping at our flanks, as a jackal does at the flocks in the hills."

Joab did not argue; he had seen David in this mood before, and knew how implacable he could be. They had barely finished making camp when Asahel returned, supporting a slender, dark-skinned young man with a lean, intelligent-looking face.

"This man was lying half-dead a little to the south of here," Asahel reported. "I thought you should talk to him before we killed him."

The brook Besor was dry in its upper reaches, except during the rainy season, but here along its main course, there was fresh water. The captive drank thirstily and gulped down some figs and several clusters of the dried grapes that were produced around Hebron and Maon. As he was eating, David studied him, for something about the captive's appearance seemed familiar. The man did not seem to be an Amalekite, but with so many tribes among that people, as with Israel, and so many variations in both facial characteristics and the shade of the skin, he could not be sure of his identity.

"Where are you from and to whom do you belong?" David asked, when the man had finished eating.

The captive began to speak in a strange tongue. When he saw that he was not understood, he changed to one of the Philistine dialects which the Israelites also spoke.

"My name is Shisha," he said. "I am an Egyptian, the slave of an Amalekite. I keep my master's records."

"Are you a scribe?"

"Yes."

David knew now what it was that seemed familiar about the captive. He had seen Egyptian scribes, such as this one, keeping records of buying and selling in the caravan towns of the Arabah.

"Why were you out there alone?" David asked.

"Three days ago I fell sick, and my master left me to die," the Egyptian explained. "We invaded the south of the Cherethites, and the territory of Judah and Caleb. And we burned Ziklag."

"Are you a fighting man?"

The captive smiled and held up his hands. The fingers were slender and quite possibly deft, but they had none of the strength of a soldier. "I am a scribe, as I told you, the keeper of my master's records. When I fell sick, he decided that I was not worth saving and dropped me by the wayside. I crawled as far as I could, trying to follow the others."

"Can you lead us to the band that burned Ziklag?"

The scribe gave him a quick, appraising look. "Swear to me by your god that you will neither kill me nor deliver me into my master's hands, and I will guide you to where they will camp tomorrow night."

"I swear it," David told him. "Rest here tonight and, if you serve me well, you shall be my scribe and a free man."

The next morning, the Egyptian led David, and the four hundred men who were able to march, on the route southward. Toward mid-afternoon, Asahel, who was scouting ahead, came back with word that the Amalekites had made camp at an oasis south of Beersheba, and were celebrating their victory with a drunken debauch. Shortly after darkness had begun to fall, David sent his men into attack in the usual two-pronged advance. The battle raged through the night and part of the day until the Amalekites' resistance collapsed. A small band managed to escape on camels, but the rest were quickly destroyed.

Everywhere that day there was rejoicing as family was reunited with family. Both Abigail and Ahinoam were safe, and all David's goods were recovered. In addition, the Amalekites had taken considerable spoils from the other towns they had attacked, all of which fell to the conquerors.

The next day the journey northward began. The flocks and herds were driven ahead, the women and children marching behind them. Armed men guarded the rear against a possible raid by camel-borne bands of the enemy. It was several days before they came once again to the brook Besor, where those who had been unable to keep up were guarding gear and supplies.

Some of the men who had pursued the Amalekites objected when David decreed that all should share equally in the division of the spoils. He silenced them sternly, and announced: "Let it be decreed from this day forward that, as his part is who goes into battle, so shall his part be who guards the supplies." And ever after, this was a law in Israel.

David knew that if he brought the spoils into Ziklag, he would have to share them with Achish of Gath. Since he had no desire to do this, he resolved the problem by sending gifts to the Elders of Israelite towns in the surrounding areas, even as far north as Hebron. For, if the witch of Endor had spoken truly when she had revealed the future to Saul, the time would not be far distant when David could boldly proclaim the leadership of Judah and, with it, make a strong claim to the throne of Israel itself.

CHAPTER 9

"And the men of Judah came, and there they anointed David king over the house of Judah."
II SAMUEL 2:4

THERE WAS MUCH WORK to be done in Ziklag. The bodies which they had hastily covered over when they had passed through about a week earlier needed to be exhumed and buried with proper ceremony. The few roofs that remained standing had to be repaired and those which had been destroyed, replaced. Fortunately, the walls of the houses were made largely of hard-packed earth, and so had not been totally demolished in the fire set by the Amalekites after their raid. The work of building shelter went on apace and, during the period of rebuilding, tents were erected to house the people of the band.

Meanwhile, Joab and a small detail of guards had been sent out to watch for the return of the Philistines from the battlefield in the Vale of Jezreel. Toward the evening of the second day, Joab and his men were seen approaching the town from the north. Hoping to obtain news of what had happened in the battle between Saul and the five kings, David met them beside the well near the ruined gate. With Joab was a small man whose clothes were dust-stained from travel, and whose face was smudged with ashes as if he were in mourning.

When the stranger saw David, he fell to the ground before him.

David took his hand and lifted him to his feet. "Who are you?" he asked kindly. "And whence do you come?"

"I am an Amalekite," the visitor replied. "I have just escaped from the camp of Israel."

"Can you tell me how the matter went?"

"The Israelites fled before the Philistines," the Amalekite said, "but not until many of them had fallen dead on the battlefield."

"What of Saul and Jonathan?"

"Saul is dead and Jonathan with him. The king's sons, Abinadab and Melchishua, died also."

David's eyes narrowed. "How do you know Saul and Jonathan are dead if you fled the field of battle?"

"I was on Mount Gilboa. I looked down and saw Saul leaning upon his spear. He was going to destroy himself because he was gravely wounded and the chariots of the enemy were almost upon him. But he did not have the strength to kill himself, so he begged me to kill him." He paused in his account and gave David a quick, appraising look, as if he were trying to decide just how much he should tell.

"Go on," David said impatiently.

"Since I was sure Saul could not live—he was gravely wounded and had collapsed upon the battlefield—I took my spear and slew him."

"What proof can you give of this?"

The Amalekite fumbled in the breast of his robe and removed two objects that glittered in the late afternoon sun. At the sight of them a sigh went up from the crowd, for many recognized them.

"Here is the crown that was upon Saul's head and the bracelet that was upon his arm," the Amalekite said ingratiatingly, holding them out to David. "See, I have brought them to you."

There was no denying now that Saul was dead. And knowing Jonathan, David was sure that Saul's eldest son had fallen beside his father, just as the Amalekite had said. For Jonathan, he felt the same pain he would have felt had he received news of the death of his own brother. And even though Saul had more than once tried to kill him, he could not forget the man who had been the hero of his childhood. Impulsively, David tore his clothing in a gesture of mourning, and stooping to pick up a handful of black dirt and soot from the remnant of the wall, he smeared it upon his face, as was customary among the Hebrews when mourning. Behind him, the women had already begun to weep for Jonathan, who had been much loved by all.

"How is it that you were not afraid to lift your hand to destroy the Lord's Anointed?" David demanded curtly of the Amalekite.

The man looked about him wildly, realizing now that he had made a serious mistake in coming to David with the tale of how he had yielded to Saul's entreaties and killed him. Before he could answer, David turned and gave an order to one of the young men standing beside Joab.

"Fall upon him," he directed. "And destroy him."

The Amalekite screamed in terror. His cry ended in a bubbling moan as the spear of the soldier designated as his executioner was thrust through his throat.

"Your blood be upon your own head," David told him as the man lay dying. "For your own mouth has testified against you saying, 'I have slain the Lord's Anointed.' "

By tradition, a week of deep mourning followed the death of a loved one. On David's order, it was strictly observed in Ziklag after the news of Saul's death was received. The first three days were the most intense. During that time, David did not emerge from his tent, and the people went about with their faces smeared with dirt and soot, and their clothing torn in tribute to the dead.

At the end of the mourning period, David emerged. In the presence of his people, he washed the soot from his face and put on a fresh and untorn robe. Then he struck the strings of his harp and, while all listened, sang a lament. The Egyptian scribe called Shisha, renamed Jasher in the Hebrew tongue, set down the words as David sang them. The chant was to become the most celebrated of all tributes to Israel's first king and the men who had died with him upon the slope of Mount Gilboa:

"The beauty of Israel is slain upon thy high places:
How are the mighty fallen!
Tell it not in Gath,
Publish it not in the streets of Askelon;

Lest the daughters of the Philistines rejoice,
Lest the daughters of the uncircumcised triumph.

Ye mountains of Gilboa,
Let there be no dew, neither let there be rain, upon you, nor fields of offerings:
For there the shield of the mighty is vilely cast away,
The shield of Saul, as though he had not been anointed with oil.

From the blood of the slain, from the fat of the mighty,
The bow of Jonathan turned not back,
And the sword of Saul returned not empty.

Saul and Jonathan were lovely and pleasant in their lives,
And in their death they were not divided:
They were swifter than eagles,
They were stronger than lions.

Ye daughters of Israel, weep over Saul,
Who clothed you in scarlet, with other delights,
Who put ornaments of gold upon your apparel.

How are the mighty fallen in the midst of battle!
O Jonathan, thou wast slain in thine high places.

I am distressed for thee, my brother Jonathan:
Very pleasant hast thou been unto me:
Thy love to me was wonderful,
Passing the love of women.

How are the mighty fallen,
And the weapons of war perished!"

Asahel had been sent north to determine what had really happened on Mount Gilboa; he returned as David was chanting the poem of lamentation. Asahel stood with his two brothers and Abiathar, the priest, in the front ranks of the crowd. When David finished his dirge, he nodded to the four to follow him to his tent. They found seats on cushions scattered about on the carpeted floor.

"The battle went against Saul's army as you were told," Asahel reported. "Jonathan died first, after fighting valiantly, and with him his brothers, Abinadab and Melchishua. Saul was wounded by many arrows and fell upon the field."

"Dead?"

"Not as it was told to me. But he was mortally wounded; and lest the Philistines take him prisoner and make sport of him, he begged his armorbearer to thrust him through with the sword. The youth was afraid, so Saul took the blade and fell upon it, thus taking his own life."

"I knew the Amalekite lied when he told of killing Saul," David said soberly. "A man of great courage would fall upon his own sword rather than beg an enemy to kill him."

"Abner was able to save more than half of the fighting men," Asahel continued. "They withdrew across the Jordan, near Beth-shan, where the Philistines could not follow. They are in Jabesh of Gilead now, and some of the other cities beyond the Jordan."

"That leaves the Philistines in control of the whole land west of the river, except Judah," Joab pointed out. "No doubt they will attack Hebron next."

"Unless we get there before them," David agreed. "That is why I called you to meet here."

Joab's eyes brightened. "If you are crowned king in Judah before Achish and the other Philistines return home from Jezreel, the people will rally behind you. We must move at once."

"Only if it is God's will," David reminded him. "First we must consult the ephod."

"I will bring it," Abiathar offered and left the tent.

While they waited, David questioned Asahel further. When he was told how the Philistines had defiled the bodies of Saul and Jonathan by stripping them and fastening them to the wall of Beth-shan, his face grew grim and angry. He relaxed only when he heard that men from Jabesh, the leading city in the Gilead area across the Jordan from Beth-shan, had retrieved Saul's body in a sudden raid by night, and given it a decent burial outside their city.

"The men of Jabesh shall be rewarded for their kindness to the

Lord's Anointed," he decreed. "And the Philistines shall rue the day they defiled the bodies of Saul and Jonathan."

When Abiathar returned bearing the jeweled ephod, David put his hands upon it and lifted his eyes skyward, speaking the question that was uppermost in his mind.

"Shall I go up into any of the cities of Judah?" he asked the Lord, who had always answered him in the past; and as on other occasions, he once again heard a voice speaking clearly in his heart, assuring him of the course he should follow.

"Have the people make ready to march, Joab," he ordered as he removed his hands from the ephod. "It is the Lord's will that we go to Judah, to the city of Hebron."

The distance to Hebron, the capital city of Judah, was only a day's march for a band of fighting men, but by now David's subtribe had swollen in number and possessions until it formed a great caravan. Progress was, therefore, much slower as they made their way northward.

News of Saul's death and the debacle in the Vale of Jezreel had already spread through the country. The people of Judah were apprehensive lest the Philistines complete their victory by sweeping through the region with their massive army and destroying all the Hebrews in their path. The sight of David's large band of skilled fighting men and the obvious wealth he possessed gave them courage now. An increasing number fell in behind David until, as the caravan drew near to Hebron, the long line of people and possessions amounted to a triumphal procession. Large crowds emerged from the city to greet them joyfully with music and dancing.

David did not actually enter Hebron in spite of the ebullience of the welcome; he remembered all too well what had happened at Keilah, and had no desire for a repetition of that near disaster at this critical point in his career. Instead, a camp was set up outside the walls for part of his band and their families, while the rest were quartered in neighboring villages and towns. True to his promise, one of his first acts upon settling down at Hebron was to send messengers with gifts to the people of Jabesh across the Jordan to thank them for their kindness in rescuing the bodies of Saul and Jonathan from the Philistines and giving them a proper burial. This done, he waited for the Elders of Judah to approach him with the proposal he had anticipated when he decided to come to Hebron.

Nor did he have long to wait. His own family was one of importance in Judah, as was that of Zeruiah, whose sons, Joab, Abishai, and Asahel, were his chief lieutenants. Besides, David had been careful to send gifts to Judah from the spoils he had taken in his raids upon the Amalekites and the Edomites; in so doing he had built up a considerable tide of good will for himself.

Only a week passed before the Council of Elders of Judah, made up of the oldest and wisest men from each of the major families, approached him. They solemnly proposed that he be named king of both Judah and Israel in Saul's stead. To this David gracefully agreed. The next day, in a great ceremony at Hebron, the crown of Saul was placed upon his head, and the armlet brought to him by the Amalekite clamped upon his arm.

Only one event marred the pleasure of the occasion for David. This was the news, brought by the men he had sent to Jabesh-gilead with gifts and thanks, that Abner had named Saul's son, Ishbosheth, King of Israel.

The court of Ishbosheth, David learned, was at Mahanaim, a town in the hills east of Jabesh in territory assigned by Joshua to the tribe of Manasseh. It was not likely that Ishbosheth would be able to exert much authority here in Judah, where David now reigned as king. But by crowning Saul's son king, Abner had brought about a grave situation which David had hoped to forestall: the division of the Israelite tribe into two camps. As a divided nation, and inevitably a weakened one, Israel was in a poor position to defend herself at a time when all of her strength was needed merely to survive.

IV.

THE CITY OF DAVID

"The strong hold of Zion: the same is the city of David." II SAMUEL 5:7

CHAPTER 1

"And they sat down, the one on the one side of the pool, and the other on the other side of the pool." II SAMUEL 2:13

THE ANCIENT RELIGIOUS CENTER of Mizpeh stood upon the loftiest hill in the central ridge of Canaan. There Samuel had called the people together after the terrible defeat when the Ark of the Covenant had been seized by the Philistines. And from the shrine at Mizpeh, he had sent the fighting men down to defeat the enemy, when the Lord discomfited the Philistines with a great storm.

Because it was the finest watch point in that region, Saul had kept observers upon the summit of Mizpeh to follow the movements of the enemy. David continued this practice when he became king of Judah for two reasons: one of these was his natural desire to be forewarned in case of any attack by the Philistines; the second was the need to keep watch on the tribe of Benjamin, dwelling in the area around Gibeah only a short distance away.

Saul had come from the tribe of Benjamin. After his death, it had remained loyal to Ishbosheth, even though Saul's son now ruled from the city of Mahanaim, upon the eastern side of the Jordan. As David, now king of Judah, had grown stronger, it had been obvious that Ishbosheth's forces must one day either cross the Jordan and attack him, or else eventually yield the whole of Israel to him. In the first several years of David's reign in Judah, a state of armed truce had existed between the two portions of the Israelite nation. But when the watchers upon Mizpeh brought word to David one day that Abner and a considerable force had crossed the Jordan and were moving westward, David knew that the time of decision had come at last. Without hesitation, he mobilized his forces and moved to meet the threat by drawing up his army in preparation for battle at Gibeon, a short distance north of Mizpeh.

Gibeon was the site of many flat terraces, leveled through the centuries from the ring-like beds of limestone that made up its base. These, heavily planted with vineyards and fields, made the area a veritable garden. At the east end of the city was a great pool, or reservoir. Cut from the limestone, the pool was walled with blocks of stone and plastered to hold in the water which poured into it from a large spring nearby.

By common consent, the opposing armies of David and Ishbosheth met for a parley with only the pool between them.

During the years since the death of Saul, David had sought to unify all the tribes under one ruler, for Samuel had anointed him to be the king of Israel, not simply the ruler of Judah. Moreover, David was convinced that only in this way could his dream ever be realized of a single great nation lying between Assyria and Egypt.

As yet, however, little progress had been made toward unification, largely because the men of Benjamin were reluctant to relinquish the kingship which Saul's anointing by Samuel had given to them. In addition, many of the smaller tribes of Israel were distrustful of Judah because of its greater size and wealth. David, on the other hand, could not very well give up his own claim to the throne of Israel; his anointing by Samuel was proof of God's will that only he should rule. Because of this impasse, there had been fighting of a sort between the two factions ever since Saul's death several years before; but David had not let Joab follow his natural inclination and attack Ishbosheth's forces. Instead, he hoped, with the help of Abner, who was the real power behind Ishbosheth, to join the people into one nation. This hope now appeared doomed by Abner's maneuver in crossing the Jordan and approaching Judahite territory.

The years since the defeat and death of Saul and Jonathan on Mount Gilboa had been kind to David. One of his earliest acts had been to take steps to continue the state of friendship which had existed between him and Achish, the king of Gath. Each had recognized the natural benefit to be gained through respecting the other's borders. At the same time, freedom from the necessity to defend his western frontier had allowed David to devote his time and his tremendous energies to building up his own position in Hebron, even though he was, technically, still a vassal of Achish.

Remembering that many of Saul's difficulties had arisen from his inability to keep a strong force of fighting men under arms at all times, David had adopted the practice of many rulers in that area; he hired a band of mercenaries, six hundred skilled fighting men armed with weapons of iron. Led by a stalwart soldier named Ittai, they came largely from Gath. As David knew from experience, that city produced some of the finest fighting men in that part of the world.

David's purpose in hiring mercenaries was twofold: not only did he add a strong segment to the forces of Judah, but he also acquired a personal army which would be loyal only to him in case of rebellion among his own people, a rebellion which might arise at any time as a result of the taxes he levied upon them to pay for the strong fighting forces he now maintained. Having proved himself already a skilled and brave warrior, David thus gave evidence of his knack for brilliant statesmanship. This skill, even more than his fighting abilities, he would display more and more in the years to come.

One of his first political maneuvers was to plant spies in the household of Ishbosheth and Mahanaim. These had already reported discord between Abner and the rather weak and corpulent Ishbosheth. The source of the dissension was the arrogant action of Abner in taking for himself a concubine of Saul named Rizpah. She was, it was reported, a woman of rare beauty and allure. Taking a dead king's wife or concubine would naturally leave a man open to suspicion as a pretender to the throne; and it would certainly seem that by taking Rizpah, Abner was attempting to strengthen his position. But in this case, the difficulty was compounded, because it was reported that Ishbosheth desired Rizpah for himself.

Knowing all this in advance, David had requested a parley as soon as he learned that Abner had crossed the Jordan. He had even agreed that it could take place in the territory of the tribe of Benjamin, rather than in Judah, an act of magnanimity and tribute to Israel's former king that was certain to make a good impression upon the other tribes. Joab, always suspicious of Abner, had objected at first to the plan. He feared that any compromise with Abner would result in a high place for Saul's former chief captain in the combined kingdom. But David had convinced his fiery lieutenant that a compromise was best, if there were any chance of its resulting in unified rule for the nation and a mutual front against its enemies.

Nor could David complain that the recent years had been other than kind to him in his personal life. Both Ahinoam and Abigail had conceived and presented him with fine sons: Amnon by the former, and Chileab by the latter. He had made an exceedingly shrewd move, also, in taking as his wife Maacah, the beautiful daughter of Talmai, king of Geshur.

Her father's kingdom, though small, was from David's standpoint in a highly strategic region. Lying just west of the Sea of Chinnereth on the other side of the Jordan, Geshur was north of Gilead, the center of Ishbosheth's kingdom, as well as across the route, southward, from the capital of the Syrian kingdom of Damascus. Thus, through acquiring an ally by marriage, David had also put a friendly force athwart Ishbosheth's flank, as well as a stumbling block in the path of any Syrian move southwestward on the part of powerful Damascus. All in all, then, he approached the parley at Gibeon in a very strong position. But he did not assume an arrogant demeanor because of it. His manner of procedure, learned that day in the valley of Elah when he had faced Goliath, was to seek out the will of the Lord and carry it through, swiftly and ruthlessly wherever actual fighting became necessary, but by less bloody means when that was possible.

The two forces eyed each other somewhat suspiciously across the width of the pool in Gibeon. The bright-colored trappings of the leaders were reflected in the clear, cool water that poured from the spring. The greetings were courteous, but wary. When they had finished with the amenities, Abner said, "Let the young men arise and play before us."

It was customary at parleys such as this to select an equal number of young warriors from each side to engage in battle before the assembled armies, the belief being that this type of trial by combat would give some inkling as to how a battle between the armies would end. Twelve of the followers of Ishbosheth were therefore pitted against twelve of David's men. The combat took place upon a leveled terrace beside the pool. The fighting was close and bloody since the area was small, and there was little room for maneuvering. In less than half an hour, all the young men from both sides lay dead upon the bloody battleground.

David had hoped that his group would triumph quickly and thus discourage Abner and his supporters from pursuing further military action. But as the battle waged, both sides were roused to such a fever pitch of excitement that, when the last of the young combatants fell, others from each side took up the conflict. Shortly a furious battle was raging up and down the terraced hillside upon which the village of Gibeon stood. The actual fighting lasted only a short while, however; when Abner saw that the forces of Ishbosheth were getting the worst of it, he gave the order to withdraw. Since David had no desire for further bloodshed between fellow Israelites, he sent orders to Joab and Abishai to leave off the pursuit.

David had been given no opportunity to talk privately with Abner. When he saw the other commander appear alone near the bottom of the hill, he started down the slope but was only halfway down when a slender, swiftly moving figure appeared between him and Abner. It was Joab's brother, Asahel.

"Asahel! Stop!" David shouted.

Joab's younger brother wore no armor, since even in battle he was concerned chiefly with carrying messages. If Asahel engaged the far more experienced Abner in a fight, a tragic outcome was certain. Asahel, however, either did not hear, or chose not to listen; instead he raced on, rapidly closing the gap between Abner and himself.

"Are you Asahel?" David heard Abner ask.

"I am," Asahel answered, increasing his pace.

"Turn aside from following me," Abner warned. "Why should I kill you and earn the hatred of your brother, Joab?"

David called again, hoping to stop Asahel. But the fleet-footed brother only ran on, getting nearer to Abner at every step. When Abner was finally forced to halt and defend himself against attack, David was still too far away to intervene.

It was really not a contest, for Asahel had no chance. Driven by an expert hand, Abner's spearpoint penetrated deep into the young man's chest. Abner, pausing only to draw out the weapon, continued on his way through the underbrush. David raced down the hill to Asahel's prostrate form. There Joab found him a few moments later, standing over the dead body of one he had loved as a brother.

"Who did this?" Joab demanded.

"Abner. He warned Asahel not to follow him, but your brother went on, anyway."

"Abishai," Joab called to his brother who had just appeared at the edge of the clearing where Asahel had fallen. "The blood of our brother cries out for vengeance. Only the life of Abner can end the feud between our families."

"So be it," Abishai said grimly. "We will go after him now and shed his blood upon the ground as he did with Asahel."

Nothing was to be gained, David knew, by reminding them that Abner had tried to keep Asahel from attacking him. To the brothers in their grief there was only one answer: Abner must die in retribution. As David followed the two men carrying the body of Asahel to the camp of the Judahites, his heart was heavy. Asahel's death, and the abysmal failure of his initial attempt at reuniting the nation under one rule, were heavy blows. With a full-scale war in prospect, the two factions in Israel would inevitably be forced farther and farther apart, and the task of the victor would now be made even harder.

But David had not taken into account other forces that were already at work in the court of Ishbosheth at Mahanaim: one was the dissatisfaction of the leaders of Israel over the weakness and indecision that characterized Saul's heir; the other, and even more powerful, was the desire of a man for a beautiful woman.

CHAPTER 2

"So Abner came to David to Hebron."
II SAMUEL 3:20

THE WAR THAT FOLLOWED the failure of the conference at Gibeon was not a contest of great armies meeting each other in battle. It was, rather, a series of skirmishes, largely between men from the tribe of Benjamin and David's personal troops. With his superior force of trained mercenaries, David could have swept across the Jordan and taken Ishbosheth's capital at Mahanaim without any great difficulty, but in so doing he would have aroused the hatred of many families in Israel whose men would have been slain by his troops. In spite of Joab's objections, therefore, he did not pursue open warfare against the other faction, particularly since his spies had brought word of further bad blood between Ishbosheth and Abner over Saul's beautiful concubine, Rizpah. In view of these reports, he was not surprised when emissaries from Abner appeared in Hebron shortly afterward.

The message they brought was characteristic of Abner; it was direct and brief. "Make a compact with me," the Son of Ner offered, "and my hand shall be with you, to bring all Israel to you."

It was a moment of triumph for David. But he was careful not to let the emissary see his elation, for one thing still remained to be done to wipe out the pain and shame that Saul had caused him when he had been driven out of Gibeah.

"Tell this to Abner," he directed the emissary. "I will make a league with you, but I require one thing. You shall not see my face unless you bring Michal, Saul's daughter, when you come."

Abner was as good as his word. Not only did he take Michal from her husband, Phalti, but he told the Elders of Israel, as was reported faithfully to David by his spies: "You sought for David in times past to be king over you. Now do it, for the Lord has said, '*By my servant David will I save my people, Israel, from the Philistines and from all their enemies.*' "

David had not told Joab of the message from Abner. He knew that Joab's hatred of Abner, many times intensified by the death of Asahel and the failure of the lieutenant and his brothers to destroy Abner immediately afterward, would make negotiations difficult. That Abner would expect a high place in Israel in return for delivering the former kingdom of Ishbosheth was also certain. Therefore, as soon as David learned that Abner was coming to visit him for the final discussions, he sent Joab and Abishai, with a force of soldiers, on a foray deep into Edomite territory. This journey, which would take several days, would keep them out of Hebron during the delicate and important negotiations.

Abner arrived in Hebron with twenty men—and Michal. She was even more beautiful in maturity than she had been as a young girl, but David could not tell whether Abiathar's warning that she might have come really to love Phalti and, therefore, would resent being plucked from her husband's household was actually the case. When he saw her eyes begin to smolder with anger at the sight of his other wives and their children, however, he knew that, in one respect, at least, Michal had not changed: her intense jealousy and quickness to anger were the same as ever.

"My steward, Shisha, will see that you are comfortable, Michal," he said courteously in greeting. "I am glad to see that the years have been kind to you."

Though David had been true to his promise in setting the Egyptian free after he had led the band to the Amalekite encampment following the sacking of Ziklag, Shisha had chosen to stay on as the chief of David's own household. He managed David's flocks, herds, and possessions, which now amounted to a considerable fortune. This position he filled with great skill and loyalty, but in addition, he had come to exercise a considerable influence in the political organization of the kingdom of Judah.

"Is a king's daughter to be as one of these?" Michal's contemptuous gesture included David's wives, their children, and the women of the household.

"Each of them is the wife of a king," David reminded her sternly. And he could indeed feel proud as his gaze swept across the women standing there, each luxuriously dressed, as befitted the wife of the king of Israel's most powerful tribe. In the front rank of his household stood the tall, dark-skinned Maacah, daughter of King Talmai of Geshur. With her was his son, Absalom, a curly-haired, dark-skinned boy who was already his father's favorite among all the royal offspring. And no less regal in appearance were Abigail and the gentle Ahinoam, with their children.

"Maacah is the daughter of King Talmai," David continued, speaking directly to Michal. "Her family were kings in Geshur when your father, Saul, was a shepherd, guarding his father's flocks on the hills of Benjamin."

Michal only shrugged, but David could see that she was impressed. When she turned to follow Shisha, he knew that he had won the first skirmish at least, though, knowing Michal, he was sure it would not be the last.

By bringing him Michal, Abner had fulfilled his part of the bargain. David was not required to make any actual concessions to Abner in return for this demonstration of good faith; Abner's indignation at Ishbosheth over Rizpah was so great that he asked none. But it was understood between them that, when the consolidation of the two kingdoms was complete, Abner's position would be a high one, possibly that of governor under David for the former domain of Ishbosheth. Thus, David would not only be gaining a capable administrator for the rich lands east of the Jordan, but he would be able to control them more closely than Saul had ever been able to do. At the same time, he would be keeping his own center of activities in the important area facing the traditional enemy of Israel, Philistia.

"I will go and gather all of Israel to my lord, the king, that they may make a league with you," Abner said. "Then you may reign over all that your heart desires."

"See that Ishbosheth is not harmed," David directed.

"It shall be as you wish; he is but a weakling and can do you no harm."

"What of the offspring of my brother Jonathan?"

"There is but one, a lame lad named Mephibosheth. He, too, is safe and lacks for nothing."

"Go in peace, then," David said, embracing Abner in parting. "It pleases me that the hand of the Son of Ner is no longer raised against my household."

With the problems of state settled for the moment, David was anticipating a renewal of his former intimacy with Michal. He knew her to be petulant and given to fits of irrational anger. But he also remembered very well the days following their wedding in Gibeah, when he had experienced in her arms the tumultuous lovemaking of a man and a woman exploring together the intimacy of marriage. As it happened, however, he was forced to postpone seeing Michal, for Joab strode into his chamber late that afternoon. His face was black with anger.

"Abner was here in Hebron," Joab accused him. "Why did you send him away when you knew he came to deceive you and learn your plans?"

"Abner came to make a league with me to rule over Israel," David said.

"At what price?"

"None was named."

"Then he made a fool of you! Don't you see how he connived to place you in his debt, as he did with Ishbosheth, so that he can tell you what you can and cannot do?"

David controlled his anger with an effort, for he was aware of the intense strain under which Joab had been laboring since the death of Asahel. Hatred for Saul's former chief captain had always been one of the driving forces in Joab's make-up; it had only been increased by the suspicion that the price of Abner's yielding the kingdom of Ishbosheth could be the generalship of the armies of Israel.

"No one tells me what I can do except the Most High," David said quietly.

"Where is Abner now?"

"On the way back to Mahanaim. He left several hours ago."

"You are my kinsman," Joab flung at him. "Why did you not kill him in payment for the blood of my brother?"

"I could not have loved Asahel more if he had been of my own blood," David said. "But I also heard Abner warn him not to come on at pain of losing his life. You have no right to hold Abner guilty because of Asahel's death, Joab."

It was the nearest the two had ever come to an open break; but David knew that the future of Israel depended upon his going through with the negotiations which had been all but finished when Abner left for Mahanaim. He had placed the welfare of Israel above his own on more than one occasion; he did not propose to place Joab's pride above it now.

For a tense moment, David thought his old companion at arms would draw his sword and attack him. Finally Joab turned abruptly and left the room. David was so relieved that the angry scene had ended without a complete break that he made no issue of the other's discourtesy, a decision he was soon to regret.

The following morning, Ittai, the Philistine who captained the mercenary band David had hired from among the soldiers of Gath, brought news of the final act in the tragedy of Abner and the sons of Zeruiah. He was admitted to David's presence as the king was eating a light meal and singing for the children, one of whom, if his plans worked out, would one day rule a great kingdom in his stead. Amnon, the first-born of Ahinoam, was sturdy and strong, while Chileab, the son of Abigail, was slight of stature and inclined to weakness, in spite of the strength of his mother. But Absalom, the son of Maacah of Geshur, was every inch a prince and already ruled the youngsters of the household with an iron hand.

"What is it, Ittai?" David had found a sturdy and dependable supporter in the leader of the band from Gath.

"The body of Abner, the son of Ner, lies beside the gate of Hebron," Ittai said. "He was slain by the sword of Joab."

David put down the harp upon which he had been playing; his face was suddenly grim with anger and pain.

"How did this come about?"

"Yesterday, after Abner left your presence, Joab sent messengers to follow him as far as the well of Sirah."

"I know the place," David said. It was only a short distance from Hebron.

"The messengers requested that Abner return to Hebron. Joab met him at the gate."

"Did they fight there?"

Ittai shook his head. "One of my men saw the whole thing. Joab met Abner at the gate and took him aside, as if to speak to him privately, but instead he smote him under the fifth rib and he died there."

"When did this happen?"

"Just after the rising of the sun."

"Bring twenty of your men and follow me," David told Ittai. "We will go and bring the body into the city."

Joab's impulsive action had placed David in a very difficult position. He could not order Joab's death, since the right to avenge the shedding of blood with the shedding of blood was guaranteed by the laws brought down by Moses from the mountain in the wilderness. On the other hand, he could not let the murder go without taking some sort of action against Joab, lest he offend the other tribes whom Abner had represented yesterday in the negotiations concerning the unification of the kingdom. All these things were going through David's mind as he left the palace with Ittai and twenty of the mercenaries. The answer did not come to him until he saw Abner's body lying beside the city gate. The blood had already begun to dry upon the dead man's robe, and flies were swarming around his body.

"I and my kingdom are guiltless before the Lord forever of the blood of Abner, the son of Ner," David announced to the crowd which had already gathered there. "Let it rest on the head of Joab, and let there not fail to be in the house of Joab one who has an issue or is a leper, or who leans upon a staff, falls upon a sword, or lacks bread."

It was a terrible curse to hurl upon the man who had been David's right hand, but nothing else, he knew, would suffice to assure the Elders of Israel that Abner's death had been none of his doing.

"Rend your clothing and gird yourselves with sackcloth," David continued. "And mourn for Abner who was a friend." He himself tore the hem of his robe and, stooping to pick up a handful of dirt, spat upon it and smeared it on his forehead in the traditional sign of mourning. As the soldiers supporting the bier marched through the city to David's own home, where Abner's body would lie in state until it could be buried, David followed behind as one of the mourners. He did not see Abishai or Joab in the crowd and when, a short time later, he was informed that they had left for Bethlehem, he drew a deep sigh of relief.

Abner was buried with great ceremony at Hebron. David himself, wearing sackcloth, and with ashes smeared upon his face, walked behind the bier.

"Know you that a prince and great man has fallen this day in Israel," he said in a final eulogy, as the body was carried into the tomb. "The Lord shall reward the evildoer according to his wickedness, even the sons of Zeruiah."

Just what effect Abner's death would have on the proposal he had brought to Hebron to name David king of the whole nation remained to be seen. It would depend, he knew, on how much the Elders of Israel could be influenced by Ishbosheth, who would certainly try to hold the crown as long as he could. Fortunately for David, that part of the problem was soon resolved. A few weeks later, two men who announced themselves as Baanah and Rechab, the sons of Rimmon, a Beerothite of the tribe of Benjamin, arrived in Hebron with the news that Ishbosheth was dead.

CHAPTER 3

"And they anointed David king over Israel."
II SAMUEL 5:3

WHAT PROOF do you bring that Ishbosheth no longer lives?" David demanded of the newcomers.

Baanah had been carrying a package wrapped in cloth under his arm. He placed it on the floor, took one corner of the fabric, and unrolled it with a flourish, revealing the severed head of a man with sightless eyes that stared up at the ceiling.

"Behold!" he said triumphantly. "The head of thine enemy, Ishbosheth!"

A cry of horror had gone up from the onlookers at the sight of the macabre gift brought by the newcomers. On David's order, it was covered at once with a towel, hiding the glazed eyes which, it almost seemed, were accusing him, although he had played no part in Ishbosheth's murder.

"How did this come into your possession?" David demanded sternly.

"When we heard that Abner had come to Hebron to make a league with you to be king over all the tribes, we decided that it would be better for all if Ishbosheth were dead," Baanah explained. "Then, not even the tribe of Benjamin would have reason to support a son of Saul against you." It was a shrewd argument, and the confident manner of Baanah showed that he expected David to be swayed by it.

"Go on," David told him.

"Ishbosheth was lazy and it was his habit to lie down in the middle of the day," Baanah explained. "Knowing this, my brother and I took up sacks, as if we were bringing wheat into his household; when we saw him lying there asleep, we smote him with a knife and cut off the head of the son of your enemy, Saul, who sought your life. This day the Lord has avenged my lord, the king, of Saul and of his seed."

David stared at the two men for a long moment before he spoke. And at what they saw in his face, they began to lose much of the air of self-confidence and bravado which had marked them when they had strode into the palace a short time before, and demanded an audience with the king.

"When one came to me saying 'Saul is dead' and thought he brought good tidings, I took hold of him and slew him in Ziklag," David said finally. "Why, then, should I not do the same when wicked men have slain a righteous person in his own house and upon his own bed?"

"But we did you a service—" Baanah started to protest.

"Take them out and slay them," David commanded Ittai curtly. "Cut off their hands and their feet and hang them over the pool, as a lesson to any who would seek favor with me by murdering those I have sworn to protect."

As the murderers of Ishbosheth were being led from the room, he turned to Michal. "I swore to Saul to hold his seed inviolate, along with that of Jonathan, and I will not break my oath. Your brother's head shall be buried in the sepulcher with Abner. As they were comrades together in life, let them lie together in death."

With both Abner and Ishbosheth dead, and David guiltless in their deaths, even the tribe of Benjamin had no further reason to oppose his elevation to the kingship of Israel. The week-long coronation ceremony at Hebron began the next day. It started with the solemn signing of a covenant between David and the Elders of the combined tribes who had supported the house of Saul. The kings of Israel ruled by divine appointment; they were anointed by a representative of God, as Samuel had anointed David when he was a mere lad. But they also were required to sign a solemn covenant with the Council of Elders, who served as an advisory body to the rulers; in this covenant, they swore to act at all times in accordance with the laws of God, and with no other thought than furthering the welfare of the people as a whole.

On the day before the actual crowning was to occur, David went to the apartment which had been set aside for Michal's use. Matters had not gone well between them, and he had visited her only occasionally since her arrival in Hebron; now he had come to propose a move which, he was sure, would appeal to Saul's old tribe, the Benjaminites. He had sent word ahead to her that he was coming; but when he entered the room, he found her dressed in a simple robe of linen cloth, which, nevertheless, set off her slender loveliness as effectively as could have any queenly garment. In spite of the obvious coolness of her welcome, he was far from insensitive to her beauty, for whatever vicissitudes had beset them since his flight from Gibeah, she had still been his first love.

"Dismiss your women," he told her. "I would speak to you alone."

Michal did not give the order, but the young women with her discreetly withdrew, leaving the two of them alone.

"Are you angry with me for bringing you back, Michal?" David asked. "I was only fulfilling the oath I swore to you in Gibeah that I would one day reclaim you as my wife. But if you wish to return to Phalti, you are free to go."

When she tossed her head without answering, he went on: "Tomorrow I shall be crowned king of Israel with the crown of your father. I have come here to ask you to stand beside me."

He saw the quick flash of surprise in her eyes. For an instant, there was even a softness there, and he was reminded of the days when they had first been married. Then her expression changed. She pressed her lips together tightly, and her eyes grew hard.

"If you think you can convince the tribe of Benjamin that they should so easily forget my father, you are mistaken," she said sharply.

"I am not trying to convince the tribe of Benjamin of anything," he told her. "If they choose to rebel, Ittai and his men can subdue them in less than a week."

"It would be quite like an upstart from Judah to use force against a smaller tribe," she flung at him. "But you cannot subdue the men of Benjamin as easily as you did the Philistine giant, who moved so slowly that any shepherd lad could have struck him down. My people still know how to use the sling; they could pick your Philistine mercenaries off, one by one."

"I could easily have killed your father with my spear, if that had been my real desire," David reminded her. "It happened in the gorge of Hammahlekoth, when I came upon him as he slept. Yet I spared him, and when an Amalekite sought payment from me by claiming that he had killed Saul, I had the man destroyed. You saw how, when the sons of Rimmon boasted of killing Ishbosheth, I destroyed them, too, for I had sworn a vow to your father to respect his seed forever." He paused and then spoke the final words. "But my patience is not endless, Michal."

As he turned on his heel to leave, she caught him by his sleeve. "David," she said.

"Yes, Michal?"

"I am an ungrateful shrew. If you wish me to stand beside you tomorrow, I shall do it."

"Why would you change your mind?"

"You should know me well enough by now to realize the answer. When I came here and found that you had taken other wives, I was jealous, especially of the daughter of Talmai."

"Maacah has been a good wife to me and borne me a fine son. Having her father between me and the kingdom of Syria provides an important protection to our people."

"I can see that now," she admitted. "Will you forgive me for letting jealousy distort my thinking?"

He wanted to believe she was sincere, that her change of face was not brought about by desire for the glory of sharing the coronation with him tomorrow, and thereby being able to lord it over the other wives. But he was beginning to understand Michal better. He could not help feeling some doubt that her motives were entirely as she had described them. Yet, in spite of everything that had happened, he still hoped that by some miracle they might be able to recapture the happiness they had known during those first months at Gibeah, so for the moment, at least, David allowed his doubts to be assuaged.

The coronation was a colorful affair, with representatives from all the tribes gathered at Hebron. The Elders met in solemn conclave, while David swore in the name of God to uphold the covenant he had made with them. It was an explicit document, binding him to respect the rights of the people, both individually and collectively, and to obey the laws given to Moses on Mount Sinai and see that they were enforced.

After David took the oath upon the sacred ephod, he knelt before Abiathar, chief of all the priests in the nation. Abiathar broke a cruse of oil and poured it upon David's head in the symbolic act of anointing, repeating the earlier and far more simple ceremony in the house of Jesse at Bethlehem many years before.

David could not help feeling a sense of pride as he rose and ascended the dais, where Michal, lovely and imperious in a royal robe of Phoenician purple, stood just behind the throne chair. But he also felt a deep sense of humility too, and of gratitude to the god who had not failed him.

"A song!" someone in the crowd shouted. Others took up the cry at once, and when a harp was thrust into his hand, he ran his fingers over the strings. As the melody poured out, he sang the words that came welling up from his heart in a poem of praise and thanksgiving to God:

"When Israel went out of Egypt,
The house of Jacob from a people of strange language;
Judah was his sanctuary,
And Israel his dominion.

The sea saw it, and fled:
Jordan was driven back.
The mountains skipped like rams,
And the little hills like lambs.

What ailed thee, O thou sea, that thou fleddest?
Thou Jordan, that thou wast driven back?
Ye mountains, that ye skipped like rams;
And ye little hills, like lambs?

Tremble, thou earth, at the presence of the Lord,
At the presence of the God of Jacob;
Who turned the rock into a standing water,
The flint into a fountain of waters."

When the week of feasting and celebration was ended, David called a council of his captains and advisers. Ittai was present as captain of the royal guard. From the Elders of Israel came Hushai, an Archite, who dwelt in the hill country northwest of Ramah, and had been a follower of Samuel. The priesthood was represented by Abiathar and his brilliant young assistant, Zadok. Sitting unobtrusively at one side, with his tablets, his sheets of parchment, his pens and styli at hand, was Shisha, often called Jasher in Israel, who would record the proceedings.

As David looked out over the group, his spirit was sad, for two familiar faces never before absent from one of his councils of war were not there today, Joab and Abishai. He had banished them from his sight following the slaying of Abner.

"What of the Sons of Zeruiah?" he asked Abiathar. "Is there any word of them?"

"They dwell in Bethlehem in the house of their father, and await the time when the king once again will welcome them into his presence."

"Without their voices, this is not like the councils of old. But they sinned grievously in killing a man who came in peace and must justify themselves before they can once more attend the councils of Israel."

He looked around the group, and rejoiced that he had such stalwart men at his back, men whose loyalty he would never think of questioning. Nor did it occur to him that much of the loyalty they gave him was inspired by his own thoroughly kingly presence as he sat at the head of the council.

Just thirty years of age, David was in the prime of life, handsome and strong, with clean-cut features. His eyes were deep-set and capable of warming with a sudden, intense luminosity which sometimes startled a stranger. And while he could be stern and unrelenting when the occasion demanded it, his expression was most often gentle and understanding. Children, in fact, did not hesitate to run after him in the streets of the city, begging for a song about the thrilling adventures of Israel's heroes and their exploits. They knew he would often stop and sit upon a wall or a rock, while they gathered around him and he wove a spell which they were loath to break when the time came to move on. Yet men respected his strength and his wisdom, and often sought his advice as counselor and judge. For quite another reason, women paused in the streets as they carried water from the well, following him with their eyes until he disappeared. With strong sons shouting at their play in the house which served as a palace in Hebron, and a beautiful little daughter named Tamar, presented to him by Maacah of Geshur, lying in her cradle, he had every reason to be content—save one.

It was because of this that he had called the council of war. Now he broached the subject that had been occupying his thoughts for a long time now. "Hebron is too far south to be an effective capital of the whole nation," he told his advisers. "I have called you together to help me decide upon another."

"The Elders of Judah will not like it if the capital is placed in the territory of another tribe," Abiathar warned.

"Do you speak as a Judahite or as an Israelite?"

"I have been so briefly under the rule of Israel that it is difficult for me to think as other than a Judahite," the priest admitted.

"And I," David agreed. "But we must all learn to think of the whole people and their welfare. Nothing is more important now than selecting the site of a capital."

"Mahanaim, the capital of Ishbosheth's kingdom, is too far to the east," Hushai pointed out.

"The kings of Gath, Eglon, and Lachish would like nothing better than to see you place it beyond the Jordan," Ittai added. "Then Judah would fall into their laps like a ripe olive from a tree."

"What about Gibeah?" Hushai asked. "The palace of Saul is already fortified, and the tribe of Benjamin would be pleased to have the site of government in their territory."

"I would rather not give any tribe reason to feel puffed up because it possessed the center of the whole kingdom," David objected.

Hushai frowned. "Surely you don't mean—"

"Only one city is really suited to be the capital of the whole nation," David said. "It lies at the edge of the strongest tribe, Judah, so our Elders will not feel that they have been passed by in the selection. And yet it is centrally enough located so that we can move swiftly in any direction against an enemy."

"And with thick walls to protect us, in case King Achish of Gath realizes you are now as strong as he is," Ittai added with a grin. "You are right, David. Nothing but the city of the Jebusites answers all our requirements."

"It must be Jerusalem," David agreed. "That is the only really perfect site for the capital of Israel."

"Just when did you decide this, David?" Hushai asked.

David smiled. "Who can say? Perhaps it was on a day when I stood upon a hill north of Jerusalem, and looked down into it, before going on to Gibeah to play for Saul. But that was a long time ago."

"When you were only a lad," Hushai agreed.

"But even then, a lad with ambition," Abiathar reminded them. "Ambition and vision, qualities that have united the whole people behind you as they have never been united before."

"You have left out the most important thing, faith in God," David reminded them soberly. "Sometimes, when I was weak, God has seemed far away. But always, when I really needed him, he was at my side. I think he will be there still when we go up to take the city of Jerusalem."

CHAPTER 4

"And the king and his men went to Jerusalem."
II SAMUEL 5:6

NIGHT WAS FALLING upon the tents of David's great encampment on the hill called Ophel, or Zion, where he had drawn up his army preparatory to the siege of Jerusalem. To the east lay a valley usually called simply "The Brook" because of the stream that ran through it. The sloping sides of the hills beyond were covered with olive groves and gardens tended by the Jebusites. To the west lay still another valley in which ran the boundary between the tribes of Judah and Benjamin.

Jerusalem was situated upon a commanding elevation, where the roads from Gaza, Joppa, Shechem, Jericho, and Bethlehem crossed. Strategically, this was an ideal spot for the principal city of a nation which could expect attack from all sides once the fact became known that it was embarking upon a program of expansion. Not only was the city strategically placed for defensive purposes, however, but when Israel took the offensive, a swiftly moving army could either strike eastward by way of Jericho, across the Jordan into Moab, or northward, through Canaan toward the Vale of Jezreel and a gateway to the rich lands of Gilead across the Jordan.

The taking of Jerusalem was the first important task David had set himself after his accession to the kingship of the combined tribes. The occupation of so commanding and heavily fortified a center would do more than anything else to give a feeling of unity to the still loose confederation of which he was the ruler. Once they took Jerusalem, they could move southward into Edom and the Arabah. There they could secure sources of iron ore, and capture men skilled in smelting and working the metal which, to a warring nation, was as precious as gold. Most important of all, a small force of highly trained men could hold Jerusalem against even a massive invading force. The Jebusites themselves had on more than one occasion turned back attempts to seize the stronghold.

From the elevation of Ophel, where David had set up his camp, he could look down into the fortified city of the Jebusites. The city stood upon a commanding escarpment, part of it man-made, that towered above a great spring which furnished water for the city. From where he stood, he could see the inhabitants going about their daily tasks in the city and working on the threshing floor which lay just outside it. They were quite confident, David realized, of the strength of the massive walls that surrounded the city. In some places, these walls were as much as eight or nine paces in width.

None of this was really new to David; as a boy he had brought the flocks of his father's sheep from Bethlehem a number of times to graze on the surrounding hills. Tradition had it that upon the elevation where he stood, perhaps at his very feet, Abraham had long ago prepared an altar and placed his only son, Isaac, upon it, preparatory to sacrificing him to the god who had guided him to this land, far from the Hebrews' traditional home at Haran. The story, learned by every Hebrew child at his mother's knee, went on to tell how Abraham had lifted a bronze knife to slay his own son, only to have his hand stayed by the voice of God at this proof of his faith and obedience.

Once inside Jerusalem, David did not anticipate any great difficulty in subduing the city, for the inhabitants were relatively few in number. Centuries of dependence upon the protection of the great walls had created a confidence in their own invulnerability, but once those walls were gone, they should make an easy prey. In fact, when his army had first made camp on the hill called Ophel, the Jebusites had contemptuously hurled at them the challenge that the blind and the lame could defend their stronghold against attack, and that this massive army would ultimately fail and creep away in defeat too, as had others before them.

David had not planned a long siege. For one thing, there was the difficulty of feeding his forces. After the first few days of foraging in the immediate neighborhood, everything they ate would have to be brought in by muleback from surrounding towns in Judah and Benjamin. For another, although he had no concern for the loyalty of the mercenaries, so long as they were paid from his personal fortunes which, however, could not long stand the drain of such an expenditure, he knew that he could not hold for long the rest of the army he had gathered for this particular venture unless some spectacular action took place soon. Thus, in these early days of his kingship, David found himself in much the same quandary that Saul had been in on more than one occasion. His were the same worries that had finally thrown the unstable son of Kish into periods of raging and senseless violence.

Shortly after they had set up camp, David had asked Abiathar to seek the Lord's will by means of the ephod. But the priest had been able to tell him nothing. David sensed that this particular venture was the Lord's way of testing his ability as ruler of the nation whose kingship he had so recently assumed. That God's will favored him in the endeavor David did not for a moment doubt, but the details of just how Jerusalem was to be captured were his alone to decide.

He found himself wishing Joab were with him. This was the first time David had embarked upon a major military venture without stocky, capable Joab standing at his back. But Joab had been removed from his position as chief captain of the armies after the slaying of Abner. More than anything else David could have done, the banishment of Joab had proved to the northern tribes and those beyond the Jordan that he intended to admit them upon an equal footing with Judah in the affairs of Israel, and not simply make them subservient to the largest and richest tribe in the nation. This fear of subservience to Judah had for a long time prevented unity in Israel.

As David gazed thoughtfully down at Jerusalem, Ittai of Gath emerged from the shadows back of David's tent. With him was Hushai, who had become one of David's closest advisers after the demotion of Joab and Abishai. The mercenary officer carried a haunch of roast meat and a skin of wine.

"It is not well to brood over the strength of an enemy before battle," he said, holding out the chunk of meat to David. "When he appears to be strongest, then is the time to look for his greatest weakness."

David bit into the meat with his strong white teeth, tearing away a great bite and washing it down with wine. "Look down there, then, and tell me what weaknesses you see," he directed.

"I see a weakness in number," the mercenary said. "And I see a weakness in spirit from having dwelt too long within the protection of a wall. Long ago, far to the west, the 'Sea People' who were my ancestors dwelt behind walls like these, but our leaders saw that they were letting themselves grow weak, so they launched upon a great journey eastward to find new lands to conquer. They were not foolish enough to attack from only one side, though; our seamen also went in great fleets along the coast while the warriors marched along the shore, carrying their possessions in great carts. Then, when they were ready to attack a city, the ships came in from the sea and the inhabitants were squeezed between the two forces as the olives are squeezed by the olive press."

"I remember the story," David said. "City after city fell before them. But finally they met the Egyptians in a great battle in the land we Hebrews called Goshen, at the mouth of the great river of Egypt. But you failed there, don't forget that."

"We have never forgotten it," Ittai said. "Nor the reason."

"After all of your victories! Why did it happen?" Hushai asked.

"Our ships were built to be driven by the force of the wind, but the mouths of the Nile extend far inland and the wind failed us," Ittai explained. "Our carts and our chariots bogged down in the marshes. Most important of all, we had grown by then as fixed in our way of fighting as we had been in our way of living in our old homeland to the west. We were not able to adapt ourselves quickly enough to meet the Egyptians so they drove us back out of Egypt."

"How did it come about that you settled in the *shephelah* and gave up the sea?" David asked.

"That, too, was not of our own doing," Ittai said. "After the battle in the delta, many of our people were sorely wounded and our ships destroyed. We were forced to settle in the first place where we could find a home, the lowlands along the coast west of Judah. But there are no good seaports in that area, so we gradually drifted away from being a seafaring people."

"You could have gone on and attacked the Phoenician cities to the north," Hushai reminded him.

"True," Ittai admitted. "And if we had advanced that far soon after the defeat in Egypt, they would now be ours and their commerce under our control. But so many of our mariners had been killed that we had lost the desire for the sea. Besides, we have never been, like the Phoenicians, a nation of merchants. In the *shephelah* we turned once again to pottery, and the smelting and working of iron tools and implements, and soon we were again land dwellers and desired the sea no more."

"I am curious about one thing, Ittai," David said. "There has always been war between your people and mine, and Saul's army was badly defeated in the Vale of Jezreel. Why do you risk your future with me when, as yet, I can hardly claim to be more than a vassal of King Achish?"

Ittai smiled. "If Achish still believes that, he is more of a fool than I think he is. Two things led me to seek service with you, David. First, your god is stronger than ours; when his Ark was captured by our people long ago and taken to the city of Ashod, the image of Dagon in the temple there twice fell to the ground before it."

"The head and the hands of Dagon were cut off too, in his own house," Hushai added.

"Whether I live or die in battle depends upon the leader I follow," Ittai continued, "and who can deny that you will be the greatest king in the history of your nation, David?"

"It will be denied soon, unless I find a way to take the city of the Jebusites. Can you tell me how that can be done?"

"Show me a breach in the walls or open the gates, and I will take it with only my men and the Cherethites," Ittai promised.

"But the breach? How can it be made?"

There no one could help, however. Finally the others moved away to their own sleeping places and David was left alone with his problem.

CHAPTER 5

"Except thou take away the blind and the lame, thou shall not come in hither." II SAMUEL 5:6

IT WAS COOL upon the hilltop at night. Oppressed with the loneliness that often assailed him when he was wrestling with a problem for which he could not see an immediate answer, David finally drew his cloak about him and started on a tour of the camp.

"If you are going out, I will send a detail of men with you," Ittai called to him, as he passed the campfire where the mercenary sat with some of his men, gambling over a game of *senit*. "The Jebusites may have scouting parties outside the walls."

"If Jerusalem is defended only by the lame and the blind as they claim, I hardly think they will trouble me," David said. But when he had disappeared into the darkness at the edge of the camp, Ittai called two of his stalwart warriors and sent them to follow at a discreet distance; they were armed and ready to help, if needed.

Jerusalem was not a large city, and the hilltop upon which it stood did not occupy any considerable territory. The towers at each angle of the fortifications were manned by guards, and torches burned along the walls, lest the Hebrews attempt to attack during the night. David's course took him well outside the band of light cast by the torches. He made his way across the terraces and through the olive groves that covered the lesser slopes of the hill below the crest called Ophel. Here it was quiet, only the sudden cry of a night bird breaking the silence. From time to time he was forced to detour around the walls of tough thornbushes about the vineyards: they had been planted to keep out goats and sheep that might nibble away at the young green shoots and destroy a whole year's crop.

The slopes of the hill were dark with massed olive groves tonight, but in the sunlight of the day, he knew, they were in full flower, a sea of pale yellow blossoms, long, slender, and of iridescent beauty.

He drew back quickly when a dark shadow loomed up before him, but it was only a large wheel of stone set upright in the midst of an olive press. When the fruit was harvested months later, the weight of the stone would press out the oil which the people used, not only in preparing food, but also as fuel for their lamps. An olive leaf plucked off a tree by a dove, David remembered, had been a sign to Noah that the flood was at last subsiding. But he saw no sign in this olive grove to give him any answer to the problem of devising a way to breach the walls of Jerusalem without destroying thousands of men in the process.

David had almost completed his circle of the hilltop citadel of Jerusalem when, on the east side of the slope, he came upon the great spring called Gihon, or "The Bubbler." The spring was one of several sources of water for the inhabitants of Jerusalem. It lay at the bottom of a depression reached by means of a rough stairway cut into the stone around it.

The pool was called "The Bubbler," David knew, because its level did not remain the same, but rose and fell as if it were fed by an underground source. Sometimes the surface was quiet and smooth; at other times, it would suddenly start to ripple and froth.

Feeling thirsty, David lay down upon the steps at the water's edge and drank deeply. Then, hoping to clear his fevered thoughts, he plunged his head into the water. The coolness was refreshing, but as he held it there for a moment, a strange sound met his ears. Oddly clear-cut and bell-like, it was a metallic sound and was repeated several times, though with no regular rhythm. Accompanying it was a scraping noise, as if something made of pottery or metal were sliding across a rock.

David's first thought was that someone was attacking him at the edge of the spring. He leaped to his feet, his hand dropping to the knife at his belt, but there was only silence and emptiness around the spring. Recalling the strange quality of the sound he had heard, David remembered something from his boyhood when he and other boys from Bethlehem had dived and swum in a deep pool in the hills outside the city. One of their favorite amusements was to have one boy click stones together at the side of the pool beneath the surface, while the others listened as they swam through the depths. But tonight there was none besides himself and, as the realization grew that the sound he heard had been transmitted through the water, an idea began to take form in his mind, an idea so exciting in its possibilities that it set his pulse to beating rapidly.

Stretching out on the rocky floor at the water's edge, David again submerged his head and listened. Once again, as before, he heard the same noise, as if metal or pottery were striking a hard surface beneath the water. But this time another sound accompanied it, a vague hum that he could not immediately identify. Then suddenly David thought he knew what it was. Unbelievable though it might be, he seemed to be hearing the sound of people's voices.

David's pulse was racing now. If he was hearing what he thought he was, he had discovered a key that might unlock the gates of Jerusalem and deliver the city into his hands. A quick glance around the rim of the pool told him he was still the only person anywhere near the spring. And this being the case, there could be only one source for the sounds he had been hearing; they must have come from somewhere within the massive rock base upon which Jerusalem stood, a rock base which served also as a source for the spring beside which he was standing.

David quickly peeled off his clothing and lowered himself into the water. It was so cold that it made him gasp. His feet found bottom while his head was still above the surface, and he was able to wade across until he could touch the base of the hill from which the current burst. Moving his hands over the rocks beneath the surface, he discovered the opening through which the water of the spring poured from its underground source to fill the pool. Taking a deep breath, he submerged and, pulling himself into the opening, worked his way through against the force of the current.

The passage was very short. Almost immediately he found himself inside a small cavern that was partly filled with water, though still shallow enough for him to stand erect with room to breathe above the surface. In the semi-darkness, he was not able to tell whether the cavern was natural or man-made; but a quick survey revealed that a well shaft had been cut down through the solid rock from above. Nor did he doubt that the shaft led to the city above, for he had heard of similar precautions being taken by inhabitants of fortified centers where a spring outside the walls could be cut off by an invading force. A faint light filtered down from the shaft. He moved nearer, hoping to be able to see up through it.

Suddenly the voice of a woman, echoing down the vertical shaft, struck his ears. Instinctively, he plunged beneath the surface of the water to hide, only to emerge somewhat shamefacedly a moment later, as he realized that the speaker could not possibly see him in the darkness of the underground cavern at the bottom of the shaft. He emerged just in time to jerk his head aside and avoid striking an earthenware pitcher that had been lowered on a long cord. Fascinated, he watched in the semi-darkness of the cavern as the pitcher filled and sank beneath the surface before it was pulled up again by means of the cord.

The pitcher was quickly lowered for another supply, while the women who had obviously come to draw water for their families chattered together happily. Their conversation was of the siege of the Israelite army and their confidence in the protecting walls, which they were certain could withstand the attack of any invader. David could not help wondering, as he crouched at the bottom of the shaft, how they would feel if they realized that they had told him, merely by lowering a pitcher into the water, just how the final capture of the city would be accomplished.

When the women had filled their jars and gone away, David moved again to a position under the shaft. He was still not able to see very well, for only the upper part of the shaft was lighted, apparently by a lamp that was kept burning at the top of the well for the benefit of those who came to draw water. But he could make out that in diameter the shaft was little more than the length of his arm. It appeared to have been hewn from the stone base of the hill upon which the city stood. That the upper opening of the shaft was inside the city walls was proved by the presence of the women, who would have not have ventured outside them after nightfall. And most important of all, if a woman could reach the well from the city and drop down a pitcher to the spring below, a man could retrace the same path, even at night.

The next day, when the morning meal was finished and the task of policing the camp completed, David ordered the army to gather before him. As he stood upon a rock so he could easily be heard, he was able to look down and see the inhabitants of Jerusalem going about their daily tasks as unconcernedly, it seemed, as if the Israelites had not been there. That very confidence, David thought, would bring about their downfall, for it had apparently lulled them into leaving unguarded the well shaft to the spring called Gihon. Then, as he looked back at his own troops at the edge of the camp, he saw something which gave him final assurance that the plan he had formulated last night would be successful. It was the stocky figure of Joab, wearing the garb of a common soldier, standing among the men who had been gathered from the tribe of Judah for this venture.

"Men of Israel," David told the waiting group. "I have discovered a way by which Jerusalem shall fall into our hands as a ripe olive falls from the tree."

A cheer rose from the men at the words, for the prospect of acquiring considerable booty in a campaign was as much of a lure as the glory of war or the conquering of new territory.

"I require a man of unusual strength and skill, a warrior who will think only of the mission he is to accomplish and not of his own safety," David continued. "This man may be going to his death, so I will not order him to undertake the mission. But if he succeeds in smiting the Jebusites, thereby winning the victory for us, he shall be chief captain in the armies of Israel."

Almost before the words were out of his mouth, David heard the answer he had been hoping to hear. It was the voice of Joab, claiming the right to undertake the mission for himself.

David did not speak until Joab reached the open space before him. Their eyes met for an instant, but it was long enough to show

David that he and Joab understood each other. By allowing him to volunteer for the hazardous task, David had made it possible for him to win back his own position without giving offense to any whose loyalty might still lean to Abner and the house of Saul.

"For what purpose does the Son of Zeruiah approach?" David was careful not to show any warmth at the sight of Joab. To do so might offend the men of the other Israelite tribes who had served under Abner and Ishbosheth. As far as Judah was concerned, no odium had been attached to Joab's slaying of Abner; it had been regarded merely as the working out of the old law of Moses, which decreed that for one man's blood, the blood of him who killed him must be shed by the family of the victim.

"The king asked just now for a man of great strength, able to fight and not afraid to lay down his life," Joab said. "Such a man stands before you, a soldier of Israel from the tribe of Judah and the family of Zeruiah, bearing arms in answer to the call sent out to all who love the Lord God and worship him."

"The Son of Zeruiah is as welcome as any other to bear arms for Israel," David told him, "and to volunteer for the hazardous duty of which I spoke." He raised his hand and looked out over the army standing before him. "Return to your duties now, while I plan the battle with our commanders and with him who has offered to risk his life that it may be successful."

The conference on strategy which was held shortly afterward included the captains of a thousand, together with Joab, Ittai, Hushai, Abiathar the priest, and the scribe Shisha who would record the deliberations. David related his discovery of the night before. When he had finished, Abiathar said quietly, "The Lord led you to that spring, David. Nothing else but the working out of God's will could have revealed to you accidentally what was so well hidden."

"Now that the Most High has shown us the way, we must follow it quickly before the Jebusites realize an unguarded gate to their city lies through the pool on the east side of the hill," David said. "I asked for a strong man just now, because it will take such a one to climb that shaft without a rope."

"No better man could have been selected for the task than Joab," Ittai said heartily.

The others concurred, but Joab did not presume upon the position which had been given him. He understood that he must still complete the task for which he had volunteered before he could assume his old position as chief captain in the army.

"When will the attempt be made?" he asked.

"Tomorrow night, in the late hours just before morning, when no one is likely to come to the well and discover us. At the same time, a mock attack will be made on the west side, to divert the attention of the Jebusites. Ittai's men will be ready before the main gate. When you and your men, Joab, open the main gate from the inside, Ittai's men will rush in."

"Would it not be better if I went alone?" Joab asked.

David shook his head. "That would be risking too much on one throw. Once you are up the shaft, a rope can be let down and ten men can quickly climb up beside you. Then even if you have to fight your way to the gate, there will probably not be many guards around at that time of the morning and you should be able to reach it."

"May I choose the men?"

"All but one."

"And the tenth man?"

"Will be myself."

There was a moment of silence; Hushai was the first to break it. "Have you forgotten the league you made with the Elders of Israel, David?"

"I promised to rule over them fairly, to lead them into battle against the enemy, to serve the Lord and obey his laws," David said sharply. "But nothing in the covenant says I cannot be one of the ten who go with Joab."

"There is nothing in the covenant," Hushai agreed. "But don't forget that Saul failed as a leader of the nation because he was a warrior only. You, David, are both warrior and king, Israel's brightest jewel after the Lord God himself. We cannot let you risk your life in a task that any warrior could do."

David looked slowly around the group. What he saw in their eyes told him they agreed with Hushai, but it was Ittai of Gath who voiced the final argument.

"I am only a mercenary and the leader of a band of mercenaries," he said. "But I owe a debt of leadership to my own men for the confidence they have placed in me. If you risk your life, David, and it is cried out in the midst of the battle that you are lost, I will lead my men away in retreat before they are destroyed."

For a moment David felt a rush of anger, but it was gone as soon as it had arisen. The nation would go on, he reminded himself, whether or not he was successful in capturing Jerusalem now or years later. His duty was to the future, not to either the present or the past.

"You are right, of course, my old friends," he said finally. "God's greatest blessing to us has been that he gave me counselors such as you."

"You are wrong there," Abiathar corrected him gravely. "God's greatest blessing to you and to Israel is that this day you have truly become king of all the people."

CHAPTER 6

"Whosover getteth up to the gutter, and smiteth the Jebusites . . . he shall be chief and captain."
II SAMUEL 5:8

IT WAS SOME TWO HOURS before dawn and the moon had already set when David led a party consisting of Joab and his band of ten men toward the east side of the hill upon which Jerusalem stood, with the pool of Gihon below it. Meanwhile, a band of David's men was preparing the diversionary attack at the west gate, to draw the defenders away from the main gate and reduce the possibility of anyone realizing that men were at work in the spring of Gihon.

Silently the men climbed down into the deep depression where the spring lay. Only the gurgling of the water disturbed the quiet of the night. The attacking party wore only daggers. Their swords had been bound into a compact bundle which would be hauled up the shaft after Joab reached the top. Securely looped about Joab's neck was a coil of strong rope. Once he had made the initial ascent, by far the most difficult part of the whole affair, he would let down the rope so that the remaining ten could climb up it.

David waded into the water with Joab close behind him. "We are at the opening of the spring," he whispered, when he felt the surge of the underground current tug at his body. "Just sink a little beneath the surface and you can enter the chamber inside."

The pressure of Joab's fingers upon David's arm told him his words were understood. He submerged, pushing on through the passage, then broke the surface to find himself once again in the cavern where he had seen the pitcher on his previous visit. An instant later, Joab appeared behind him, and David tugged twice on the cord attached to his waist. The other end of the cord was held by the men who waited outside in the darkness. Two tugs was the agreed-upon signal that he and Joab were safely inside the cavern; three would be the signal for the ten to follow inside, using the cord as a guide to lead them through the opening into the cavern.

Compared to the pitch blackness of the night outside, the faint amount of light filtering down through the shaft above made the cavern seem almost bright. "By the tents of Israel!" Joab exclaimed in a whisper. "They could not have opened a better route into the city!"

"It is still a hard climb," David reminded him. "You had better start before some early riser comes to the spring."

It took but an instant to check Joab's equipment for the hazardous job ahead: the dagger at his belt, the rope about his shoulders, and the tightly wrapped bundle of swords, which David now dropped to the floor of the spring, where he could easily find them later with his foot.

"Remember, now," he told Joab, "as soon as you get to the top, drop the rope so that I can attach the bundle of swords. You may need one of them to secure the rope at the upper end of the shaft. The moment you've done that, I will signal the others to come in."

Joab nodded and David moved into position directly beneath the shaft. Standing there, he was able to reach upward and touch the rim of the bottom end of the shaft, but it would have been quite impossible to obtain a sufficient handhold on the rough surface alone to hoist himself up into the opening. He set his feet squarely on the floor of the subterranean pool and squatted, so that Joab could step first on his flexed knees and then up to his shoulder. From this position, Joab would be able to guide himself with his palms against the inner surface of the shaft. When David straightened up, the lower rim of the shaft would come to just below Joab's waist.

As he steadied himself against the considerable burden of Joab's weight, David reached up and worked first one hand and then the other beneath the soles of Joab's feet. Then, with a hoist from below and a sudden swing upward on Joab's part, the climber's body was drawn up into the shaft to a point where he could spread his legs apart and support himself by the pressure of his feet against the rocky sides.

"God go with you," David whispered, as Joab began the climb.

It was a far from easy task for the climber. He must first move a foot and then a hand, followed by the other foot and the other hand, holding his body inside the shaft all the while by the strength of his powerful arms and legs pressed against the walls. Progress was necessarily slow, but a man of lesser strength could hardly have accomplished the feat. Ignoring the rain of pebbles and dust that struck him in the face, David looked upward and watched Joab's progress. Then, suddenly, the fall of dirt and pieces of rock ceased.

"I am inside a room and can see a passage leading away from it," Joab reported.

Shortly, the lower end of the rope Joab had carried dropped down and struck David upon the shoulder. Submerging quickly, he found the bundle of swords lying at the bottom of the pool and secured the rope to its lashing. As Joab hauled them up the shaft, David gave three tugs on the cord, attached to his waist. He then took up a position by the side of the opening, so that he could guide the soldiers who came through. It had been agreed that no more than three would enter the cavern at one time, since the presence of more men in the small space would crowd it too much. When the head of the first soldier broke water beside him, David quickly steadied him and guided him out to the middle of the pool.

David, Joab, and the ten had rehearsed several times the procedure by which they planned to send eleven men up the rocky shaft into the city. The first soldier placed himself directly under the lower opening of the well, and got ready to boost the second up on his shoulders. The second man would then be able to seize the rope and climb the shaft. The third man of each group of three, David boosted himself. By using the rope to help them climb, it took the ten men only a short while to join Joab at the top of the well shaft. The rope was left in place in case it became necessary for them to make a retreat by the same route.

When David's head broke the surface of the water, a great din greeted his ears, telling him that the diversionary attack had already been launched. He hurried up the hill, too excited by the thrill of battle to feel the cold, though his clothing was soaking wet. Not far from the main gate to Jerusalem, he met Ittai and his men, waiting in the darkness.

"How did the matter go?" Ittai asked.

"Perfectly. Joab said there is a chamber at the head of the shaft with a passage leading away from it."

From the far side of the hill, the clamor of the diversionary attack was growing louder. The group waiting before the main gate could see the confused movement of torches along the walls and hear the men shouting and cursing as they collided in the darkness.

"The Jebusites boast that Jerusalem is defended by the lame and the blind," Ittai said with a chuckle. "It sounds as if they are running into each other inside the walls."

"The noise on the west side is creating confusion," David agreed. "Look how the torches borne by the defenders of the walls are moving in that direction."

There was still no sign from within the city that Joab and his party had been able to accomplish their aim, and David was beginning to feel a little apprehensive. Then, from the main gate, there came a sudden flurry of shouting, the crash of sword on sword, and the scream of a mortally wounded man. Behind him, David could hear the soft hiss of swords being drawn by the mercenaries who were the shock troops of his army. Then he heard the groan of hinges as the main gate was opened, and Joab's exultant shout: "Jerusalem is taken! Long live David, King of Israel!"

When Ittai gave the order to advance, David heard himself shouting the battle cry of Judah, and, sword in hand, found himself running with the mercenaries. Then he was through the gates and facing a Jebusite warrior. The man was brave, and certainly far from either lame or blind, but against the skill David had gained during the years when he had been hunted by Saul, the Jebusite had no chance. There were a few moments of thrust and parry; then David cut the other man down and sped on to follow Ittai.

Stunned by the presence of Israelite troops inside walls which they had considered completely impregnable, the inhabitants of Jerusalem had little stomach for battle. In a short time, all resistance had ended. Just as dawn was breaking over the hills toward Jericho, David marshaled his army outside the main gate. There, Joab, his sword still bloody from the fighting and his tunic stained and torn from the climb up the rocky wall of the shaft, marched proudly forward to be named once again to his old position as chief captain of the armies of Israel.

When the ceremony was completed, Joab joined David and his other advisers, while they feasted on the spoils taken from Jerusalem.

"Ittai tells me you ordered those spared who did not fight against us, David," he said.

"That is true."

"But why? Always before, we have destroyed all who were our enemies."

"The Jebusites have never attacked us," David pointed out. "We have dwelt in peace with them in the very heart of our land since the time of Abraham."

"Yet you took their city."

"Only because Israel needed Jerusalem for a capital. Besides, these people have skills we badly need."

"What skills? They are neither metalworkers nor even skilled potters."

"The Jebusites are versed in a different art, that of buying and selling for profit. They are able to recognize value when they see it and make others recognize it."

"The skill of a merchant!" Joab exclaimed contemptuously. "A sword in the hands of a skilled fighting man can take with one thrust everything a merchant has gained in his whole life."

"But thriving trade can produce the wealth to hire even stronger warriors. What I am saying, Joab, is that Israel can no longer be simply a nation of warriors, herdsmen, farmers, or even keepers of vineyards. To become truly great, we must trade with the countries around us; and for that we will need the skill of the merchant as much as we need the blade of the sword."

"A city of merchants is like a hollow shell," Joab warned. "You saw what happened in Jerusalem, once they had no walls to protect them."

David smiled. "With you to lead us in battle, we will soon have no need to fear attack from any side. I have missed you and Abishai. May nothing ever part us again."

CHAPTER 7

"And Hiram king of Tyre sent messengers to David." II SAMUEL 5:11

ISOLATED FOR several centuries in the midst of the Israelite tribes, the city of Jerusalem had not expanded to any great extent. At the time of its capture by David, a man could easily walk around the walls in less than half an hour. It was far too meager in size even to serve as a garrison for David's continually growing army, so one of his first activities following the capture of the city was to enlarge it. He set about this with all the energy which had made him the great leader he had come to be.

The first expansion of Jerusalem was accomplished by extending the walls on the hill called Zion to encompass a larger area. There David planned to build a home for himself and a structure to house the government, as well as a temple for religious worship. Before he had progressed very far, however, a delegation arrived in Jerusalem with a message which was to usher in a whole new period of growth and expansion for Israel, as well as further glories for its king. The delegation came from King Hiram of Tyre, the powerful king of the southernmost among the great Phoenician trading cities. They not only proposed an alliance between David and Hiram, but also guaranteed the assistance of skilled builders and material in furthering the program of Israel's expansion.

Israel's single seaport of Joppa was poorly adapted for anchoring large trading ships. The Phoenician coast, on the other hand, abounded in major ports, the greatest of which was Tyre. The proposed alliance, therefore, appealed to David, because it gave him access to the sea and the considerable advantage of commerce with one of the great trading nations of the world.

As for the Phoenicians, their coast was often mountainous in the extreme, with only very narrow areas of hills close to the sea. They possessed nothing resembling the rolling area of the *shephelah* which was one of Israel's greatest prizes, although the presence of the Philistine cities nearby prevented its full use by the Israelites. The Phoenicians would thus be able to obtain food, hides, and similar materials from David; in return, Hiram could supply skilled artisans, such as stonemasons and woodworkers, who would build the splendid new city on the site of the old Jebusite center of Jerusalem. And since Israel possessed little in the way of timber suitable for such building, the alliance also promised to Hiram a market for the fine cedars cut in the mountain ranges called the Lebanon, which lay east of their seacoast.

Most important of all, perhaps, at least from David's standpoint, the Phoenicians were not a warlike people, and there was little danger to Israel in an alliance with them. Hiram's emissaries were, therefore, treated with great courtesy. They were sent back to their ruler with a message that David and Israel would be honored to sign a treaty of peace and friendship with the great city-state of Tyre.

The period that followed the signing of the treaty was one of great prosperity and growth for Israel and for its strong and handsome king, now in the prime of life. The palace built by the Phoenician artisans was large and luxurious. David filled its many chambers with new wives from surrounding areas, thereby encouraging friendly relationships with the rulers of many small nations, as he had done with the king of Geshur.

The children's quarters in the new palace were soon filled with princes and princesses of all ages. Of them all, David favored those borne him by Maacah. Their beautiful, dark-skinned daughter, named Tamar, was indeed a fitting sister to the handsome stripling called Absalom. The latter, though not the eldest son, an honor that had fallen to Amnon, son of gentle Ahinoam, was the undisputed ruler of the children in the royal household.

Even with the large harem befitting his wealth and station, David had been careful to keep Michal as his chief wife lest the tribes that had followed Saul's son, Ishbosheth, be offended. But as his power waxed far greater than anything Saul had been able to gain for Israel, the two grew farther and farther apart. He still visited her occasionally, but the old remembered rapture eluded them now. And as the days passed, she became more and more shrewish in temper, while David grew less and less tolerant of her continuing irascibility.

And then something happened which, for the moment, took David's thoughts away from his household and the beauty and magnificence of his capital city. Since the death of Saul, most of the country west of the Jordan had been under the titular sovereignty of the five Philistine kings who had joined to defeat Israel on the slopes of Mount Gilboa. Even after he was crowned king of all Israel, David had continued to maintain the fiction that he was a vassal of King Achish. By so doing, he hoped to avoid a war with the Philistines before he could complete the new fortifications guarding Jerusalem, and build up the military strength of the rest of the kingdom to its highest level. But now, with Jerusalem in David's possession, not even Achish of Gath could doubt that David was rapidly growing strong enough to meet the Philistine kings on equal terms. Facing the new threat as they had faced the power of Saul, they gathered a huge army, and then, by a swiftly executed maneuver, managed to penetrate deep into the territory of Judah and threaten Jerusalem itself.

Southwest of Jerusalem lay a broad plain known as the Valley of Rephaim. The Philistines had easy access to this plain by way of the Vale of Elah and several other passes in the hills. A number of roads converged in this plain and, for this reason, the Philistines were able to place a considerable army almost within sight of Zion, before David could mass his own forces to stop them.

Had the extension of Jerusalem's walls been complete, David could have withdrawn inside the fortress while the enemy wasted his strength trying to breach them, but serious breaks in the fortification remained. If David were to maintain a position of independence from domination by his former overlords, he would have to inflict a serious defeat upon the enemy, in spite of the vulnerability of his position.

At first news of the Philistine attack, David called for Abiathar and the ephod. "Ask the Lord, 'Shall I go up to meet the Philistines and will they be delivered into my hands?'" he instructed the priest.

Abiathar put his hand upon the sacred vestment and prayed; then he gave the answer without hesitation. "The Lord has said to you, 'Go up, for undoubtedly I will deliver them into your hands.'"

David at once called together the captains of his army. Always eager for hand-to-hand combat, Joab urged a frontal attack upon the Philistines, and largely because the enemy forces were now too close to Jerusalem for any effective maneuvering to be carried out, David had no choice but to agree. While the enemy was still about an hour's march from the hill of Zion, Joab led forth the army of Israel; that same day, at a place called Baalperazim, the two armies clashed. The fighting was bloody from the beginning, but the forces David threw against the attackers were far different from the untrained soldiers recruited in Saul's time who were all too prone to shout the traditional cry of retreat, "Every man to his tent, O Israel!"

In the front lines of the battle were skilled mercenaries from Gath and Capthor. Behind these were the men of David's own band, toughened by the long years when they had been hunted in the wild maze of hills and chasms in Judah. Supporting these troops, in turn, were the levies, skilled sling-wielders from the tribe of Benjamin, and bow-men trained to shoot over the heads of their own ranks and rain down arrows upon the enemy.

By nightfall, the Philistines had been pushed back almost to the entrance of the Valley of Rephaim. As the sun went down, they withdrew into the hills in order to regroup their forces. The battlefield was littered with the small images called *teraphim*, which every Philistine fighting man wore in the hope that the tiny likenesses of their household god would bring them luck in combat. And since the loss of one's personal *teraph* was considered a deeat, the Israelites gathered up all of these that they found upon ne battlefield and burned them.

David had not taken part in the actual battle. He was still mindul of the advice given him by Hushai and the others when he had ished to climb the shaft above the spring called Gihon. He had atched the fighting from a hill that afforded an excellent view of ne entire battlefield; from time to time, as it became necessary, e had been able to send messengers to the various bodies of roops, with instructions for changing tactics. After nightfall, when ne enemy had withdrawn into the hills, the commanders came o this hill to report to David. As the list of the wounded, the dyng, and the dead mounted, David's face grew more and more grim.

"We have lost more men this day than we can afford," he said hen the tally was finally entered upon the papyrus rolls on which hisha kept his records. "If we lose that many tomorrow, we shall ave lost the battle."

"For every man who falls, two spring up in his place," Joab omplained. "Had it not been for the valor of the Pelethites and ne Cherethites, our flanks would have been turned already."

Benaiah, a squat, powerful warrior whose stature was oddly at ariance with the height of most of the mercenaries from Capthor hom he commanded, spoke. "Praise from the son of Zeruiah is usic to my ears," he said. "But we cannot hold on tomorrow as e did today."

"Perhaps the Philistines may not hurl as many men against s," Abiathar suggested.

David shook his head. "From where I watched, I could see reforcements marching through the passes from the north," he aid. "We will face even more tomorrow."

"Then it will not go well with us," Joab said heavily, "unless we etreat to Jerusalem and fight to hold the breaches in the walls."

"Let us not forget that it is the Lord who will give us victory r defeat tomorrow," David reminded them. "Remain here, while pray before the ephod and seek some revelation of the will of od."

Even the mercenaries, who did not worship the god of Israel but arried their own small *teraphim* upon their bodies, did not object, or on more than one occasion, David's prayers had been rewarded with a plan which had turned defeat into victory. Recognizing his wish to be alone while he communed with the god who had guided him through so many difficulties, even Abiathar did not offer to accompany David. The priest placed the linen-wrapped package, with the ephod inside it, in David's hands and stood aside with the others.

It was cool at the top of the hill, but when David placed the ephod about his shoulders, as he had a right to do, being both priest and king, and touched the jeweled embroidery upon it, he experienced once again the warm, comfortable feeling of a higher presence which he had first experienced that night overlooking the Valley of Elah. And as he stood there, looking out across the plain of Rephaim toward the camp of the Philistines, a picture began to take form in his mind.

It was a familiar picture and yet a strange one: familiar because it was the valley below him that he saw, the same valley that he had been watching most of the day while the battle ebbed and flowed; yet it was strange because even though his eyes told him the valley was dark and the moon had not yet risen, the picture he saw in his mind was one of full sunlight as it had been at noonday. And as he watched this inward picture with a wondering gaze, he saw many things he had not noticed before in the heat and excitement of the battle.

A grove of mulberry trees stood on the far side of the valley; he had seen it many times, and had sometimes stopped to pick fruit there when approaching Jerusalem at the end of a long day's march. Yet now it was as if he were really seeing the grove for the first time. He could see how the thick branches grew close to the ground and were borne down by the weight of the foliage and the fruit to form a solid green barrier, a screen where a considerable body of men could easily hide with little danger of being discovered. And as he studied the mental picture of the grove, he seemed to hear a voice deep within his soul saying, "Do not go up, but circle around behind them and come upon them over against the mulberry trees."

It was a daring plan and, by reason of its very daring, a completely logical and simple one. From a position at the rear of the main Philistine force, a small body of skilled fighting men could sow confusion and defeat within the enemy ranks. Even the timing presented no problem, for, in this climate, a breeze always sprang up just at sunrise. The swaying of the tops of the mulberry trees in the wind would be the signal for those hiding in the grove to attack.

David was smiling when he came down from the top of the hill. "This is the way the Lord would have us fight the enemy tomorrow," he explained to the waiting group. "Ittai and Benaiah, with their men, will make a wide march between midnight and dawn, and will hide in the grove of mulberry trees on the far side of the valley until the sun rises. When I give the signal, we here in the valley will pretend to retreat. Then when the enemy is launched in pursuit of us, those in hiding will fall upon the rear of his army. The dawn breeze that stirs the branches will be their signal to advance."

"By Asherah, the spouse of Bail!" one of the mercenary captains cried. "It will be as simple as cracking a nut between two stones!"

"If the cracking is well done, the meat of the nut will be sweet in our mouths before tomorrow's sunset," David promised. "Each of you will give orders to your men according to their part in the battle. I shall watch from the top of the hill here."

"You have left me nothing to do," Joab complained.

"Yours shall be the most important part," David told him. "You will have the task of pursuing the enemy when he retreats westward."

Joab brightened. "We might even push them as far back as Gath; with that territory in our hands, Philistia would be conquered and we would have no enemies."

"You forget the East and the North and the South," David told him. "Before the kingdom of Israel is completely carved out, I promise that you shall wet your lance in the Red Sea, the Euphrates River, and the Great Sea at the foot of Mount Carmel."

None answered him; of them all, only David had the vision to dream such a dream.

CHAPTER 8

"And they set the ark of God upon a new cart, and brought it out of the house of Abinadab that was in Gibeah." II SAMUEL 6:3

THE FORCES under Ittai and Benaiah began a wide swing around the Philistine camp shortly before midnight in order to allow time for a brief rest in the mulberry grove before the actual battle began. By then the moon had risen above the grim and silent mountains of Moab to the east, and the sky was bright with stars.

David sat alone before his tent, experiencing once again the loneliness that comes with heavy responsibility. His thoughts ranged far afield, for if the plan of battle the next day proceeded as he hoped it would, the way westward would lie open through the valleys of Judah to the Philistine centers, and the enemy, whose encroachments for more than a century had gradually shrunk the boundaries of his own tribe of Judah, would be pushed back into a small area encompassing little more than the cities upon the seashore. Then the importance of Philistia as an antagonist to a young and growing Israel would no longer be of consequence. It was a heady thought and an exciting one, and the night was far advanced before David was finally able to sleep.

The sun had just risen over the hills of Moab when the Philistine army, confident of victory, marched once again into the Vale of Rephaim to meet the Israelite forces. Just as the shields of the foremost antagonists clashed, Joab, acting upon David's command, sounded the order to retreat toward the stronghold of Jerusalem.

As David had hoped, the Philistines pushed forward eagerly, shouting their battle cries at this promise of victory.

For a few moments David feared that Ittai and Benaiah, waiting for the breeze to sway the treetops before launching their own attack, might delay too long. Then the morning wind fanned his own forehead, and, at the same moment, he saw the tops of the mulberry trees across the plain begin to move. He felt a tremendous surge of elation as the mercenaries came pouring out from the protection of the grove to fall upon the rear of the Philistine army.

Joab, too, had been waiting for that moment. David heard his exultant shout as he plucked the great *shophar* from behind his back and blew a mighty blast upon it to signal the troops to fight again. Then he plunged into the thick of the battle, swinging his own great sword. Behind him, the bowstrings twanged as a rain of arrows arched over the heads of the foremost Israelite troops and poured down upon the enemy. The slings of the Benjaminites whirred as they, too, sent a rain of stones pouring in upon the Philistines.

Once Ittai and Benaiah had launched their attack from the rear, the outcome of the battle was not long in doubt. The Philistines made no further progress toward Jerusalem; instead, as the sun rose higher, they started retreating westward, with Joab in eager pursuit. Long before dark, the fighting had moved so far westward that David could no longer see it from his vantage point on the hill. Although Joab was not able to carry out his hope of capturing Gath and other Philistine centers, the victory was still so great that it relieved the threat of the enemy against Israel for years to come.

In honor of the great victory, David ordered a period of feasting and celebration throughout the nation. To a greater degree than he had hoped, Jerusalem had now become the true political capital for the united kingdom of Judah and Israel. But one thing remained to be done before his plan could be complete: Jerusalem must be made the religious capital as well. To do this, the Ark of the Covenant would have to be moved to the new capital from Gibeah.

After it was recovered from the Philistines more than twenty years before, the Ark had been brought to Gibeah, where it was kept in the house of a very pious man named Abinadab. But with the moving of the capital, Jerusalem had now become the logical place for the Ark to rest. Before having it transported to the new capital, David ordered a magnificent new tabernacle prepared to house it, a tent even more luxurious than had been the one at Nob.

On the day appointed for the transfer, a great crowd, led by David, went to Gibeah, which was a two-hour walk away. At the house of Abinadab, they were greeted by his two sons, Uzzah and Ahio, who had guarded the Ark. The priests placed the Ark upon a cart which Ahio drove on the trip back to Jerusalem. Uzzah walked beside the vehicle, while David walked in front.

David wore only the simple linen ephod of a lesser priest, symbolizing his humility and obedience to the will of God. He was still the sweetest singer in Israel and, as he walked, he played the harp and chanted songs of praise and thanksgiving. The people followed joyfully behind him. Many of them played psalteries and horns, and marked the rhythm of their progress with timbrels and the clashing of cymbals. It was a day of great rejoicing. David's heart was filled with joy, for he was bringing the Ark, the sacred symbol of God's presence, to its proper resting place in the new capital of Israel.

But then tragedy struck. As they were passing a threshing floor by the wayside, one wheel of the cart carrying the Ark ran over a stone, and the vehicle was almost overturned. Instinctively, Uzzah, who was walking beside it, took hold of the Ark to steady it, a right reserved only for a priest.

David was at the head of the procession when a sudden cry of fear went up from those who were following the cart. He ordered a halt and went back to find Ahio kneeling beside his brother while those around him moaned and wept in fear.

"The oxen shook the cart and Uzzah must have feared the Ark would topple from it," Ahio explained. "The people here say he put his hand to the Ark and fell dead at once."

A babble of voices confirmed the account. David had no way of knowing whether the tragic death of one who had so recently guarded the Ark was indeed an accident, as it appeared to be, or an indication of God's displeasure with the whole affair. But he would not go against the will of the Lord, if it was indeed God's wish that the Ark should not be brought into Jerusalem that day.

"How shall the Ark come to me?" He addressed the question as much to himself as to anyone in the crowd, for the tragedy of Uzzah's death presented him with a difficult decision as to just what should be done with the Ark.

"Do not risk the anger of the Lord," answered a bearded man, who had been walking behind the Ark. "In good time, his will concerning the sacred Ark will be revealed to you."

The man who had spoken was tall, broad-shouldered, and in the prime of life. He was not at all frail and old, as Samuel had been; and yet, something in his eyes, a burning purpose and conviction that, David sensed, could not be quenched by any personal concern, reminded him of the old prophet who had anointed him so long ago in Bethlehem.

"Who are you?" he asked.

"This is Nathan, my lord king," Ahio told him, "a prophet who speaks the will of the Lord. He often prayed before the Ark when it was in our home."

"Are you indeed a prophet of God?" David asked the tall man.

"The Lord has sometimes spoken through my mouth," Nathan replied. "And I have served him all my days."

"What shall we do with the Ark, then?"

"A man named Obed-edom dwells nearby. He and all his household worship the Lord and keep his commandments, so let the priests carry the Ark to his house and leave it there. If the Lord favors the house and those that dwell therein, then you can be sure he will not be angry if the symbol of his sacred covenant is brought into Jerusalem."

"See that it is done," David directed Nathan. "And then follow me into the city. I would have you near me, so that the Lord may speak to me through your heart and through your voice."

It was three months before Nathan brought word to David that good fortune had come upon the house of Obed-edom because of the Ark. Once again a great procession went down to bring the sacred symbol of God's presence into the city. As on the former occasion, David led the procession, wearing a simple linen ephod like the least among the priests and Levites, and playing upon the harp. In fact, so great was his happiness because God had finally favored bringing the Ark to Jerusalem that, as on the occasion of his own wedding procession in Gibeah years before, he sang and danced with the others in the joyous procession. And in all of Jerusalem, only one person looked upon his joy and his expression of it with disfavor—Michal, his wife.

David had scrupulously made Michal the chief among his wives and the titular queen of the kingdom, since she was the daughter of its former king. But the fact that he had increased the power and glory of Israel far more in a short span of years than her father had ever been able to do during his whole reign was like a canker of envy eating at her heart. As the years went by, she had grown more and more shrewish in temperament, particularly when it became evident that her father's rude castle upon the hilltop of Gibeah was smaller even than the courtyard of David's magnificent new palace upon the crest called Zion, in Jerusalem.

Michal had watched the procession enter Jerusalem with the Ark. When David returned to the palace to change from the linen ephod to more regal robes, she met him at the door of his quarters.

"How glorious was the king of Israel today!" Her voice was shrill with sarcasm. "In his linen ephod, he uncovered himself in the eyes of the handmaids of his servants, as a vain fellow exhibits himself."

David looked at her and was not surprised to discover that she was no longer anything more to him than a spiteful and shrewish woman. He could feel nothing but pity for her now, pity for what she could have been as his wife and chief helpmate. Yet out of spite and envy she had chosen to thrust it all aside.

"It was the Lord who chose me, instead of your father and all of his house, as ruler over Israel," he said coldly. "Therefore, I will play before the Lord and I will be base in my own sight. But the maidservants of whom you spoke, with them I shall be in honor."

Michal turned white at his tone and his words. For a moment she hesitated in the doorway, as if she hoped for some sign of his relenting. But when David returned to his dressing and paid no more attention to her than if she had been a servant, she turned quickly and left the room.

The break with the house of Saul was complete. From now on it was David, and David alone, who ruled in Israel.

V.

A WOMAN CALLED BATHSHEBA

"Is not this Bathsheba, the daughter of Eliam, the wife of Uriah the Hittite?"

II SAMUEL 11:3

CHAPTER 1

"See now, I dwell in an house of cedar, but the ark of God dwelleth within curtains."

II SAMUEL 7:2

DAVID'S NEW PALACE in Jerusalem was more magnificent than any other structure in Israel. Built upon the easternmost of two elevations separated by a depression known as the Valley of Hinnom, it dominated the whole "City of David," as Jerusalem was called after its capture from the Jebusites.

The work of extending and rebuilding the walls of Jerusalem had been interrupted temporarily by the Philistine attack in the Vale of Rephaim. But once the enemy had been severely punished and driven back almost to Gath by Joab's determined pursuit, work was resumed. The wall was completed at about the same time that the skilled Phoenician artisans from Tyre finished building David's own palace. The fortifications included a strong tower and revetment above the Gihon spring, so that sentries watching in this tower were able to see anyone who might try to follow the same route that Joab and his men had taken when they climbed the well shaft into Jerusalem. Even if an enemy party should succeed in entering the subterranean passageway, they could be spotted immediately and captured when they appeared within the revetment.

David's teeming family and harem occupied a large section of the palace. One wing, however, was left for the chief administrators of the government. With the borders of the nation steadily expanding, the administration was necessarily becoming more and more complicated. At its core was the Egyptian scribe Shisha. He had proved as loyal to David as had Ittai of Gath, Benaiah, the commander of the mercenaries who made up David's own guard, or even Joab who commanded the soldiers of the entire nation.

The health of the priest Abiathar had begun to fail shortly after the conquest of Jerusalem. In time, the position of chief among the priests was assumed by his brilliant young disciple, Zadok, who was also one of David's closest advisers. And since the keeping of adequate records was a most important factor in proper government, a young man called Jehoshaphat had been trained by Shisha to become recorder. David's older sons, who were active young striplings by now, were each given a district to rule as governor. Absalom, his favorite, was assigned to David's own tribe of Judah. By establishing his sons as governors, David hoped to induct them early into the responsibilities of strong leadership.

Much yet remained to be done before David could translate into reality the dream that had come to him in the Wilderness of Paran. He was still beset on many sides by powerful nations who hated the Hebrews. They hated David, in particular, because he was a strong, aggressive leader who showed promise of being able to weld the often quarreling tribes into a single fighting force. Such a force, striking out from the central stronghold of Jerusalem, might well be able to conquer each of them in time.

Had these surrounding nations, the Ammonites who inhabited the hill country to the east, the Moabites, east of the Salt Sea, and the Syrians of Damascus to the north, joined forces, they could have shattered David's dream at one stroke, and reduced him once again to the status of a vassal, as he had been to King Achish of Gath. But it would be several centuries yet before such a confederation of states and kings could forget their petty jealousies long enough to join forces.

David was justly proud of his fine new palace. The stones had been hewn and fitted together by skilled Phoenician workmen. The broad roof was supported by columns and beams of cedar hewn from the heavily forested mountains of the Lebanon. David, moreover, had captured much booty in his campaigns; the major part of it was used to adorn the palace and fill his treasure chests against the time when the expense of the next military campaign would make severe inroads on his coffers. The palace looked down upon a thriving metropolis, for David's wisdom in not destroying the Jebusites was already being proved in the expanding trade which had come to Jerusalem. The city was now a central market for the whole nation, as well as an important crossroads for caravans from all directions.

With all this prosperity, David had every reason to be content. That he was not content hinged upon one factor which troubled his conscience and kept him from enjoying to the full his good fortune and the magnificence of his palace: he had not yet prepared a dwelling place of comparable splendor for the sacred symbol of God's presence, the Ark, and therefore for the Most High himself. David had insisted that Nathan, the prophet, keep him apprised of his whereabouts so that he might be able to consult the most holy man in the nation whenever the occasion demanded. He now decided to summon Nathan to Jerusalem.

"Do you see how I dwell in a house of cedar, but the Ark of God dwells within curtains?" David asked, when the tall prophet with the long beard and hair of a Nazarite came into his audience chamber and stood before him. "Speak the words of the Most High, and tell me whether this should be."

"Go do all that is in your heart, for the Lord is with you," Nathan assured him. A great happiness surged through David, for the prophet's words seemed to indicate that he could now set about building the house of God, which he had planned as proof of his own gratitude for the way in which the Most High had led him to his present position of eminence and splendor. His happiness was quenched, however, when Nathan came into his presence the following morning.

"Last night the word of the Lord came to me again," the prophet announced.

"And what is the will of the Most High?" David asked.

"Thus saith the Lord: '*Shall you build a house for me to dwell in when I have not dwelt in any house since the time I brought up the children of Israel out of Egypt even to this day, but have walked in a tent and a tabernacle? In all the places where I have walked with all the children of Israel, did I speak a word with any whom I commanded to feed my people Israel saying, why have you not built me a house of cedar?'* "

Nathan paused, then continued, " '*Now therefore,*' the Lord said unto me, '*say to my servant David, I took you from the sheepcote, from following the sheep, to be ruler over my people Israel and I was with you wherever you went and have cut off all of your enemies out of your sight and have made you a great name, like unto the name of the great men that are in the earth. Moreover I will appoint a place for my people Israel and will plant them that they may dwell in a place of their own and move no more.*' "

"Does the Most High then forbid me to build a house for him?" David asked.

" '*When your days are fulfilled and you shall sleep with your fathers,*' saith the Lord," the prophet answered, " '*I will set up your seed after you and will establish his kingdom. He it is who shall build a house for my name and I will establish the throne of his kingdom forever. I will be his father and he shall be my son. If he commit iniquity, I will chasten him with the rod of men, and with the stripes of the children of men. But my mercy shall not depart away from him, as I took it from Saul, whom I put away before thee. And your house and your kingdom shall be established forever.*' "

David had never failed to obey the edicts of God, whether they came to him through the words of a prophet such as Nathan, or through the familiar, comforting voice which, on a few occasions, he had heard within his own soul. Although God seemed to have found his hands too bloody from the many battles he had fought for Israel to let him build the sacred temple, he had at least given David the assurance that David's own house would rule in Israel after his death, an assurance which had never before been given to any man.

To prove his gratitude for God's promise that his house should rule in Israel, David resolutely set to work to expand the kingdom. And here his inspired wisdom in selecting Jerusalem as his capital quickly became apparent.

About a half-day's swift march to the east, the most important road from Egypt intersected the caravan trails that led from the *shephelah* to the district of Gilead across the Jordan. There David was able to observe practically the whole domain of Israel, as well as the enemy territory which surrounded him. Even more important, he could move forces rapidly in any direction from the capital. At the same time, he was sure of being able to return to the citadel with equal swiftness, should an attack develop from another source. Thus, he had gained a rather remarkable mobility of operation which made it possible for him to cut down the size of the forces which he would have to maintain permanently.

In any major military operation, such as the attack upon the Philistines which David was now planning, the Israelite tribes lying to the northwest—Issachar, Naphtali, Asher, Dan, and Zebulon—were of no great importance, since they were rather small and largely incapable of independent action. The major source of David's strength had always been his own tribe of Judah, until he had acquired the territory assigned to the sons of Joseph in Gilead, following the death of Abner and Ishbosheth. With these forces behind him now, David dared to launch a major offensive operation against the Philistines. He hoped to remove the threat they posed to his military security, before he looked eastward to the rich tablelands beyond the Jordan.

Moving directly to the northeast by way of Beth-horon, the highly disciplined forces of David's own band, along with the mercenaries and levies which accompanied them, were able to conquer the region around the Vale of Jezreel, the key to the northern entrance into Gilead across the Jordan. Pushing on westward, then, in the shadow of Mount Carmel, David's forces reached the shore of the sea and turned southeastward, driving past Gezer into their old haunts in the neighborhood around Hebron and Ziklag. From this commanding position, they were able to swing westward again to the shores of the Great Sea, and squeeze the enemy into a smaller area than the Philistines had ever occupied before, limited largely to the cities of Ekron, Ashdod, Ashkelon, Gaza, and Gath.

Thus, in one swift operation, David was able to gain control of the important caravan trails through the area around the Vale of Jezreel, and also encompass his old enemies so thoroughly that they were never again strong enough to mount a major attack against him. In the course of this campaign, David's first promise to his chief captain was fulfilled: Joab was able to wet his lance in the waters of the Great Sea.

David now looked eastward, where lay the greatest prizes of all for the expansion of his kingdom.

CHAPTER 2

"And so the Moabites became David's servants, and brought gifts." II SAMUEL 8:2

SINCE THE TIME of Moses and the exodus from Egypt, the Hebrews had nursed a grievance against the Edomites and Moabites who lived in the wild country east of the Salt Sea, and in the waste lands of the Arabah to the south. On their journey to the Promised Land of Canaan, the wandering tribes led by Moses had turned back at Kadesh, in the south, when the fears of advance scouts had convinced the people, over the protest of Joshua, Caleb, and a few others, that it would be dangerous to enter by the route they were then pursuing. Instead, they had sought permission to pass east of the Jordan, along a caravan road connecting Egypt with Damascus and the cities of the upper Euphrates valley.

This route, called the King's Highway, had been in existence for at least a thousand years and was one of the most heavily traveled roads in that region. But the kings of Edom, Moab, and Sihon had refused them passage because they felt that the presence of so large a group of strange tribes within their boundaries might seriously threaten their own security. Rather than fight with the inhabitants of Moab and Edom at a time when his own forces were not yet trained and skilled in warfare, Joshua had led the children of Israel by a route farther east, bypassing much of the kingdom of Edom and all of Moab. He had then turned westward again into Sihon, the country of the Amorites. In a brief but bloody campaign, Joshua had captured the Amorite capital of Heshbon and had pushed on northward, seizing the rich and fertile plains of Gilead and much of the territory of King Og of Bashan. Thus, in a series of well-executed campaigns, Israel had gained some of the most fertile territory in the whole region on the east side of the Jordan.

The Moabites had prudently not opposed the victorious Joshua in his conquest, but from time to time there had been brief skirmishes as well as major wars between them, alternating with periods of uneasy peace.

In David's own time, Nahash, king of the Ammonites, in the territory just north of Moab, had been more friendly, perhaps because he recognized in the young king of a now united Israel a foe too strong for him to oppose. Except for a few border skirmishes, there had been little trouble between the two kingdoms, and when David at last decided to move against Moab, it was with the assurance that King Nahash could be expected to remain at Rabbath, his heavily fortified capital in the hills east of the Jordan.

Led by Joab, David's armies crossed the Jordan and launched one of the swift campaigns for which they had become famous. Had Moab possessed any large walled cities, the campaign might have dragged on while these were placed under siege. But its inhabitants were mainly nomads, who drove their flocks from oasis to oasis and rarely joined forces, so Joab's skilled fighting men quickly conquered them. As was customary in order to keep an enemy from gathering strength again, David ordered two-thirds of the fighting men of Moab killed and placed the kingdom directly under his own control. However severe this penalty upon a vanquished foe might seem to be, it was actually more humanitarian than that meted out to the Amalekites in the time of Saul. Then, on Samuel's orders, the curse of *herem* had been placed upon the enemy, and everything living among them was destroyed.

The conquest of Moab was only the first step in David's great plan to gain the minerals and trade of the vast region south of the Salt Sea called the Arabah, which he had inspected on his journey into the wilderness many years before. Moving south along the King's Highway, he next seized the major oases and strongholds in the country of the Edomites. Continuing southward, his forces soon came into the region where the great iron and copper mines were. Thus, God's promise that his people would find in the Promised Land a region whose "*stones are iron and out of whose hills thou mayest dig brass*" was being fulfilled centuries after the fleeing tribes had passed through this area under the leadership of Joshua and Moses.

David's victories in the Arabah were a serious blow for the Philistines. For centuries, long caravans driven by the dark, hawk-faced Bedawins among the Amalekite and Edomite tribes had transported this ore to the Philistine cities, particularly to the great smelting center of Gerar. By cutting off the sources of the copper and iron-bearing ores in Edom and placing them under his personal control, David was able to strike a heavy blow at the main sources of strength of the Philistine cities on the coast.

About halfway from the southern tip of the Salt Sea to the head of the Gulf of Aqabah, an arm of the Red Sea, David and his troops came late one afternoon to a narrow defile, opening through the sharp jagged cliffs on the eastern side of the Arabah. Outside the pass, the sun was shining brightly, but as they began to move warily between perpendicular walls of stone, the shadows deepened, making it dark as night. David was reminded of another narrow spot where he had almost lost his life when a torrent came rushing down it from the hills above. The path they were following was rocky, for they were moving along the bed of a stream. Advancing slowly, cursing when the stones slipped beneath the tough soles of their sandals, the soldiers made their way through the narrow pass with Joab and David in the lead.

Before he had died of his wounds, a prisoner captured among the Edomites had gasped out a strange tale of an oasis within the stronghold, ringed in by walls of sandstone, where Moses had struck a rock to bring forth a spring of water. The fact that a small stream trickled through the narrow pass they were now negotiating tended to support the assumption that there was a spring somewhere beyond the defile through which they were passing, and from its location, David and Joab were fairly sure that this was the place of which the dying prisoner had spoken.

As they marched on, the defile became more twisted and the space between its vertical walls narrowed until the looming sandstone cliffs above seemed to meet overhead. Then, suddenly, they rounded a sharp turn in the passageway and found themselves in a strange pocket, or enclosed valley, fed by a great spring. The floor of the valley was carpeted with a lush growth of grass. Trees were growing on both sides of the stream and, in the steep slopes forming the pocket, the openings of caves in the reddish sandstone showed where previous inhabitants had dwelt. But the Edomites, who had formed the population of this village, which the prisoner had called Sela, had long since fled before the invaders.

Joab paused at the entrance to this beautiful hidden oasis and wiped the red dust from his face with a muscular forearm. "We need build no walls here to have an impregnable fortress," he commented approvingly.

"God has indeed built it for us," David agreed. "I never saw this place before, but I think I've known it would be here ever since God led me into the Arabah years ago."

Joab gave him a startled glance but did not comment; no man in Israel would have denied that a special sort of communion existed between their king and their god.

"If we left a small group of men here, they could spy out the caravans of the Edomites and fall upon them and then retreat into the pocket after the attack," Ittai observed.

"This will be one of our strong points for the control of Edom," David agreed. "There is water and shelter, and food can be brought in to supply the garrison."

That night, as he lay looking up at the bright canopy of stars visible above the dark, looming mass of the rocky cliffs, David thought how far he had come in the years since he had lain, uncertain as to his future, within that other gorge. He had almost lost his life then in the flood, only to receive, through the assurance of God's confidence in him, the strength he needed in order to go on. And in that moment of triumph and satisfaction it did not occur to him that he might ever lose the favor of the Lord.

Leaving a garrison to hold the hidden and deserted village of Sela behind, the army moved southward. A few days later, as they were trudging across the ridge of a watershed, they saw ahead of them a deep blue tongue of water. David felt a sudden surge of triumph, for he was certain that this could be none other than the gulf which he had been told connected with a great and mysterious ocean stretching endlessly eastward.

"Look there!" he cried to Joab. "I did not speak idly when I promised that you should wet your lance in the Eastern Sea!"

CHAPTER 3

> *"David smote also Hadadezer, the son of Rehob, king of Zobah, as he went to recover his border at the river Euphrates."* II SAMUEL 8:3

A TUMULTUOUS WELCOME awaited David, Joab, and the army when they returned to Jerusalem after the conquest of Moab and Edom. They had captured much booty—ornaments and utensils of gold and silver, copper cooking pots and iron tools and weapons. Most of the precious metal David dedicated to the Lord against the day when his son, as he had been promised through Nathan the prophet, should build a house where the sacred Ark would dwell. The remainder was distributed to the people of the kingdom.

Many matters of state had accumulated during David's absence, and he was busily occupied with them for several months. Besides, there were always quarrels to be settled within his own household. To his detriment, perhaps, David was as lenient in dealing with his own family as he was forthright in battle. As had been the case almost since the day of his birth, the young prince Absalom was the source of much of the trouble. His physical prowess and ruthlessness had earned him the position of leader among the princes, although Amnon and Chileab, the older brothers, bitterly resented this fact. They were always ready to complain to David about their more aggressive brother, as was his younger brother Adonijah, now almost grown. David, on the other hand, could see little fault in Absalom, for the young man was just such another as he had been in his youth—handsome, ruddy, and spirited. As vain and egotistical as he was handsome, Absalom did not hesitate to use his father's fondness for him to strengthen his own position in the king's household and in the king's favor.

David did not have long to enjoy the pleasures of home, however. A few months after his return, Hushai, who was entrusted with handling the relationships with surrounding states and watching lest these states plot against Israel's welfare, brought disquieting news. David at once called a meeting of the council, including the military leaders, the chief priests, and the Elders of Israel.

"Hushai has a matter to bring before us," David announced to the group. "It concerns us all, so it is best that we should all hear of it at the same time."

The bearded councilor rose to his feet. "Joab and our armies have won great victories over the Philistines and over Moab and Edom," he said. "The Amalekites are no longer strong enough to trouble us. But we are still beset by enemies to the east and the north."

"King Toi of Hamath is our friend," Joab pointed out. "He has sent presents to David and assured us of his good will."

"But Hamath is far to the north," Hushai said. "The Syrians of Damascus could cut him off west of Mount Hermon if he were to try to help us."

"True," Joab admitted. "But then there is King Nahash of Ammon. He is our ally."

"King Nahash has been friendly toward us," Hushai agreed. "He is old, however, and most of the affairs of his kingdom are in the hands of his son, Prince Hanun, who is ambitious. In fact, I have word from our spies in Rabbath that Hanun seeks to make powerful allies against us."

"By the tents of Israel!" Joab exclaimed. "Who would dare to join him?"

"The King of Zobah has already made a pact with Ammon on the south, and with the Syrians of Damascus on his northwestern boundary," Hushai said soberly. "Word of it came to me only yesterday from a caravan that had stopped at Damascus."

Everyone present understood the threat to the safety of Israel that such a confederation would constitute. The question was not so much whether King Nahash would be able to control his son, or if Ammon alone might pose any serious danger to Israel. It was Zobah that was to be feared, for like David, Prince Hadadezer, its leader, was clever and ambitious. And like Israel, his kingdom of Zobah was expanding as rapidly as he was able to enlarge its borders.

"This is grave news indeed," Benaiah said. "With Zobah and Damascus as allies, the Ammonites can put an army into the field that would outnumber us nearly two to one."

"Hadadezer has many chariots," Ittai added. "He needs them to hold his northeast border against the Assyrians."

So far, David's army possessed few of the wheeled vehicles. Not accustomed to that kind of warfare, he had hitherto preferred to fight in the narrow valleys of central Canaan or in the mountain country east of the Jordan, where chariots were of little value. But should Hadadezer move into the Jordan Valley with a large chariot force, the advantage would be heavily in his favor. It was David himself, however, who pointed out the greatest danger posed by an alliance of Ammon, Zobah, and Damascus.

"Hadadezer is a strong and resolute leader of men," he said. "No doubt he intends to weld the three kingdoms into one under his rule."

"Then we would have a conqueror upon our very doorsteps," Joab said. "Rabbath-ammon must be taken at once before the alliance grows too strong for us."

"The capital of Ammon must be conquered," David agreed. "But while we were laying siege to the walls of Rabbath, Zobah and Damascus would not be idle."

"What is in your mind, David?" Ittai's eyes had begun to gleam, for David and the Philistine mercenary leader often thought alike.

"Let Hushai first tell us everything he learned from the caravan."

"The alliance has already been made," Hushai said. "In fact, in Damascus the Syrians are boasting that David will soon be destroyed and Israel with him."

"Why does Hadadezer not move, then?" Joab asked.

"His boundary on the Euphrates is threatened by the Assyrians," Hushai explained. "As the caravan was nearing Damascus from the east, they saw large numbers of Hadadezer's soldiers moving toward Tadmor and the Euphrates, where the Assyrians have gathered."

"This Hadadezer must be as clever as we were told he is," Joab said. "It is sensible to secure one border before you attack another, but by doing so he has played into our hands. While he is busy on the Euphrates, we can take Rabbath and prepare ourselves to withstand attack and perhaps a siege of Jerusalem."

"Joab's counsel is well thought out, as always," David admitted. "With a stronghold like Jerusalem, we could be sure of withstanding any siege, so it is tempting to consider letting Hadadezer bruise and batter himself against the walls of Zion. But if that happened, he would only withdraw into his own country to gain more allies and strike once again."

"As you would do," Ittai agreed.

"I have tried to put myself in his place and think what would be his course," David admitted.

"And the answer?"

"Hadadezer seeks to destroy us in one blow, with Syria and Ammon as his allies. But he is occupied at the moment with the Assyrians on his northeastern border. So now would be the time to crush him, with the help of our allies."

"We have no allies except perhaps King Toi of Hamath and Talmai of Geshur, your father-in-law," Joab objected. "And neither of them is strong enough to be of any value to us."

"You forget the Assyrians," Ittai reminded him with a grin. "They are our enemies, too! Or will be if they continue to move westward as they have been doing."

"An ally need not fight beside you, Joab," David pointed out. "Neither is it necessary for him to be friendly, so long as he fights a common enemy."

"And divides the enemy forces," Ittai added.

"Zobah is the strongest part of the alliance that includes Syria and Ammon," David went on, "not only because it has the largest army but because it has the strongest leader. But Hadadezer is occupied on the banks of the Euphrates. If we strike at his rear from Gilead and also from the territory of Dan, the very least we can accomplish will be to cut Damascus off from Ammon and possibly from Zobah as well."

"Leaving them to be destroyed separately," Joab agreed. "When do we march against Zobah and Hadadezer?"

"Give him a week to reach his farthest boundary and become embroiled with the Assyrians while we are preparing our forces for a rapid march," David said. "Hanun no doubt has spies in Jerusalem, so we will pretend that we are preparing to attack Ammon. But when we do move, we will strike northward instead, into Zobah, before Hadadezer can withdraw from the Euphrates."

David turned to the chief captain. "I promised that you would wet your javelin in the River Euphrates, Joab, but I didn't dream that it would be so soon."

For the march northward, David selected a route that traversed the hills of central Canaan. Where the Vale of Jezreel cut through the central range of Canaan at the foot of Mount Gilboa, he divided his army into two parts: one under the command of Joab, the other under his own leadership.

Joab's force turned east to Beth-shan and crossed the Jordan. He was to strike almost directly northeast driving a wedge between Zobah and Damascus to the north and Ammon to the south. Meanwhile the forces under David's command were marching through an area of tumbled black basalt rocks, from which they could look down occasionally upon the intense blue of the lovely lake called Chinnereth.

Following the shore of the lake through an area so fertile that it seemed to be a veritable Garden of Eden with the heavily forested and well-watered hills of Galilee on their left, they came to the Jordan, a short distance north of where it tumbled into the Sea of Chinnereth. Crossing the river there, they skirted the foothills of snow-capped Mount Hermon, with the grays and browns of the desert to the south.

While they were still in sight of Mount Hermon, the desert lands began to give way to a broad, terraced plain around Damascus. Soon the city itself could be seen in the distance, fairyland green with the delicate feather dusters of palm trees rising above its white buildings, a scene of such startling beauty that it seemed a mirage dreamed up by a thirsty desert traveler. By-passing Damascus, David's army moved through the foothills of Mount Hermon and approached Hadadezer's center of Beerothai.

The choice of a route through the hill country had been intentional, for here chariots would be of little value. On the plains around Damascus, however, chariots could move freely and cut David's troops to pieces. David was thus using the same tactic he had employed long ago in fighting the Philistines. And in attacking Hadadezer while the armies of Zobah were preoccupied with the Assyrians, he was carrying out still another tactic, learned during his days as a guerrilla leader: that of the attack from an unexpected quarter. The results were a further and striking proof of the genius for military strategy which had made David, after Joshua, the greatest warrior in Israel's history.

Descending swiftly upon Beerothai, David took the town almost without shooting an arrow. At the same time he outflanked Damascus and rendered it comparatively helpless. From Beerothai, he drove through the hill country and attacked the rear of the Zoban army while Hadadezer was pressing his own foray against the Assyrians, who had crossed the River Euphrates near its junction with the Balikh.

The battle that ensued was fierce and swiftly carried out. When it was over, Hadadezer's army had been defeated, and the thousand chariots which had made it the most formidable force in that region were in David's hands. The greater part of the vehicles he ordered destroyed. He took only a hundred back with him to Jerusalem, in order to accustom his army to their use and to form a nucleus for building his own chariot corps for future battles.

Belatedly, the Syrians of Damascus realized that they had been outmaneuvered and sought to reverse the defeat of Hadadezer. But David's swift-flanking operation had put them at a considerable disadvantage. Forced to fight alone against a victorious Israelite army, they too were dealt a strong defeat in the hills north of their capital. As a result, David was able to leave garrisons in both Zobah and Damascus to hold that territory against a possible future uprising against him.

It was indeed a victorious army that returned to Israel along the King's Highway. Of them all, Joab was the most jubilant, for as

David had promised, he had now wet his lance not only in the Great Sea to the west, but also in the Gulf of Aqabah, an arm of the almost legendary Eastern Sea, and, finally, in the River Euphrates.

CHAPTER 4

"And David gat him a name when he returned from smiting of the Syrians." II SAMUEL 8:13

NEVER BEFORE in Israel's history had its major enemies been rendered so completely helpless. The Philistines were contained within a small perimeter surrounding their seacoast cities. Egypt troubled itself little about the Hebrews, although Pharaoh still held a nominal suzerainty over all of Canaan. To the east across the Jordan, Ammon remained unsubdued, but with Zobah and Damascus defeated, the siege of the heavily fortified capital of Rabbath could safely be postponed to a better season.

David had every reason to feel satisfied as he rode into Jerusalem on one of the captured Syrian chariots, while the people lining the streets shouted their acclaim. Behind his chariot marched the battle-hardened mercenaries of his personal bodyguard, followed by carts and sledges bearing an enormous treasure in gold, silver, and precious gems, most of which he had declared dedicated to the great temple God had promised him would be built by his son.

David's chariot was almost at the gate leading to his own palace when his eyes fell upon an extraordinarily beautiful woman standing in the crowd. Her hair was dark and, unlike most of the women among the watchers, she had covered it only partly with a gauzy scarf which did nothing to hide its lustrous beauty. As her eyes caught and held David's for a long exciting moment, she dropped the scarf she had been holding across her face just below the eyes. Her face, in full view now, was of dazzling loveliness. But it was not so much her beauty that held David as it was a feeling almost of sharing a secret known only to the two of them. Although he was sure he had never seen her before, he was equally certain that he would see her again, and his pulse quickened at the thought.

During David's absence many questions of state had arisen which must be decided, either by him alone or in conjunction with the Council of Israel. When these were settled, he was able to turn his attention to cementing further the ties which, he hoped, would hold the tribes together after his death. For this purpose, he sent for his steward Shisha, and the recorder Jehoshaphat, whose task it was to keep an accurate account of the nation's history.

"Is anyone left of the house of Saul?" David asked them. "I wish to show him kindness, for Jonathan's sake."

"A servant in your household named Ziba was once a servant of Jonathan," Jehoshaphat said. "He would know."

"Send him to me," David directed, and when Ziba, a graying, portly man, appeared, he asked him the question.

"Jonathan had a son who is lame in his feet," Ziba answered. "He is called Mephibosheth."

"Where is he?"

"In the house of Machir in Lodebar."

David knew the region well. It lay at the eastern edge of the Jordan Valley, not far from the old capital of Saul's son, Ish-bosheth, at Mahanaim. From Ziba's words, it did not appear that Jonathan's son was likely to be a danger to David in any way, even though he still lived in an area which had been loyal to Saul's family after David became king of Judah. But by bringing the lame son of Jonathan to the capital and being kind to him, David knew he would please those who opposed him in Israel. And at the same time he would have Mephibosheth in a place where he could be easily watched. This precaution was particularly necessary, since from time to time there were mutterings of discontent in the tribe of Benjamin from which Saul had come.

"Go bring Mephibosheth to Jerusalem," David directed Ziba. "And tell him to fear not, for his father and I swore blood brotherhood together."

Less than a week later, Mephibosheth was ushered into David's presence. David saw at once that there was little to fear from him, for the young man walked with crutches and stumbled forward to prostrate himself at David's feet.

"Fear not," David told Jonathan's crippled son. "I will show you kindness for your father's sake and restore to you the lands of Saul. Moreover, you will eat bread at my table."

"What is your servant that you should look upon such a dead dog as he?" Mephibosheth asked as he touched his forehead to the floor. David could not repress a stab of pain that a son of Jonathan, who had been so strong and courageous, should thus cringe before him.

"I have given to your master's son all that pertained to Saul and to all his house," David told Ziba. "You and your sons and your servants shall till the land for him."

"According to all that my lord the king has commanded his servant, so shall your servant do." Ziba stooped to help his master to his feet and assist him from the room.

The sight of Jonathan's crippled son had depressed David, and the constant wrangling that went on in his household did nothing to raise his spirits. With each of his elder sons striving for a position of prominence in David's sight in the hope of inheriting the crown of Israel, and with the younger sons carrying tales to him about their doings, he found more reason than ever to admire Absalom. That stalwart youth settled his grievances with his brothers in his own way. More than one of them had appeared at the prince's table with bruises attesting to Absalom's prowess as a fighter.

Restless and fretful from the inaction imposed upon him by residence in Jerusalem, David almost welcomed an attempt by Prince Hanun of Ammon, following the death of King Nahash, to revive the old Syrian confederation and attack Israel. In a swift campaign which David himself led, the Syrians were ruthlessly put down, and for a brief period he was able to revel once again in the joy of battle and conquest. When it was over, Joab went on to lay siege to the heavily fortified Ammonite capital of Rabbath, but political matters necessitated David's presence in Jerusalem. There, once more, he fretted against the bonds that kept him tied to the capital and the constant bickering in his own household.

It had been a long time since David had been able to pluck the strings of a harp and sing the songs that he and the people loved so much. But the sweet singer of Israel who had once danced for joy before the Ark of God, wearing only the humble linen ephod of a lesser priest, had long since become a graying man in his late forties. His face was lined with worry from the cares of administering a kingdom where tribe still fought against tribe for ascendancy, and where those who had followed Saul still muttered among themselves and sometimes talked openly of rebellion, claiming that, since David belonged to the largest and richest tribe, he must of necessity favor Judah over the others.

There was a great deal of resentment in Israel, too, over the fact that the rich treasures captured in the wars, as well as the gifts brought by neighboring kings to cement friendship with Israel, had not been distributed among the people. The ordinary man of Israel was accustomed to seeing the Ark in its luxurious tent called the Tabernacle. He could not understand the feeling of guilt that assailed David when he looked upon his magnificent palace of cedar and stone and remembered that, because of the blood that had stained his hands in the process of carving out the kingdom over which he now ruled, God had chosen to deny him the right to build a temple to the glory of the Most High. Nor could the average man understand that there was any profit in storing up vast treasures with which another would one day build a temple; those same treasures might have eased his own burden, and lessened the amount of taxes collected to maintain the king's household and the army of mercenaries that guarded Israel's borders.

At times David wished he were back in the wilderness living the life of a guerrilla chieftain, raiding the Philistines or the Amalekites, and demanding tribute from towns whose inhabitants he protected from enemy attack. Life had been far simpler then.

He had no reason to trouble himself about anything except day-to-day living—the planning of a swift foray against the enemy, and the excitement of battle with a foe as eager to take his life as he was to prevent its being taken.

As king of Israel, however, he had given up this fundamentally simple life; now his every action was guided by protocol and ceremony. Decisions could be made only after weighing what the effect might be upon the various principalities which were now subject to him. For if he did not seriously weigh every decision, petty jealousies might be set aflame and new bickering arise between kings who were always ready to undermine his own rule in the hope of bringing about its overthrow. His whole day now was rigidly governed by the duties of his office, and except in the late hours of the night, he had hardly a moment to himself.

Each morning the Egyptian scribe Shisha, now one of the most important men in the kingdom, presented himself before David with the recorder Jehoshaphat. Shisha gave a detailed report of all the affairs that needed the king's attention, and secured David's decision regarding them. In addition, all important documents, communications with foreign rulers, matters covering public works, finance, the armies, and the multiple affairs of a growing and thriving kingdom must be approved and, in many cases, the documents concerning them sealed with the royal seal.

Next would come a conference with "The Thirty," headed by Joab, as general of the armies of Israel, when he was in Jerusalem. In the nature of an honorary military body composed of mighty men whose prowess and loyalty were unquestioned, "The Thirty" formed an advisory council dealing with strictly military affairs. After them would come the chief priests to discuss matters of ceremony and worship, since David, as the Anointed of God, also officiated over those who served before the Ark and the altars of sacrifice. The life of the people and the unity of the kingdom were closely bound up with religious worship, for David had never assumed that he reigned other than as God's agent, with the Most High the ruler of them all. Failure to humble himself in the early days of his rule had denied to Saul the full approval and support of the prophet Samuel, who had headed the priests in that day, and David did not propose to add to the divisive influences which were still at work inside the nation by fanning the flames of religious controversy.

The routine tasks finished, it was customary for the king to sit as the last court of judgment in controversies between individuals in the kingdom. Such cases had already been ruled upon, in most instances, by the Councils of Elders in the various cities and villages, but every man had a right to carry his controversy to the king as a final court of appeal whenever there was time for it to be heard. Inevitably, David made enemies, for only in rare instances was it possible to render a decision which would appease both sides in these controversies, and usually one went away jubilant while the other was unhappy, thereby increasing the ranks of the malcontents who were always ready to grumble.

Each day a large crowd of these petitioners gathered, hoping for an audience with the king. But even if he had sat all day as a court, it would have been impossible to hear all the complainants, and the greater portion of them had to be sent home unheard. There they could naturally be expected to grumble and magnify their grievances against the king, who they felt was too busy with the affairs of empire to listen any longer to the troubles of his people.

With all these cares bearing down upon him from every side, David was often oppressed with a dark melancholy. He felt cut off even from the loving sympathy of his wives, who, often as not, took advantage of their evenings with him, as well as the days, to press the claims of their own sons to positions of favor. Gradually his temper, usually sunny and untroubled, became short. He found little pleasure in food, drink, or even sleep. He often awoke in the night to toss and turn for hours upon the magnificent bed of carved ivory from Egypt which had been sent to him by King Hiram of Tyre. At other times, he would pace the rooftop where he slept in warm weather, vainly seeking an answer to the difficulties which beset him.

David had almost stopped composing songs. But in one of these periods of deep depression, he did write a psalm which was to go down in the archives of Israel as his personal cry of lamentation:

O Lord God of my salvation,
I have cried day and night before thee:
Let my prayer come before thee:
Incline thine ear unto my cry;
For my soul is full of troubles:
And my life draweth nigh unto the grave.

I am counted with them that go down to the pit;
I am as a man that hath no strength,
Free among the dead,
Like the slain that lie in the grave,
Whom thou rememberest no more:
And they are cut off from thy hand.

Thou has laid me in the lowest pit,
In the darkness, in the deep.
Thy wrath lieth hard upon me,
And thou hast afflicted me with all thy waves.
Thou hast put away mine acquaintance far from me;
Thou hast made me an abomination unto them:

I am shut up, and I cannot come forth.
Mine eye mourneth by reason of affliction;
Lord, I have called daily upon thee,
I have stretched out my hands unto thee.
Wilt thou show wonders to the dead?
Shall the dead arise and praise thee?

Shall thy loving kindness be declared in the grave?
Or thy faithfulness in destruction?
Shall thy wonders be known in the dark?
And thy righteousness in the land of forgetfulness?
Unto thee have I cried, O Lord!
And in the morning shall my prayer prevent thee.

Lord, why castest thou off my soul?
Why hidest thou thy face from me?
I am afflicted and ready to die from my youth up;
While I suffer thy terrors I am distracted.
Thy fierce wrath goeth over me;
Thy terrors have cut me off.

They came round about me daily like water;
They compassed me about together.
Lover and friend hast thou put far from me,
And mine acquaintance into darkness.

And then something happened that changed David's whole life and brought him new vigor. He saw once again the woman whose lustrous beauty had so stirred him on the day of his triumphal return from the defeat of the Syrians of Damascus.

CHAPTER 5

"And David sent messengers, and took her."
II SAMUEL 11:4

IT WAS A HOT NIGHT in Jerusalem, and even upon the elevation where David's palace stood, hardly a breeze stirred. For a week he had not even sent for one of his beauteous concubines to share his couch when he retired. Instead he tossed and turned half the night, oppressed by the deep melancholy which bedeviled him so often of late. His depression was intensified by the fact that Joab and the armies had found the fortifications of Rabbath-ammon stronger than they had expected them to be, and were now bogged down in a long and costly siege.

David had retired early that evening, after an exhausting day of listening to the quarrels and complaints of the petitioners who had come before him. He had gone immediately to sleep, only to awaken a little before midnight in the grip of one of the nightmares that were so frequent an occurrence now. Wearing only the tasseled loincloth in which he had been sleeping because of the heat, he left the pavilion that had been set up for him on the rooftop to give him privacy from the prying gaze of the people of the city, many of whom also slept upon the roofs of their houses.

The moon was shining brightly. As David looked out across the city, which already had begun to burst the bounds even of the new wall, and spill out in a pattern of white-walled houses upon the slopes around it, he could not help a feeling of pride, for during his tenure as king, Jerusalem had grown and prospered more than in all its previous history as a Jebusite stronghold.

Remembering the coolness of the water upon his body that night when he had explored the subterranean cavern of Gihon, David was almost tempted to leave the palace and make his way to the spring. But he dismissed the thought quickly, since it would mean summoning the guard, who was sleeping on the other side of the roof, as well as explaining to the captain of the guard at the gate his reasons for leaving the city alone.

To the east, the looming shadows of the hills reminded him that Joab and the army were at that moment camped before Rabbath. For a moment he wondered whether he had been unwise in sending such a large portion of his forces across the Jordan to lay siege to the last enemy stronghold that still held out against him. But, he knew, Rabbath must be conquered lest it be a rallying point once again for the forces ever ready to oppose him. There had been no choice except to supply Joab with as many soldiers as could be spared and assume the costs of a long siege.

David was turning back to his couch when a light in the city below attracted his attention. It was a small light, as if from an oil lamp, visible upon the rooftop of a house only a short distance below the palace. Curious as to who would be about at this time of night, he went to the parapet surrounding the roof and looked down. At what he saw, he knew he should turn away, for it was a sin, according to the ancient law, to look secretly upon the nakedness of any person. But after that first glimpse, no power on earth could have drawn his eyes away.

Upon the roof of a house below the palace, a woman was bathing in the light cast by an oil lamp. Apparently secure in the knowledge that at this time of night everyone in the city would be asleep, she appeared to have no fear of any prying eye. She was taking her time about the bath, leisurely enjoying the coolness of the water upon her skin in the hot night air. Almost voluptuously, she rubbed her body with a cloth, lifting the cloth, dripping with water, and squeezing it to let the water cascade over her shoulders and down her back.

She was sitting in a large basin such as was used for ablutions by people who had no recessed tub in the house, and he was able to see only a small part of her body. That would have been enough to tell him she was extremely beautiful. But he knew even more about her for another reason; he had recognized her instantly as the same woman whose gaze from the crowd had stirred a deep fire within him on his return from the conquest of the Syrian armies. Much of his discontent in recent weeks, he admitted now, had been because of the desire which that one glimpse of her had aroused in him, and the fact that he did not even know her name.

The woman's hair was just as he remembered it, lustrous and dark. It cascaded down over her shoulders, almost to her waist, as she sat in the bath, and David was sure her skin was rosy and glowing, her body warm and pulsing with life. Again and again she poured the water over her body, her full breasts lifting as she raised her arms to dip water from the basin with a small jar and lift it above her shoulders.

A pulse was throbbing at David's temple with an insistent beat and his hands clenched the parapet that ran around the edge of the roof. The hoarse, rhythmic sound in his ears he identified as his own breathing, but he made no effort to control either it or his hammering pulse, caught up as he was in a surging tide of desire.

Finally she put down the water jar and, rising to her feet, reached for a towel with which to dry her body. Then, as if she wanted to enjoy to the utmost the coolness of the water upon her skin as a relief from the turgid heat of the night, she stepped out of the basin onto a small rug lying beside it, and lifted her hands to comb her fingers through her hair, which had become wet from her splashing.

Standing upon the rug like a lovely marble statue he had once seen in the palace of Achish of Gath, the woman was even more breathtakingly beautiful than David had dreamed she would be. Fairly tall, with long, slender limbs, sweetly rounded hips, and full breasts, her whole body as she began to dry herself with the towel was the very epitome of grace. But it was not simply admiration for her loveliness that held David rooted to the spot:

rather it was the intense desire that washed over him, sweeping away all thought of sin or of punishment should he take her, as every part of his being demanded that he should.

When the woman had finished drying herself and put on a robe of some light stuff that hid her flesh from his eyes but still could not hide the limpid grace of her body, David stumbled across the rooftop to where the guard lay asleep at the head of the stairway leading to the floor below. He was still a half-dozen paces from the sleeping man when the soldier came awake, as he was trained to do, fully alert and with his hand on his sword.

"What is it, my lord king?" he asked.

"Come to the edge of the roof."

The man looked at his master oddly, for David's voice was hoarse with emotion, but he followed him to the parapet around the roof. The light still burned on the housetop below. The woman was moving about now, emptying out the water and setting the basin and the jar aside before spreading out her own bed, a thick pallet of the kind used by almost everyone except royalty and those who could afford the luxury of one of the low Egyptian beds made of carved ivory.

"Look there and tell me whether you know that woman," David directed.

The man leaned upon the parapet and studied the house below. "Is not this Bathsheba, the wife of Uriah, the Hittite?" he asked.

David stiffened but not at the knowledge that the woman was already married. Her dark-haired loveliness and the fact that she was obviously older than a mere maiden had made it almost certain that she must belong to another, for even had she been a widow, a woman of such beauty would hardly have remained unmarried long. Instead, it was the identity of her husband that had startled him. Uriah was a sub-captain among the mercenary forces he employed, a man whom he had fought beside on several occasions, and whom he knew to be a brave, if rather stubborn and uncompromising individual. Nor did David make any attempt to repress the thrill of satisfaction that came to him at the memory that Uriah was even now with the forces before Rabbath, and his wife quite alone in the city.

"Go down and rouse my steward," David directed the soldier. "Tell him to bring the woman called Bathsheba to me."

"But she is the wife of Uriah, my lord," the soldier stammered. As an Israelite, he was fully cognizant of the ancient law concerning adultery.

"Uriah is a Hittite," David said sharply. "He does not worship our God."

The fact that Uriah was a heathen constituted flimsy ground for breaking one of the most rigid laws of Israel, but the fire that had been stirred in David by the nude beauty of the woman called Bathsheba could be quenched only in her arms. Even if Uriah had been an Israelite, David would have taken her for himself, though it meant tearing her from her husband's embrace.

"Do as I say," David snapped. "Have the woman brought to me at once."

The soldier hurried across the rooftop and disappeared down the steps. Below, in the palace, David could hear people moving about as the steward of his personal household was aroused, and soon he saw two men carrying a torch leave the palace and make their way through the streets to the home of Uriah. A short while later, they emerged from the house, accompanied by a slender figure. She was muffled in a long cloak with a scarf wrapped around her hair to hide her identity in case others were also abroad that night.

As soon as the three had entered the palace, David went to the pavilion where he had been sleeping and dropped the side flaps. It was now a private apartment, richly furnished with cushions and coverlets, since the air upon the summit of Zion sometimes turned chilly toward morning. A small, intricately carved table stood at one side. He filled two of the silver cups standing on it from a skin of wine, which had been wrapped in a moistened cloth to keep it cool. His heart was beating like that of a shoolboy courting his first girl, for it had been years since he had been filled with anything like this heady sense of excitement and anticipation.

When David heard light footsteps upon the roof outside, he did not go to meet them. But as the fingers of a slender, feminine hand groped through the hangings, he took hold of the flap and drew it aside so that the woman called Bathsheba could step into the tent. When he let the flap fall again behind her, the two of them were alone upon the rooftop. On pain of incurring the wrath of the king, whose word could mean instant death, no man would trouble them until it was David's will that they should emerge from the richly appointed pavilion. Even the guard had descended to the foot of the stairway to take up his post beside the door there.

Bathsheba did not speak, but David could read in her warm, almost mocking gaze, neither fear of him nor indignation at being taken from her home in the middle of the night. Instead, her eyes burned with much the same light of desire that moved him, and, though she took not a step toward him, he knew that she was willingly his for the taking.

"Show thyself!" David said hoarsely.

It was a command more properly given to a female slave or concubine whom the master considers taking to his couch. Bathsheba, however, seemed not to resent it. Slowly she reached up and unwound the scarf of fine byssus wrapped about her head and veiling her face. As she dropped the scarf to the rug on which she stood, her beautiful dark tresses fell to her waist. She was even more dazzling at close range than she had appeared from afar.

Her eyes were dark and luminous, the lashes black with kohl and the lids shadowed with the stibium paste sold by Phoenician merchants to fill the cosmetic boxes of rich Israelite women. But the rich color in her cheeks needed no source in a cosmetic box of alabaster, nor did the color of her full, moist lips demand any embellishment. David drew a deep breath. "By the horns of the Ark itself," he said hoarsely. "You are even more beautiful than I remembered!"

The woman did not speak, but a smile parted her lips, revealing the pearly whiteness of her teeth and the moist pink tip of her tongue as it touched them for a second. Only when her fingers fumbled at the knot of the cord that bound the soft robe of almost transparent cloth, which she wore under the enveloping cloak, and he was forced to help her untie it, did he realize that she was in the grip of a desire fully as great as his own. Her fingers were trembling, and the touch of them upon his own was like fire. When the knot was finally loosened, she stepped back with a quick, graceful movement and drew the robe aside to reveal that it was her only garment. Then she shrugged her shoulders and let it fall in a soft heap of fabric at her feet.

"My love! My own love!" David cried, knowing that at last he was to find the perfection of bliss he had never quite achieved before, even in the arms of Abigail. As he stepped forward, Bathsheba came into his arms, her body as eager as his own.

CHAPTER 6

"And the woman conceived, and sent and told David, and said, I am with child."

II SAMUEL 11:5

ONCE AGAIN there was music in the palace of David in Jerusalem as skilled fingers plucked the harp strings and the voice of the sweetest singer of Israel was raised in a song of joy and triumph. It was a song that had been sung in the encampments of Israel for centuries, the words of Balaam in the wilderness. The king of Moab had ordered Balaam to prophesy the destruction of the children of Israel and their God, but the prophet's tongue could speak only praise instead:

How goodly are thy tents, O Jacob,
Thy tabernacles, O Israel!
As the valleys are they spread forth,
As the gardens by the river's side,
As the trees of lign aloes which the Lord hath planted,
And as cedar trees beside the waters.

He shall pour the water out of his buckets,
And his seed shall be in many waters,
And his king shall be higher than Agag,
And his kingdom shall be exalted.

God brought him forth out of Egypt;
He hath as it were the strength of an unicorn:

He shall eat up the nations his enemies,
And shall break their bones,
And pierce them through with his arrows.

He couched, he lay down as a lion,
And as a great lion: who shall stir him up?
Blessed is he that blesseth thee,
And cursed is he that cursed thee.

By day, David went joyfully about his tasks with a zest he had not known for a long time. His mood of joy was contagious, and women smiled upon him when he rode through the streets, while men shouted greetings of praise and allegiance. And each night, with the coming of darkness, he hastened eagerly to the pavilion upon the rooftop, where Bathsheba soon came through the opening of the luxurious tent and into his arms.

At first there had been little need for talk: the urgency of their common desire was so great that it seized them and drove them to new heights of passion and bliss until, all desire spent, they fell asleep in each other's arms. David would have shouted the news of their love from the housetops, but Bathsheba was more practical. At least an hour before dawn each night she left the pavilion and returned home, accompanied by David's personal servant. And each evening she delayed her departure to the palace until the streets were dark, and the people of the city had gone into their houses for the night.

In the grip of a rapture greater than ever he had known, David was able to thrust from his soul, for the moment at least, any stirrings of conscience. These would have warned him that not even the king was above the law, and that, through lying with the wife of another man, even though a heathen, he was committing one of the ten great sins forbidden to the Israelites by God's own law given to Moses upon the mountain. But Uriah had been many months absent with the armies besieging Rabbath in Ammon, and no one dared to accuse the king, so even though word of the adulterous relationship had spread through the town, there was no public condemnation of either of them.

When their passion was sated at last, David began to find new pleasures merely in being with Bathsheba. She was intelligent and able to hold her own in the discussion of topics usually reserved for men. From Uriah she had learned much about the lands in which David and his armies had fought and about the political forces at work, not only in Israel, but in the farthest reaches of the kingdom. David found a new joy in talking with her, a quiet pleasure which his other wives, so often preoccupied with petty concerns and conflicts of the harem, had never given him.

"When I think that I might have lived out my days without even knowing there was such a one as you, my dearest," he told Bathsheba one night, as they sat before the open flap of the pavilion, "I thank the Most High that I happened to see you that day when I was riding through Jerusalem, and again on the night you were bathing upon the rooftop."

"Such a thing as our love could not just happen, David," Bathsheba said. "I came to love you the first day I ever saw you."

"It was the same with me," he agreed, thinking that she was referring to the day when he had noticed her in the crowd as he rode through Jerusalem in triumph. "I will never forget the way my heart leaped when my eyes found yours."

"For a king and a wise man you know little of women, beloved." There was a note of tender mockery in her tone.

"What do you mean?"

"The first time I saw you was long ago, when I left my father's home to live in Jerusalem."

"And you loved me then?" he asked incredulously.

Rising with the lithe movement of her sweet body which he knew so well, but which never failed to stir him, Bathsheba poured two cups of wine and gave him one before settling upon the cushions at his feet. "I not only loved you then," she confessed, "but I decided that one day I would lie in your arms."

"You could easily have brought yourself to my attention," he pointed out. "Beauty like yours is not seen every day, even by kings."

"I wanted to come to you only when you needed me," she explained. "When you needed me not just for my body, but for the love I could give you and the peace you could find in my arms."

"I have needed you for a long time, then," he told her soberly.

"For many months all zest for life seemed to have gone out of me—and then you came."

"I saw that in your eyes the day you rode through Jerusalem," she agreed. "And I knew then that the time had come when I could help you with my love. That was why I smiled at you."

"It was like the sun breaking through the clouds after a storm," he told her.

"Did you consider seeking me out and taking me then?"

"Perhaps I would have. Your face kept entering my thoughts and I knew no peace because of you. Then I happened to see you bathing upon the rooftop and sent my servant for you."

Her smile contained all that is the mystery of woman. "It was not merely chance that directed your eyes toward me that night, beloved, but because I knew you needed me and my heart was crying out to you."

David gave her a quick glance. "I am the singer of songs, yet your words are as if spoken to the strains of a lyre," he said, and then his eyes began to twinkle for at last he had understood her meaning. "Tell me, how many nights did you bathe there upon the rooftop before I saw you?"

"Surely my lord the king does not think his humblest and most loving servant would set out to trap him," Bathsheba said demurely.

"How many nights?"

"Three," she confessed. "And it is a good thing the air was warm, else I might have died from a chill."

"Why did you choose those particular occasions?"

"Night after night I watched you move about upon the rooftop long after others were asleep," she admitted. "I knew what was troubling you, for I had felt the same uneasiness that drove you. So I took the one way I could find to be sure of catching your eye." Her eyes twinkled again. "Everyone knows the most beautiful women in Israel are your wives and your concubines, so I had to find a new way to draw your attention to me."

He leaned down to kiss her, tasting the full sweetness of her lips and feeling them stir with passion beneath his own.

"Compared to you, all others are like old hags in the market place," he assured her. "Surely, even in his fondest dreams, no man has possessed such a treasure before."

She came into his arms then, nor did the fact that she had admitted trapping him into sending for her diminish by one iota the lure she had for him. In fact, part of her attraction lay in the knowledge that she had wanted him quite as much as he wanted her.

Almost a month had passed, but neither David nor Bathsheba had ever spoken of the fact that she was another man's wife, a fact which they must eventually face under the laws of Israel. Instead they were content to dwell, for the time being at least, in an enchanted realm of bliss. Then, one night, she came to the pavilion, but when David tried to take her into his arms, she gently pushed him away.

"We have something to discuss," she said gravely. "I am with child."

"You could not bring me more welcome news," David cried happily, and picked up the harp that was lying upon a cushion beside him. "Sit here and I will compose a song of joy in praise of the son you will bear me."

"I cannot bear you a son!" she cried. "Have you forgotten that I am the wife of another?"

"I know only that you are my beloved, more precious to me than all my possessions."

"But everyone knows Uriah has been with the armies before Rabbath-ammon for several months and could not have gotten me with child."

David's hand dropped away from the harp strings, for at last he understood what was troubling her. "The law would condemn you as an adulteress," he said thoughtfully. "But I, too, would be guilty, because it falls as heavily upon the man who seduces the wife of another as upon the woman."

"I will not let you be named!" she cried. "If I swear it could be any of several who visited my house, no man would be judged guilty with me."

"Do you think I would let you sacrifice yourself to save me?" he asked. "You can swear that I brought you here and forced you to lie with me. After all, I did send my servants for you."

"But I came willingly, even eagerly." She lifted her head proudly. "I would not deny it, even to save my life."

David put his arm about her waist and kissed her tenderly. Then he led her to a seat upon the cushions and poured a cup of wine for her. "We must think clearly about all this," he said. "Perhaps there is still a way out."

"How could there be? My husband is away and I am pregnant by another man. The punishment for such a crime is clear under the law—stoning until dead."

"Not if your husband were the father of the child."

"But *you* are its father. We both know that."

"*We* know it," he agreed. "But who else does? Have you told your servants that you are with child?"

"No, I couldn't even be sure myself until today."

"Then it can hardly be more than a month since you conceived."

"Less than a month. Perhaps only about three weeks."

"Suppose your husband would visit you in Jerusalem and a child is born to you a few weeks early. Who could say that Uriah was not the father?"

"But Uriah is before Rabbath-ammon."

"A chariot can make the trip in a little more than a day," he said. "I will send a letter to Joab at once, instructing him to have Uriah bring me a report of the fighting there. Naturally he will go to his home as soon as he arrives in Jerusalem. No man could be blamed for wanting to be with his wife as soon as possible after his return home, especially such a wife as you."

"Must I lie with him again?" she asked. "It will be almost like a sacrilege after the bliss we have known together."

"There is no other way," he told her. "We must think of the child you bear now, not of ourselves."

"What will happen after that?"

"If Uriah were to put you away, I could marry you later." David pointed out. "Then the child you bear would grow up in the palace as my own son, which he actually is."

"But how can we persuade Uriah to divorce me without telling him the truth?"

"I know Uriah of old. He is ambitious to rise as an officer, and if Joab offers him the captaincy of a thousand in return for divorcing you, I do not think he will refuse."

"For the captaincy of a thousand, he would sell his own father and mother into slavery!" Bathsheba said.

"Then we have nothing to worry about," David assured her. "Go home now and remain in your house. Your husband will visit you before three days have passed."

There were certain rewards for being a king after all, David reminded himself as he stood upon the rooftop and watched the torch carried by the servant escorting Bathsheba back to her home. A king could move mere individuals about like the pieces in a game of *senit*, and who was to say that anyone involved would be the worse off? Not Uriah, certainly, for he would realize his ambition to become the captain of a thousand men. Not Bathsheba, who would become a queen. And certainly not himself, for he would have the precious jewel of her love and her body as his own.

Early the next morning, David called for a scribe and had a letter written to Joab. He instructed the chief captain to send Uriah to Jerusalem by the same chariot that carried the letter, with a report of the situation at Rabbath-ammon.

CHAPTER 7

"And David sent to Joab, saying, send me Uriah the Hittite." II SAMUEL 11:6

URIAH THE HITTITE was not happy at being ordered to leave the battlefront in order to bring a report of the fighting to the king. "Why must we hurry so?" he demanded, when the chariot taking him to Jerusalem halted at the ford of the Jordan opposite Jericho for the horses to drink. "This is a pleasant place to stop and refresh ourselves, and perhaps to bathe in the stream."

"I was ordered by the king to bring the messenger from my lord Joab to Jerusalem as quickly as I could," the chariot driver told him. "Were I in your place and married to the most beautiful woman in Jerusalem, I would be in a hurry to get home." He gave Uriah a sidewise glance as he spoke, for there was already talk in Jerusalem concerning Uriah's wife and the king, but the Hittite seemed to suspect nothing.

"Can the embrace of a woman compare with seeing an enemy's blood spurt forth when your spearpoint finds his heart?" Uriah demanded contemptuously.

The chariot driver shrugged, for after all, Uriah was an officer and it was not his place to tell him he was also a fool. Come to think of it, he decided, this fellow deserved to be cuckolded, if he cared no more than that for a bundle of loveliness like Bathsheba.

"Why did Joab select me to bring messages to the king?" Uriah went on angrily as the chariot rolled up the farther bank of the river. "He could have written it all down in a letter."

The chariot driver had his own ideas about why Uriah was being recalled to Jerusalem, but he was not going to reveal them. The anger of the king was a formidable threat indeed, and, up until the past several weeks, David's temper had been so fractious that all who were not required to be in his presence had kept away. Besides, there was little doubt that the Hittite was about to be bought off in exchange for his wife, and if he were such a fool as not to know what a valuable treasure he possessed, why should he be warned?

Not far from the Jordan crossing was the village of Jericho. In Joshua's time, it had been a powerful fortress city, with giant walls protecting it from attack. Situated as it was, on the east-west caravan route leading from Moab and Ammon to the seacoast, at the very entrance to the Promised Land, Jericho had seemed an insuperable obstacle to further progress on the part of Joshua and his men. But then a great earthquake and fire—not uncommon occurrences in this land, as was evident by the black basalt boulders which were tumbled about everywhere, and the sulphurous fumes bursting forth sporadically from cracks in the rocks—had shaken down the walls of Jericho and destroyed the city. Now it was little more than a village, but a very beautiful one with palm trees and fruit orchards growing everywhere, since frost seldom visited the lowlands here along the Jordan.

Uriah would have been happy to stop at Jericho and taste the wine for which it was famous, but the chariot driver insisted that they go on in order to reach Jerusalem before night fell. Behind the town and the great spring that provided it with water rose the forbidding mass of a rugged, naked, and arid mountain height, covered with a wilderness of craggy gullies. The road to Jerusalem led around the foot of the mountain, and by the time the chariot reached the capital, it was late in the afternoon.

At the palace, Uriah was met by David's chamberlain, Shisha. "I trust that my lord has had a pleasant journey from Rabbath," the Egyptian said courteously. "The king waits to hear your report."

"Let us get on with it, then," Uriah said. "I must get back to Rabbath as quickly as I can."

Shisha's eyebrows lifted, but he was a prudent man and a loyal servant, so he made no comment as he led the Hittite into David's audience chamber. Nor did the king wait for Uriah to reach the dais, but stepped down to greet him. "You must be weary from your journey, so I will not keep you long from your own house," David said warmly. "Tell me only how the fighting goes before Rabbath-ammon. We can speak tomorrow of the details and the messages you will take back to Joab."

Uriah could not but be warmed by David's welcome. Though not a clever man, he was, as Bathsheba had told David, a very ambitious one. And as he followed David to the throne chair on the dais, his mind was working busily.

"My lord Joab sends his greetings to the Anointed of your god," he said. "And wishes you long life and good health."

"It pains me to remain here at Jerusalem while brave men such as you and Joab suffer before Rabbath," David told him. "But I have no choice."

Uriah had been able to think of only one reason why he had been singled out to come to Jerusalem. Word of his prowess in battle must have come to the king, and as a result, he had been selected for some military honor. If he played his part well and conducted himself in a manner likely to gain David's approval, he felt that he should have an excellent chance of gaining promotion, something he very greatly desired.

"We must make up to you for the privations you have suffered, Uriah," David said. "Tell me, has the fighting been severe?"

"The Ammonites shut themselves up inside the walls and will not come out to fight," the Hittite said contemptuously. "I myself have challenged their champion, as you did Goliath of Gath, but they are craven and fear to meet my weapons."

Small wonder Bathsheba had so little respect for her husband, David thought, and could not help feeling a moment of revulsion that such a clod as Uriah was now to be lying with the woman he himself loved so deeply. But there was no other way to be sure of having Bathsheba for himself, and once Uriah had spent the night in his own house, the matter could be concluded swiftly. The

Hittite would be given his captaincy, and Bathsheba would be free under a law which permitted a man to divorce his wife merely by announcing that he was putting her away.

"Go down to your home and wash your feet," David told Uriah. "We will talk again on the morrow."

David slept soundly that night, sure that his plan was working out well. In the morning he sent for Shisha to prepare a decree elevating the Hittite to the position of captain of a thousand in the armies of Israel. "Bring the document to me for my seal when it is written," he directed. "But before you give him the commission, make it clear to him that he must put away Bathsheba."

"No doubt Uriah will be glad to do as you wish, my lord king," Shisha said. "But that will not complete the matter."

"What do you mean?"

"Uriah did not go to his own house last night."

David stared at the scribe incredulously. "You must be wrong, Shisha. I myself sent him."

"I realized you would want to know everything he did, my lord, so I set one to watch him. It was reported to me just now that the Hittite did not go near his home last night—"

"But I sent a mess of meat to him there."

"The meat was received by the servant of my lady Bathsheba and a feast was prepared in honor of Uriah's return. But he slept in the servant's quarters of the palace and has not set foot across the doorsill of his own house."

This was disquieting news indeed. For David's well-laid plan to work out smoothly, Uriah must spend at least one night at his house, thereby establishing in the eyes of the law that he was the father of the child Bathsheba would bear. Now the fool had disrupted everything by not rushing into her arms, as any normal man would have done after an absence of several months.

"Did he give any reason for this strange behavior?" David inquired.

"No, my lord king. But I suspect he thinks to make you deem him worthy of greater honor because he puts service to you above everything else, even the embraces of his wife."

"He would serve me best by doing as I directed," David snorted angrily. "Send him to me at once."

"I hear and obey my lord," Shisha said. "But if I may advise you—"

In his perturbation over Uriah's unexpected action, David started to lash out at the faithful scribe for his temerity. But then he remembered Shisha's long service to him, and restrained himself.

"What do you suggest, Shisha?"

"The Hittite is a stubborn man," the Egyptian said. "If he suspects you have reason to want him to visit his own home, he might be even more reluctant to do so."

CHAPTER 8

"And it came to pass in the morning, that David wrote a letter to Joab, and sent it by the hand of Uriah." II SAMUEL 11:14

URIAH WAS CONFIDENT and pleased when David summoned him for another private audience. "May my lord the king have long life and win great victories over his enemies," he said, bowing before the throne chair upon which David sat. "Only name the greatest among them and I will thrust him through with my sword."

"My greatest enemy is the city of Rabbath," David said, but he could have added with equal truth that at the moment Uriah also fitted that category.

"Then give me leave to return to my lord Joab, and I will tell him it is your wish that we scale the walls by assault."

"That would mean losing too many men," David objected. "The archers on the wall can shoot down upon attacking troops and crush them with stones hurled from the heights."

"If we but had machines like the Assyrians have to launch great stones against the walls, the city would fall sooner."

"Soon we must use catapults, as the Assyrians do," David agreed. "But the defenders of Rabbath are small in number; when their food begins to run out, they will weaken and can be taken with less bloodshed."

"The wisdom of my lord the king is above that of all others,"

Uriah said fawningly. "It is known that your god speaks directly to you through the holy ephod."

"Why did you not go down to your house when you came from your journey?" David asked. "The servants tell me you slept here in the palace."

Uriah drew himself up proudly. "The Ark, Israel, and Judah live in tents, and my lord Joab and his servants are encamped in the open field. Should I then go to my home to eat, and drink, and lie with my wife? As you live, I will not do this thing!"

David was a little taken aback by the vehemence of the words. Here, he realized, was a man even more stubborn than Bathsheba had led him to believe. And there was the added difficulty that Uriah must be bent to his will without the Hittite knowing what was happening.

"Stay here today and rest in your house," David temporized. "Tomorrow I will let you depart."

It hardly seemed likely that Uriah's stern conscience would keep him from going to his own house during the day. And once there, Bathsheba could be relied upon to seduce her husband into exercising his marital rights. But lest Uriah still prove adamant, David decided upon an additional precaution. If the Hittite became drunk, he could be taken to his house and left there for the night, with no memory of what had happened, when he woke up in the morning, and no reason to claim that the child Bathsheba would bear was not his own.

"Return at sunset and we will eat the evening meal together," David told him. "I would do you further honor for your bravery in battle."

Uriah departed, pleased with the prospect of dining with the king. David was busy with affairs demanding his attention until it was time for the evening meal, but when Shisha came to tell him that the Hittite awaited his summons, the scribe also brought the distressing news that Uriah had still refused to go near his own home during the day. In the light of the man's stubbornness, it was not easy for David to be pleasant to him during the long ordeal of the evening meal. But he knew he must do nothing to arouse Uriah's suspicion until he was drunk enough not to remember anything he had done, and the next morning awakened in his own bed with Bathsheba beside him.

Unfortunately, Uriah proved to have a tremendous capacity for wine. Although David plied him with it steadily throughout the evening, when finally he departed shortly before midnight, Uriah was still able to stand on his feet. After instructing the servants to guide him to his own house, David went to bed, hoping that the wine would have deadened the Hittite's stubborn convictions sufficiently to allow him to go home. David did not sleep well that night, however, for not only had he been forced to drink more wine than was his custom, but he was oppressed by the conviction that Uriah would fail him again in what, at the time of its inception, had seemed so perfect a plan.

Long before dawn, David was walking upon the roof, looking down at the housetop where Bathsheba always kept the lamp burning at night. As the sleepless hours passed, a course of action began to form in his mind. He approached reluctantly the decision to adopt it, for it was not an easy thing to determine coldly upon a man's death. But unless Uriah had indeed been duped into sleeping in his own home while in a drunken stupor, David's plan seemed to offer the only way out of the dilemma.

Nor was there much time to lose, for as soon as Bathsheba's pregnancy became known, someone was certain to go before the Council of Elders and swear to a charge of adultery against her. David himself had enemies in Israel who would gladly choose that means of attacking him, in the hope of exposing him as the man who had committed the adulterous acts with Bathsheba. And once the machinery of the law had been set into effect, not even the king could stop it. Inevitably both of them would be charged and found guilty, to die the most horrible of all deaths: the traditional execution by stoning decreed under the law.

Bathsheba, David knew, would try to save him by swearing that more than one man had lain with her while Uriah was away, thus placing herself in the position of a common harlot. But David loved her too much to let her face her accusers—and the stones—alone. Besides, there was another consideration: that of the child who would die in its mother's womb when she did, guiltless though it might be.

In the final analysis, it was this last consideration that brought David to the only decision which under the circumstances seemed sensible. He felt he had no choice, and by the time Shisha came to him in the morning, he was prepared for what he had to do and had planned the method by which it must be done. One glance at the Egyptian's face told him there would be no going back.

"The servants tried to take the Hittite to his house last night as you ordered, my lord," Shisha reported. "But he resisted and made such an uproar that they were afraid and did not try to force him."

"Then he did not enter his home at all?"

"No, my lord. The whole matter would have come to public notice if they had tried to take him there by force, so it seemed best not to go any farther."

David nodded thoughtfully. Now that the decision had been made, he felt strangely unemotional about it. "Perhaps there has never been anything else we could do but what we must do," he admitted.

"It is better that one should die than two, and one of them an unborn babe."

"Or three," David corrected him.

"As well include the nation," the scribe said. "Not even the lives of ten men or a thousand men in Israel are worth the life of its king."

"Bring your writing materials," David directed him. "Uriah is anxious to return to the battlefront. He can take a letter for Joab with him."

Shisha returned shortly, bringing with him the materials necessary for writing and a small papyrus roll. The message David dictated for Joab was brief and to the point: "Set Uriah in the forefront of the hottest battle and retire from him that he may be smitten and die."

Shisha allowed the ink to dry before rolling up the small scroll. Dropping a blob of wax upon it from a candle, he held the scroll so that David could press the signet ring he wore into the wax, marking the letter with the official seal of Israel.

"Give the letter to Uriah and tell him to return forthwith to Joab and the army," David directed. "My own charioteer will take him to Ammon and wait to bring back news of what happens in the next few days."

When the charioteer returned from the battlefront, he brought a courier from Joab with him.

"The men of Rabbath prevailed against us and came out onto the field," the messenger reported. "We were upon them even to the entering of the gate, but the bowmen shot down from the wall. Some of the king's servants are dead, including your servant, Uriah the Hittite."

David did not go near Bathsheba during the traditional period of mourning, but as soon as it was completed, he sent for her and made her his wife. He did not, however, install her in the harem along with his other wives and concubines, but assigned her an apartment directly adjoining his own.

From that day forward, Bathsheba was David's favorite, and there was great joy in his heart when at last the son of their union was born. David even allowed himself to hope that his sin in breaking the law might have gone unnoticed by God. But when Nathan appeared in his audience chamber one morning, a single glance at the prophet's stern face told him that he had hoped in vain.

CHAPTER 9

"And Nathan said to David, Thou art the man."
II SAMUEL 12:7

DAVID GREETED NATHAN courteously, but the prophet did not waste time in ceremony. "I have come to bring an important matter before you," he announced.

"Speak," David told him. "The words of the prophet Nathan are always the words of God himself."

"Two men were in one city, the one rich and the other poor," Nathan said. "The rich man had many flocks and herds, but the poor man had nothing save one little ewe lamb, which he had bought and nourished. It grew up together with him and with his children. It ate of his own meat and drank of his own cup and lay in his bosom and was to him like a daughter."

"Speak on," David told him, thinking that Nathan was describing a controversy to be judged like the dozens that came before him almost every day, and daring to hope he had been wrong about the purpose of the prophet's visit.

"A traveler came to the rich man," Nathan continued, "but he would not take from his own flock and his own herd to dress meat for the stranger. Instead, he took the poor man's lamb and dressed it for the man who had come to visit him."

"As the Lord lives, whoever has done this shall surely die,"

David burst out indignantly. "He shall restore the lamb fourfold because he did this thing and because he had no pity."

Nathan leaned forward, jabbing his finger at David accusingly. "You are the man!" he thundered.

Even though he was the king, David could not help quailing before the wrath of the tall, grizzled prophet, and Nathan gave him no opportunity to defend himself.

"Thus saith the Lord God of Israel," Nathan said, " '*I anointed you king over Israel and delivered you from the hand of Saul. I gave you your master's house and your master's wives and I gave you the house of Israel and of Judah. And if that had been too little, I would have given you many other things. Why then have you despised the commandments of the Lord to do evil in his sight? You have killed Uriah, the Hittite, with the sword of the children of Ammon and have taken his wife to be your wife. Therefore I will raise up evil against you out of your own house. I will take your wives before your own eyes and give them to your neighbor and he will lie with your wives in the sight of all. You did this thing secretly but I will let it be done to you before all of Israel.*' "

It was a terrible curse and prophesy, for no greater indignity could be heaped upon a man than to have the women of his own household despoiled publicly. But every word Nathan had spoken in condemnation was true, and David knew that no matter how successfully he might have deluded himself into thinking that God would overlook his grave sin, he had always known deep in his heart that some day he must pay for it.

"I have sinned against the Lord," he said humbly. "And I deserve to die because of it."

Nathan studied David for a long moment and could not fail to see that he was sincere in his admission of guilt and repentance. "The Lord has put away your sin and you shall not die," the prophet said finally. "But because by your deed you have given great occasion to the enemies of the Lord to blaspheme, the child who is born to you shall surely die."

Not long afterward Bathsheba's son became very ill and, though the best physicians in the kingdom were in attendance, none could help the baby. David humbled himself before God and besought divine help, fasting through the day and lying at night upon the earth outside the palace, like the least of his subjects, but to no avail. On the seventh day of its illness, the child died as Nathan had prophesied.

For a long moment after the physicians had pronounced the baby dead, David stood looking down at the small form wrapped in swaddling clothes; then he turned and left the room. In his quarters he bathed and was massaged with fragrant oils, after which he dressed in one of his finest robes and went to the Tabernacle where the Ark was housed. There he worshiped God, humbling himself before the will of the Most High. But when the sacrifice was completed, he returned to the palace and, calling for food, sat down to eat as if nothing had happened.

"Why did you fast and weep for the child while it was alive," one of the servants asked, "but when the child was dead you arose and ate bread once again?"

"While the child was still alive," David said, "I fasted and wept, for I said, 'Who can tell whether God will be gracious to me, that the child may live?' But now that he is dead, why should I fast? Can I bring him back again? He will not return to me."

Bathsheba, too, grieved for the child, but both she and David acknowledged that its death was no more than a just punishment visited upon them by God, as Nathan had prophesied. As for the rest of the prophecy, that the sword should not depart from his own house, David could only wait for the will of God to be manifest and trust that the Lord would be merciful.

Then two happenings gave David reason to hope that the curse of the Lord against him had been fulfilled completely in the death of Bathsheba's first child: she became pregnant again and gave birth to a fine son whom David named Solomon, and soon afterward, Nathan appeared to bless the child who, he announced, had found favor with the Lord.

The ceremony of blessing was held in David's own quarters. Besides the king, the child Solomon, its mother, and Nathan, the chief priest Zadok was present with Benaiah, the faithful captain of the mercenaries who formed the king's personal bodyguard.

Nathan blessed the baby with these words: "His name shall also be Jedidiah because he shall be given the favor of the Lord." Then, taking a small cruse of oil, he poured its contents upon the dark head in the ritual of anointing.

David could not help comparing this ceremony with a much simpler one which had taken place long ago in Bethlehem. Then the prophet Samuel had selected him from among the sons of Jesse and anointed him to be king of Israel. And when once again he heard a voice deep within his soul, a voice he had not heard for a long time, he called the others back as they were leaving the chamber.

"You shall be witnesses this day," he told them. "The child whom the Lord has deigned to favor shall rule after me. He shall erect the house to the glory of God whose building was denied to me because of the blood that stained my hands. And he shall rule my kingdom after me wisely and shall make it great."

As if, with the birth and anointing of Solomon, God had once again shown his favor to David, word soon came from Joab that Rabbath was finally about to fall. David gathered up a great train of people and crossed the Jordan to join the armies before the walls of the capital city of Ammon and receive the surrender of its people. The spoils were great, and when David received the crown of the king of Ammon as a token of the nation's surrender, he could take pride in the fact that the last of the enemies who had hemmed him in had fallen. No more during David's lifetime would Israel be seriously threatened from without. He could now turn his energies, renewed through his love for Bathsheba and the certainty he now had that one of his sons had indeed found favor with God, to the task of strengthening the internal structure of the kingdom of Israel.

That feat, however, was to be the most difficult and painful one in the whole career of David, the king.

VI. ABSALOM, MY SON

"Would God I had died for thee, O Absalom, my son, my son!"

II SAMUEL 18:33

CHAPTER 1

"Absalom hath slain all the king's sons, and there is not one of them left." II SAMUEL 13:30

THE YEARS FOLLOWING the birth of Solomon were busy and trying for Israel's king. The kingdom far exceeded in size the Promised Land God had covenanted with Moses to give to the children of Israel. Its eastern border skirted the edge of the great desert and extended southward to where the Arabah touched an arm of the Red Sea at Ezion-geber. From there the border ran northwestward to the River of Egypt, the partially dry steam bed that marked the traditional boundary with the domain of the Pharaohs. This triangular area in the south, with its vast wealth in metal-bearing ores, its thriving cities and fertile oases, was ruled by a military governor responsible directly to David himself.

On the coast of the Great Sea to the west, the power of the Philistines had been broken and their cities reduced practically to the position of vassals of Israel and its king. Joppa, lying almost directly west of Jerusalem at the very edge of the Philistine territory, was Israel's main seaport; but most water-borne commerce for the nation still came through the Phoenician ports to the north of Mount Carmel, cities whose ties with Israel had remained intact since David and King Hiram of Tyre had made the alliance which had proved so profitable for them both.

From the northern tip of Phoenicia, the boundary of David's

kingdom turned eastward once again past Riblah, on the River Arantu in the great hollow of Syria lying between the Lebanon and anti-Lebanon mountain ranges. From there it extended into the desert to include the region north of Damascus and the district of Bashan, or Hauran.

It was a vast area, peopled by many nationalities besides the tribes descended from the sons of Jacob. Since much of it, such as Zobah, Maacah, and Geshur, was ruled by petty kings responsible to David, a considerable administrative machine was necessary to govern this vast territory. More important, constant military supervision was required to assure that its kings did not conspire together to rebel against the dominion of Israel. This was largely left in the hands of Joab, for David, the youthful warrior, had long since given way to David, the king and statesman whose main concern was keeping the kingdom whole and the nation prosperous and strong.

In these efforts David did not receive much help from his family; in fact, the battles for control being waged in his own household were almost as vicious as any he had been forced to contend with while expanding the empire of Israel. To avoid stirring up any more family animosities than could be helped, the fact that the succession to the throne had been promised to Solomon was kept secret. Amnon, David's eldest son, would normally have been considered first in the succession, although there was actually no law in Israel saying that the eldest son should follow his father upon the throne. But he was an indolent young man who preferred the pleasures of the table and the harem to the tasks which, along with all the other princes, David had set him. In fact, only one of the older sons showed much interest in the affairs of the kingdom; that was Absalom, the handsome son of Macaah of Geshur, to whom had been assigned a subgovernorship over most of Judah.

In spite of his somewhat flamboyant manner and the overweening vanity which made him wear his hair quite long, Absalom had earned the support of Joab by displaying a marked willingness to suit his actions to his own aims. Joab had not hesitated to murder Abner when the latter stood in his way, and he saw in Absalom qualities like his own which he considered essential for the welfare of the kingdom and for his own continuation as chief captain after

David's death. Joab had also bitterly resented David's action in condemning to death his fellow officer, Uriah, in order to take Bathsheba for himself. Ever afterward, he hated the woman he considered responsible for the Hittite's death and was determined to do what he could to keep her son from the throne.

During these years, Solomon, the youngest of the sons of David, grew from a slender, dark-haired boy into a handsome stripling with a gravity of manner and love of learning that sharply contrasted with the more boisterous attitudes and pursuits of the older princes. When he early showed a wisdom far beyond his years, he quickly earned the approval of men like Zadok, the chief priest, and Nathan the prophet, who had brought word that God looked with favor upon this youngest son of David. But since Solomon took little part in the rough games that occupied the others or the wine-drinking and wenching that were the favorite pursuits of the older princes, even Absalom tended to look upon him as no threat to his own ever-growing ambition. Besides, Absalom was married now and had his own house in another part of the city, so he was not quite so closely involved in the palace intrigues as some of the other princes.

And then something happened which, for the moment, seemed to put a stumbling block in the path of the handsome and impatient Absalom. That it was also part of the curse Nathan had placed upon David's offspring, following the death of Uriah, was not immediately apparent; but as time wore on, the connection became quite clear.

Among David's daughters, Tamar, the sister of Absalom, was by far the most beautiful, as her brother was the most handsome. And although she was also Amnon's half sister, he conceived such a passion for her that he could think of nothing else. Amnon could easily have asked his father to give him beautiful Tamar as his wife, since marriages between relatives with close blood ties were not at all uncommon. But the pleasure-loving prince had no wish to marry Absalom's sister, and, perhaps, be forced to share with his ambitious brother some of the power that would be his if he ever became king in his father's stead.

In this quandary, the somewhat slow-witted Amnon played into the hands of his cousin Jonadab, a wily man who was the son of

David's brother, Shimeah. Jonadab saw in Amnon's passion for Tamar a chance to improve his own fortunes by undermining the security of David's rule. Were a scandal to break out in the king's household, there would be a greater chance for his own father to be named in David's stead—should the king come to an untimely end.

"Tell me," Jonadab said to the lovesick Amnon, "why does the king's son languish from day to day?"

"I love Tamar, my brother Absalom's sister," Amnon confessed.

"Lie down on your bed and pretend to be sick," Jonadab advised him. "When your father comes to inquire after you, beg him to send Tamar to prepare your food and feed you. Then you can do with her what you wish."

As Amnon did not recognize in Jonadab's advice a plan to destroy the two leaders among the king's sons at one stroke, he easily fell in with the scheme. When David visited him as he lay upon his pretended sick bed, he begged for Tamar to be sent to his chamber to prepare food as Jonadab had advised. Seeing nothing untoward in the request, David ordered the girl to go to her half brother and prepare nourishing food for him in his illness. But when she brought the food to Amnon, he sent all the servants out of his house and took Tamar by force.

Tamar was wise enough to see the possible results of Amnon's crime, and tried to convince him that he should ask the king to give her to him in marriage. But having satisfied his desire, Amnon was tired of her and thrust her from the house in disgrace. When she went to Absalom's house and confessed her shame, she was given shelter by her brother, who swore revenge upon his brother Amnon.

Characteristically, Absalom did not denounce Amnon at once, for he could not be sure just how David would look upon his action. And not wanting a family scandal to become public, David let the matter be hushed up. Had it suited his purpose, Absalom, too, would have had no qualms about letting Amnon go unpunished, but his cunning mind saw a way whereby he might be able to destroy Ammon and remove a barrier between him and the throne. He therefore made no issue, at the moment, of the disgrace which had come upon his sister; instead he set to work planning to destroy Amnon secretly in such a way that his own part in the murder would not be known.

In addition to what he allotted each of his sons from the royal treasury, David had given them considerable property from which they drew income for their needs. To Absalom had gone a valuable piece of land at a place called Baal-hazor in the hill country north of Bethel. There he kept a large flock of sheep watched over by shepherds, who, as shepherds had been doing since time immemorial in the hill country of Canaan, moved them from valley to valley wherever grass might be found. Absalom also had rich vineyards at Baal-hazor, as vine-culture was one of the greatest sources of wealth for the landowners of Israel.

Since harvesting these two crops, the grapes and the wool, formed two of the most important activities of the people, they were also associated with two of Israel's greatest festivals. One of these was celebrated in the vintage months of fall, when the grapes were gathered from the vineyards and trod out in the wine presses. The second festival took place in the spring, when the earth was showing signs of new life after its long sleep in winter and the fleece was heavy upon the backs of the sheep. At both times there was much merrymaking and dancing, and a joyful sacrifice to the Lord for the bounty of the harvest. What was more natural than for the rich Prince Absalom to invite the whole court of Israel to help him celebrate the shearing and the abundant harvest of wool?

"Behold your servant has sheep-shearers in Baal-hazor," Absalom told his father. "I have invited the king's sons, my brothers, to celebrate with me after the shearing. Let the king and his servants go with us, I pray you."

"Nay, my son," David answered, as Absalom had expected. "Let us not all go lest we be a burden upon you."

"Then let my brother Amnon go with us," Absalom begged.

"Why should he go?"

"Amnon is the oldest; if he goes, the other princes will follow," Absalom explained. "I would fain have all my brothers celebrate my good fortune with me."

The request was actually a clever ruse to get the indolent Amnon out of Jerusalem, but David could see no harm in it. Besides, he had always found it difficult to refuse anything to the tall, handsome Absalom who was so much as he himself had been in his youth. Thus it came about that all of David's sons journeyed to Baal-hazor to help their brother Absalom celebrate the festival of the shearing.

By ordering his servants to fall upon his brother secretly on the road, where robbers would be blamed for the act, the wily Absalom had taken care that he would not be blamed for Amnon's death. But when the treacherous attack took place, the servants failed to hide their identity, and thereby exposed him as the culprit. During the milling around and confusion at the murder scene, one member of the court fled to Jerusalem with the horrifying news that Absalom had slain all the king's sons.

To David this seemed to be the final working out of the curse foretold by Nathan after the death of Uriah. First, the son conceived by Bathsheba during the early days of their turbulent love affair had died; now the sword had fallen again, as God had promised, upon his sons. In a paroxysm of grief, he tore his robe and threw himself upon the ground, to lie there in the traditional posture of deepest mourning while the servants of the household and the women sobbed with grief for the dead princes.

Jonadab, too, had been invited to the festival. As soon as he was able to determine what had really happened, he rode posthaste to Jerusalem. He arrived only moments after the first report, and attempted to ingratiate himself with the king, while at the same time indicting Absalom for the deliberate murder of Amnon.

"Let not my lord suppose they have killed all the king's sons," Jonadab soothed the grieving David. "Only Amnon is dead by the decision of Absalom, and that has been determined since the day he forced his sister Tamar."

At the news Jonadab had brought, David dared to hope that the first report had been incorrect, and he had watchers set at the gate to bring him any additional news that might arrive from the scene of the crime. These soon announced that a considerable company of people was visible upon the road leading from Baal-hazor toward Jerusalem.

"Behold, the king's sons are coming!" Jonadab hurried to report to David. "As your servant said it was, so it is."

The princes themselves soon arrived to confirm Jonadab's story, but Absalom, fearing his father's wrath, sought refuge in the household of his mother's father, the king of Geshur, and David did not pursue him. There was mourning for Amnon in the king's household, but Bathsheba was pleased. With two of the most promising contenders for the throne apparently out of the running, the field was far clearer now for her son Solomon.

CHAPTER 2

"And Joab sent to Tekoah, and fetched thence a wise woman." II SAMUEL 14:2

WITH ABSALOM GONE from Jerusalem, the faction in the court who supported Solomon for the throne, consisting, among others, of his mother Bathsheba, the priest Zadok, the prophet Nathan, and Benaiah of the king's bodyguard, could feel that they were more firmly entrenched in David's favor. But David still mourned for the handsome Absalom, whose flamboyance and occasional intrigues had considerably enlivened life at the court. Nor could Bathsheba be entirely sure that the king would feel bound by his promise to name Solomon his successor if Joab and his faction were able to persuade David that Solomon was not strong enough to hold the nation together after his death.

For one thing, Solomon was but a stripling. The question, therefore, of rule by a regent, should David die before Solomon attained his majority, was raised. In a kingdom of diverse peoples held together largely by loyalty to David alone, such a rule could easily mean the end of a united Israel, an argument which David might find it hard to resist. Also, Absalom was a more logical successor on at least two counts. He was the darling of the tribe of Judah, who had personally adopted him as their own before the affair of Amnon. With tribal intrigues as great as they were, Judah would carry a great weight in any decision as to who would rule after

David. And as the grandson of King Talmai of Geshur, Absalom could count upon the loyalty of the people of that kingdom, as well as those of the neighboring principalities in the north. Moreover, he was a skilled and daring warrior, while Solomon, though doubtless far more intelligent than his brothers, showed little prowess as a soldier and possessed none of the flamboyant characteristics which made Absalom, even in exile, a favorite with the masses.

Actually, most of the Israelites did not consider that Absalom had committed any grave crime in bringing about the death of Amnon. According to the laws of Moses, which were considered the final authority, Absalom had every right to avenge with blood the insult to his sister Tamar. In fact, his only real crime had been in not himself wielding the weapon that had cut down Amnon but sending his servants instead to set up an ambush. This was really of no major importance, though, since the law had been carried out. As first one, then two, three years passed, Absalom's crime was largely forgotten, though the memories of his colorful exploits and minor scandals were not.

Joab, particularly, viewed the gradual rise in influence of the group around the boy Solomon as a danger to the country and to himself. Since the day when he had thrown in his lot with David in the Valley of Elah, where Goliath had been killed, there had been only one brief period when Joab had not been close to David, both as general of the armies and as adviser. That had been during the months between the slaying of Abner and the capture of Jerusalem, but Joab's exploit in climbing the well shaft above the spring of Gihon in the battle for Jerusalem had restored him to the position of chief captain of the army. Now, with David growing older and more inclined to withdraw to himself, Joab watched with dismay the rise of the circle around the boy Solomon to a controlling position in the affairs of the kingdom. And with the army playing a less and less important part in the day-to-day life in Israel now that its major enemies had been conquered, he could see his own position being steadily undermined.

Characteristically, Joab took forthright action with a shrewdly devised plan to return Absalom to Israel and his father's favor. This was to be the first step in convincing David that the welfare of the kingdom, always, after carrying out the will of God, his major concern, demanded the designation of Absalom as successor to the now somewhat feeble king. For this purpose, Joab secured the services of a clever woman who lived in Tekoah, a small village at the edge of the wilderness of Judah not far from Hebron and the tomb of Abraham at Mamre. Following Joab's instructions, the woman came to Jerusalem, put on mourning as if a loved one had recently died, and presented herself at the palace. There she demanded that her case be heard and judged personally by the king.

David was able to hear only a few of those who came to the palace begging an audience, and these were usually rather carefully screened by his advisers. But Joab still possessed enough influence in the palace to have the woman of Tekoah admitted to David's presence.

"Help, O king!" she begged, prostrating herself upon the floor before the throne.

In his own sorrow for the handsome Absalom, David was inclined to be even more considerate of another's grief than he might normally have been, a fact which Joab had shrewdly counted upon in planning the scheme. Now he looked at the woman with compassion and asked, "What troubles you?"

"I am a widow," she said, as Joab had coached her. "My husband is dead and I had two sons. But they strove together in the field and, since there was none to part them, one of them killed the other."

"Go on," David told her, his interest naturally aroused by a story which so closely paralleled his own experience.

"Now the whole family has risen against me," the woman continued. "They demand that I deliver the one that killed his brother so they may kill him."

"That is the law," David reminded her. "If your husband's family demands the life of the murderer, it shall be theirs."

"But then the only coal I have left will be quenched!" the woman sobbed. "They will not leave to my husband either name or remainder on earth."

The question of law involved here was not entirely simple, since in Israel it was considered a major tragedy for a man's line to die out completely and the family land be sold. Much of the law was devoted to questions of inheritance so that the land possessed by a family would be handed down to succeeding generations. It was not a question to be decided lightly, and David wished time to think about it.

"Go to your home," he told the woman. "I will give orders concerning you later."

A less clever woman would have let the matter drop lest she anger the king by pursuing it further. But Joab had chosen his agent well, and she had not yet accomplished what she had set out to do.

"I pray you, let the king remember the Lord thy God," she begged. "Do not suffer the revenges of blood to destroy any more, lest they destroy my son."

"As the Lord lives," David promised her, "not one hair of your son's head shall fall to the earth."

This was the commitment the woman had been trying to obtain, a decision which, even though in a hypothetical case, could form the basis for the safe return of Absalom to Jerusalem and his father's favor.

"I pray you, let your handmaiden speak yet one word to my lord the king," she begged.

David studied the woman thoughtfully before he answered. Though his body tired easily these days and his hair and beard were already white with age, his mind was as clear and sharp as it had ever been. And something told him there was more to the woman's story than met the eye.

"Say on," he told her.

"Why, then, as the king shows mercy to me and to my son, does he not bring home again his own banished?" she asked boldly. "As the angel of God, so is my lord the king to discover good and bad. Therefore, the Lord will be with you."

David could see the framework of the plan clearly now, nor did he need to seek far to suspect its authorship. "Is not the hand of Joab with you in all of this?" he demanded, knowing that Joab had been working for some time to return Absalom to the kingdom.

Caught by surprise, the truth of the accusation was written in the sudden pallor that drained all color from the woman's cheeks.

"Your servant Joab ordered me to come here; he put the words into my mouth," she admitted. "Truly my lord is wise with the wisdom of an angel of God, to know all things that are in the earth."

"Go," David told her, not unkindly. "And tell Joab to come to me at once."

The woman hurried out. Joab arrived soon after, looking somewhat apprehensive, since he had no way of knowing just how David would take his stratagem of sending the woman to him with a trumped-up tale of brother killing brother. David, however, was gracious, for Joab had given him the excuse he needed to authorize Absalom's return from exile.

"You may bring Absalom to Jerusalem," David told the chief captain. "But let him turn to his own house and do not let him see my face."

CHAPTER 3

"Absalom prepared him chariots and horses, and fifty men to run before him." II SAMUEL 15:1

DAVID KEPT HIS WORD. For two years after the return of the former exile to Jerusalem he did not admit Absalom to his presence. Nevertheless, this was a busy and productive period for the wily and ambitious prince. The years in Geshur had changed him not at all. As vain and flamboyant as ever, he cut his hair only once a year, by which time the weight of the cutting equaled two hundred shekels of the Tyrian coinage which formed the main medium of monetary exchange in Israel. Nor did he overlook any chance to impress the people with his charm and his kingly qualities.

Joab had been inclined to let David decide without pressure when to reinstate Absalom in his favor completely, but the handsome prince was impatient. At the end of two years in Jerusalem, without having been called before his father, he importuned the chief captain to speak to David. Joab agreed to intercede, but had he known then what was in Absalom's mind, he might have begged David instead to send the prince back to Geshur.

When Joab begged David to admit the young prince to the palace and to his councils, David agreed. He had sorely missed Absalom, and welcomed the opportunity to have his son near him once more. At the same time, he restored Absalom to his old position as a subgovernor of the district that included much of Judah and the highly populated area lying west of Jerusalem. David's action fell in with Absalom's own plans, which were nothing less than to take his father's place upon the throne of Israel.

Absalom's first move in the elaborate scheme he had worked out to make himself king was to buy several chariots and employ a company of mercenaries as his own personal bodyguard. Wherever he went, he was now accompanied by an even greater train of guards than usually followed David on his less and less frequent public appearances. Inevitably, this show of wealth and power impressed many of the people with Absalom's importance, and to the untutored he soon achieved a stature not far below that of the king. It was generally accepted that he would gradually take over more and more of David's power.

As for David, his love for Absalom and his happiness at having him once again a member of the court tended to blind him to what was really happening. In fact, if Absalom had been willing merely to bide his time, the crown of Israel might well have become his almost by default as the ageing David grew more and more weary of the routines of ruling. Absalom, however, was both impatient and overly convinced of his own cleverness. Without consulting Joab, who had been his original sponsor, he laid plans for an actual revolt. The first part of his scheme involved weaning the people away from their almost worshipful attitude toward his father. To do this he embarked upon a clever strategy. Rising early each morning, he stood beside the main gate of the city, and there greeted those who came to Jerusalem with the hope of having their quarrels heard and judged by the king.

"Your matters are good and right," Absalom would tell the petitioners. "But no man has been deputed by the king to hear you."

Such a statement from David's own son, who was known to be a man of great importance in Israel, inevitably started a train of doubt in the minds of the visitors as to whether or not they would be heard by the king. When subsequently the greater portion of them were turned away because it was not possible for David to hear their complaints, they could hardly be blamed for remembering what Absalom had said and seeking him out again. To these disgruntled petitioners, as well as to those who had been heard and who had been ruled against, Absalom gave his commiseration and sympathy on their ill luck, adding, "Ah, that I were made judge in the land, so that every man who had a suit or a cause could come to me and I could do him justice!"

When he further took the hand of the visitor and embraced him, it was easy for a disappointed petitioner to tell himself that David cared nothing for the ordinary people, and that Absalom was the only man occupying a high place in the kingdom who would go out of his way to see that wrongs were righted and justice was done. In this way, Absalom gradually ingratiated himself with the people, not only in Judah where he was already much admired, and in Jerusalem where his lavish gifts earned him a following of ne'er-do-wells, but also in the other districts of the kingdom where those who had failed to lay their grievances before David described the glowing promises of the handsome prince. This prince, they decided, was better fitted to rule them than an ailing and ageing king.

Finally the day came when Absalom was ready to begin his revolt. But since he first planned to marshal in Judah the forces he had been building up outside Jerusalem, he knew he must leave the city without arousing any suspicion of his purpose. For this, he needed David's permission but he anticipated no trouble in that quarter, since his father had always granted him his every wish. When he came before David, his manner was subservient, as fitted that of a dutiful son.

"I pray you let me go and pay my vow which I have vowed to the Lord in Hebron," Absalom begged.

"What vow is this?" David asked him.

"While I was living in Geshur in Syria, I vowed a vow that if the Lord would bring me again to Jerusalem, I would sacrifice to him in our old homeland." It was a clever fabrication, the sort of thing David could hardly refuse.

"Go in peace," the king told Absalom, who left the court at once. Accompanied by his chariots and his mercenaries as well as several hundred of the young men of the capital whom he had invited to accompany him, he rode out of the city toward Bethlehem and Hebron. And once ensconced there, he sent messengers throughout the land, to announce the signal which he had agreed upon with a small group of dissident men whose help he had been courting for several years.

"As soon as you hear the sound of the trumpet," they were told, "then you shall say, 'Absalom reigns in Hebron!' "

There were many reasons why diverse groups chose to follow Absalom: old grievances, hope for the rich rewards he promised in booty and spoils, the lure of action for young men in a country which had not fought a major war in many years, the chance of gaining personal glory in battle, disgruntlement on the part of the tribe of Benjamin because Saul's sons had not succeeded him, and envy of the wealth and power David's own tribe of Judah possessed. Because of these considerations, the rebellious prince was able to raise a fairly large army with which he began the march upon Jerusalem, hoping to take the city by surprise before David could prepare to defend it.

Word of the rapidly spreading rebellion came to David when a man whom he had considered one of his most intelligent and trusted advisers, Ahithophel of Giloh, joined forces with Absalom. The defection of Ahithophel was a bitter blow to David, who had trusted and respected him. It was a stern and sorrowful king who gathered his advisers around him in Jerusalem.

"I have received word that the hearts of the men of Israel are following after Absalom," he told the group. "Even now he marches upon Jerusalem."

Though Joab had supported Absalom as successor to David, he had taken no part in the rebellion and had chosen to stay with the king. "If we shut the gates and man the walls, Absalom will have to lay siege to the city," he said. "I and my men stand ready to defend it."

David's eyes warmed at this vow of loyalty from his old friend and battle companion, from whom the vicissitudes of political life had separated him so much of the time in recent years.

"It would be like the old days," he agreed. "But I have never been one to fight from behind walls. Besides, Jerusalem would be damaged and its people would suffer, even though they have had no part in this controversy between me and my son. Let us retreat, instead, across the Jordan to Mahanaim, and from there rally those who are loyal to us among the tribes and the kings of the surrounding country who choose to join us."

No one pointed out that he would be re-enacting in almost every detail the sequence of events during the last days of Saul, when David had been the leader in Judah and the forces loyal to Saul and Ishbosheth had retreated to Mahanaim under the command of Abner. But the parallel was much too close for any to fail to see it; inevitably, it had a dampening effect upon their spirits. Giving the order to evacuate Jerusalem and his beautiful palace there was the most painful decision that David had ever been called upon to make. And yet he knew that it was the only way to save the lovely city where God had promised him his son would one day build a temple to the glory of the Most High.

CHAPTER 4

"Hushai the Archite came to meet him with his coat rent, and earth upon his head."

II SAMUEL 15:32

DAVID WASTED NO TIME in following up his decision to evacuate Jerusalem. Everyone who chose to leave the capital was ordered to pass through the gate opposite the brook called Kidron and take the road to Jericho that wound around the face of the slope to the east, sometimes called the Mount of Olives. David himself stood beside Kidron at a point where the shallow waters rippled over the gravel bed of the stream to form a ford. By his presence there, he hoped to encourage those who had followed him, and persuade those whom he did not consider able to make the journey to turn back.

David's wives and children followed Joab and the soldiers of the army who led the procession. Adonijah, whose mother was Haggith whom David had taken as a wife long before he was crowned king, was, since Absalom's rebellion, the leader among the king's sons. David had decided to leave his concubines behind in the harem in Jerusalem, since they would only consume food and be a burden upon the marchers. Besides, they were young and beautiful, and might stir up trouble among the young men of his party.

After David's own household marched, under the captaincy of squat, capable Benaiah, the Cherethites and the Pelethites, tall and often fair-haired mercenaries who were among the best fighters in his army. Behind them were the six hundred Gittites from Gath. But when their leader, the grizzled Ittai, David's old companion in arms, appeared, David called out, ordering them to halt.

"You are already an exile from your own country, while I must go where I may," he told Ittai. "Take back your men, and mercy and truth go with you."

"As the Lord lives and as my lord the king lives," Ittai said quietly. "In whatever place my lord the king shall be, whether in death or in life, there also will his servant be."

David was so moved by this assurance of faith and allegiance that for a moment he was not able to speak and could only wave the stalwart mercenaries on as they crossed the brook and followed the others. After them came a long line of people from the city, who had chosen to leave their homes and the safety of the walls rather than desert their king. Bringing up the end of the train was the magnificent tent of the Tabernacle with the Ark of the Covenant inside, borne upon a carrying frame by stalwart young Levites. A file of richly garbed priests followed, led by Zadok and Abiathar, but David stopped them before they reached the ford.

"Carry back the Ark of God into the city," he directed.

"The Ark should go with the Anointed of God," Zadok protested.

"If I find favor in the eyes of the Lord, he will bring me here again and show me both the Ark and its dwelling place," David said. "But if God shall say to me, 'I have no delight in you,' then here I am. Let him do to me as seems good to him."

Zadok, who was now chief priest with a son of Abiathar as his assistant, was reluctant to go back to Jerusalem. "Return to the city in peace and dwell there with your sons," David told him. "Keep watch in Jerusalem and send word of what happens to me where I dwell in the wilderness."

"God go with you and bring you safely home once more," Zadok said in parting, and ordered the procession accompanying the Ark to return to the city according to David's orders.

From the top of the hill called the Mount of Olives, David turned for one last look at Jerusalem. He could see the Tabernacle, easily distinguished by the rich Phoenician purple of the fabric from which it was made, being carried through the streets to its regular resting place. On the far side of the hill, the line of people plodding slowly down the winding road toward Jericho seemed pitifully small compared with the great armies he had more than once led to victory along this same route. From the agony of his loss and, most of all, from the pain in his heart that the son he loved had proved himself a traitor, David burst forth in a lamentation even more anguished than had been his song of mourning for Jonathan and Saul:

"My God, my God, why hast thou forsaken me?
Why art thou so far from helping me?
O my God, I cry in the daytime, but thou hearest not;
And in the night season, and am not silent.

But thou art holy,
O thou that inhabitest praises of Israel.
Our fathers trusted in thee:
They trusted, and thou didst deliver them.

Be not far from me; for trouble is near;
And there is none to help.
Many bulls have compassed me;
Strong bulls of Bashan have beset me round.

They gaped upon me with their mouths,
As a ravening and a roaring lion.
I am poured out like water,
And all my bones are out of joint.

My heart is like wax;
It is melted in the midst of my bowels.
My strength is dried up like a potsherd;
And my tongue cleaveth to my jaws.

Thou hast brought me into the dust of death.
For dogs have compassed me;
The assembly of the wicked have enclosed me;
They pierced my hands and my feet.

I may tell all my bones:
They look and stare upon me.

They part my garments among them.
And cast lots upon my vesture.

But be not thou far from me, O Lord;
O my strength, haste thee to help me.
Deliver my soul from the sword,
Save me from the lion's mouth,
For thou hast heard me from the horns of unicorns."

Overcome by his own grief, David could say no more. But then, before the Mount of Olives shut it away from view, he lifted his eyes for a farewell look at the city he loved, and a strange and wonderful thing seemed to happen. No longer did the city appear heavy with sadness and misery at the fate which had befallen it; now even the walls appeared to glow before his eyes like a beacon seen from afar off, guiding a traveler back home. And he knew, with a sudden rush of thankful understanding, that this was God's way of telling him that once again he would return to the beautiful city he had dedicated to the glory of the Most High upon the hilltop of Zion, and that whatever befell him, the Lord would not let him die, deserted and scorned, in the wilderness.

With this assurance from God, David felt his weariness and his sadness fall from him like a soiled garment dropped to the floor. His body straightened and his shoulders went back proudly. Even his eyes took on a newly confident gaze. It was no longer an old and bent man who followed the others on the road to Jericho, but a strong and resolute king leading his people to victory.

Near the foot of the hill David saw a small party moving along a path that joined the road ahead of him. As they drew closer he recognized his old friend and counselor, Hushai, who was moving rather slowly because of his advanced years.

The two men embraced warmly as they met just below the crest of the hill. Hushai sank to a rock beside the path, panting for breath after the long climb over the hill. David saw that his robe was torn and his face smeared with ashes in the traditional gesture of mourning.

"It is a sad day for Israel when its king must flee from a

traitorous son," Hushai said. "As soon as I heard of it, I came from Ataroth to join you."

A half hour ago, David might have wept with Hushai at the depths to which misfortune had brought him. But since then he had been given the assurance of God that he would once again return to the city he loved. It was a new David who had now taken command of the whole venture, a man who had shed some ten years in that moment of rededication and was now ready to launch the campaign to regain his kingdom.

"If you go on with me, you will become a burden to me," he told Hushai kindly. "Return, I pray you, to the city and say to Absalom, 'I will be your servant, O king. As I have been your father's servant before, so will I also now be your servant.' "

"Would you have me turn traitor, too?" Hushai demanded indignantly. "As I live and breathe, this shall not be!"

"Not a traitor," David assured him. "But you can be a help to me in Jerusalem by defeating the councils of Ahithophel."

"So he did go over to Absalom? I heard but could not believe it."

"Athithophel has gone over," David confirmed. "And without such a one as you there to defeat him, everything I have gained through the years may well be lost."

"What can I do alone?" Hushai protested.

"Zadok and Abiathar are there," David assured him. "Anything you learn in the king's household can be told to them."

"But we shall be only three men shut up within the walls!"

"Zadok's son Ahimaaz, and Abiathar's son, Jonathan, are to serve as my messengers," David explained. "You can send word by them of anything you hear that I should know."

Hushai got to his feet. "If I am to combat the counsels of such a wise man as Ahithophel, I had best be going to Jerusalem," he said. "May God go with you and watch over you, David."

"He will," David said confidently. "This day he has spoken to me in my heart and promised that I shall return."

David did not wait to watch Hushai enter the city, for he wanted to reach Jericho by nightfall. By the time Absalom rode into Jerusalem in a chariot, with his long hair flying in the wind, Hushai was already there, determined to squelch the revolt of the triumphant new ruler by every means he could devise.

CHAPTER 5

"And Ahithophel said unto Absalom, Go in unto thy father's concubines." II SAMUEL 16:21

NOT FAR BEYOND the Mount of Olives, David found a small caravan waiting beside the road. When he came nearer and the plump man leading it knelt before him, he recognized Ziba, who had been charged with the care of Jonathan's crippled son, Mephibosheth. The caravan was not large but the loads piled high upon the backs of the pack animals contained many loaves of bread, cakes of raisins from the vineyards of Hebron, baskets of fresh fruit, and skins of wine.

"The asses are for the king's household to ride upon," Ziba explained. "The bread and the summer fruits are for the young men to eat, and the wine that any who become faint in the wilderness may drink."

David could not help being cheered by the man's loyalty and his willingness to contribute to the welfare of a king whose rule in Israel appeared to be nearing its end. But there was no sign of Mephibosheth, whom David himself had succored by giving him the income from all of Saul's possessions and letting him live in Jerusalem as a member of the king's household.

"Where is your master's son?" he asked Ziba.

"He abides in Jerusalem," Ziba answered. "When I heard that you were leaving the city, I asked Mephibosheth what he was going to do. He only said, 'Today shall the house of Israel restore to me the kingdom of my father.' "

It was a strange situation, indeed, when a servant had held the king's welfare before his own, while his master repaid the kindness shown him by going over to Absalom at the first opportunity. With this thought came the answer to the question of what should be done to Jonathan's ungrateful son.

"All that belonged to Mephibosheth shall be yours," David assured Ziba.

"I humbly beseech that I may find grace in your sight, my lord the king," Ziba answered, as he handed over the lead-rope of the mules to one of David's servants. "May God bring you safely back to your people."

A little east of Jerusalem, David and those marching with him passed the village of Bahurim. A line of curious people had gathered by the roadside to watch the procession pass. For the most part they stood silently, though some called out greetings and blessings upon David and his household. Toward the edge of the village, however, a man came running from a house shouting curses at them. Joab's brother, Abishai, was marching beside David to guard him, since it was impossible to tell just what the sentiments of the people might be.

"That is Shimei, the son of Gera of the house of Saul," Abishai growled. "He has always hated you and loses no opportunity to speak against you."

While Abishai was speaking, a stone obviously aimed at David struck a pack mule not far from him. The animal grunted with pain and shied into the ranks of marchers, bringing the column momentarily to a halt. David stepped forward to make certain that no one was hurt. Just as he was about to speak to one of the mercenaries, he saw Shimei pick up another stone and hurl it in his direction.

"Come out, come out, you man of blood!" the Benjaminite shouted at David. "The Lord has turned upon you all the blood of Saul in whose stead you reign! Because you are a man of blood and a son of Belial, the Lord has delivered the kingdom into the hands of your son, Absalom."

"Why should this dead dog curse my lord the king?" Abishai demanded. "Let me go over and take off his head."

"If my son who comes from my own body seeks my life, how much the more may this Benjaminite do it," David said. "Leave him alone and let him curse, if the Lord has bidden him to do it."

"But if one is allowed to curse you and go unpunished, many others will dare to do so," Abishai insisted.

"It may be that the Lord will look upon my affliction and repay me with good for his cursing," David said. "Tell the column to move on."

As the people of the caravan picked up their belongings and started on their journey again, they were astounded to see Shimei running along beside the path, his voice shrill with hate and invective, cursing Israel's king and throwing stones at him until finally he was lost to view around a turn of the road. To them it must have seemed that David's fortunes were at their lowest possible ebb. But already the divine power was at work which had watched over a shepherd lad upon the hills around Bethlehem. The evidence of it was there for everyone to see in the new clearness of David's eye and the new purpose in his stride. And it was also at work back in Jerusalem, where Hushai was even then entering the gate and planning how he would defeat the counsel of Ahithophel and make Absalom play into his and David's hands.

It was the season of rains when the Jordan ran full and sometimes overflowed its banks, so David's people were forced to ferry themselves across the Jordan by whatever transport they were able to commandeer or devise. Joab and the other commanders had tried to persuade David to cross over first, but he refused. He chose instead to remain behind until his people were safely beyond the reach of Absalom, in case the rebel prince followed them with his troops at this most critical point of their escape. There on the banks of the river, the messengers Ahimaaz and Jonathan found David supervising the final details of the crossing.

"What news from Jerusalem?" he asked them. "Has Absalom entered the city?"

"He has entered," Ahimaaz said, "along with a great company of fighting men and chariots."

It was not comforting news, but it could have been worse; they might well have brought word that Absalom and his chariots were even then at their heels.

"What of Hushai?"

"He is now the chief among Absalom's counselors," Jonathan said.

"How is this so? It was said that Ahithophel advised my son in everything?"

"Ahithophel rode just behind Prince Absalom when he entered Jerusalem," Ahimaaz said. "And at first Absalom listened only to him."

He seemed hesitant to go on and David said impatiently, "Tell me everything. Hold nothing back."

"When Absalom entered your palace, Ahithophel advised him to take your concubines that you left behind and possess himself of them upon the rooftop in the sight of all the people."

David felt a sharp stab of pain that the son he loved above all others would thus publicly show his scorn and contempt for his father. For a man could dishonor another no more effectively than by taking his women and publicly despoiling them. The pain was replaced by a surge of anger, but before he gave voice to his rage, something stopped him: the memory of Nathan's familiar voice speaking on the occasion when he had told the story of the poor man whose lamb had been taken by the rich lord. Then Nathan had voiced the edict of God himself concerning David's punishment for his sin:

"Behold, I will raise up evil against you out of your own house. And I will take your wives and give them to your neighbor, and he shall lie with your wives in the sight of this sun."

"Absalom should die for this," Joab said, but David shook his head.

"It is the will of the Lord." But he could not help wondering when the remainder of the prophecy would be fulfilled, that portion where the Lord had also said: *"Now therefore the sword shall never depart from your house."*

"Why did not Absalom ride to catch us here on the banks of the river before we could cross?" Joab asked Ahimaaz.

"Such was Ahithophel's counsel," the messenger said. "He

begged to be given twelve thousand men to pursue you by night. But when Absalom consulted Hushai, he warned that my lord the king would set an ambush in the hills and trap them, so that the people would desert."

"And my son listened?"

"In Israel it is well known that even my lord the king listens to the counsel of Hushai," Ahimaaz said and grinned. "Besides, Absalom was loath to give up the pleasures of the king's harem."

"By the tents of Israel!" Joab exclaimed. "I would give much to have seen Ahithophel's face when Absalom took Hushai's advice instead of his! He was always an exceedingly proud man."

"We cannot delay in crosing the river," David said. "Ahithophel is one of the cleverest men in Israel. He will soon convince Absalom that he should follow us."

"Not any more, my lord," Ahimaaz assured him. "Before I left Jerusalem, Ahithophel had already ridden his mule through the gates. He took the road to Giloh in Judah, and I do not think he will counsel Absalom any longer."

This was better news than David could possibly have hoped to hear. For with Ahithophel out of the way and Hushai now advising Absalom, he could count on the greatest possible delay before an attack was launched against his meager forces. And every moment gained increased by that much more his chance of getting safely to Mahanaim and raising an army to meet Absalom.

"Hushai has even convinced Absalom that he should wait to gather an army from all parts of the nation before he attacks you," Jonathan added. "It is sure to be a month or longer before he will cross into Gilead."

"Meanwhile I, too, will send messengers to Dan and to Beer-sheba," David said grimly. "Israel must choose now between me and Absalom."

"I can tell you now who will be chosen," Joab cried exultantly. "Before the heat of summer comes, the Lord's Anointed will be back in Jerusalem."

CHAPTER 6

"Then David came to Mahanaim."

II SAMUEL 17:24

ONCE SAFELY ACROSS the Jordan, David turned northward along the western bank of the river, in the depths of the deep rift in which the stream flowed, known here as the *Ghor*. At its flood, the Jordan covered a far greater breadth than during the dry season of summer and autumn, when the flow was greatly diminished. Like the great Nile in Egypt, it annually replenished and fertilized the lands along its bank. And, since the weather was mild even in the dead of winter, the countryside was pleasant with the graceful, leafy branches of the willows drooping along the stream banks, and the soft, musical murmur of the river.

On the western shore a range of high limestone hills extended to the very edge of the *Ghor*. The eastern bank was flat, and in many places swampy, fringed with tamarisk and willow. Thickets of acacia, silver poplar, terebinth, cedar, laurustinus, arbutus, oleander, pistachio, and many other shrubs turned the area into a veritable jungle in many places. Occasionally the tracks of a leopard which had come down to the water to drink could be seen in the underbrush.

Flocks of cranes and wild ducks rose into flight as the advance guard stirred them from their feeding. Sparrows by the hundreds were flushed, along with the nightingale, the turtledove, the cliff swallow, the bulbul, and the wur-wur, a bird of surprising beauty and brilliance of hue whose main diet was said to be bees. When the *Ghor* gave way to the sloping rise of the hill country leading up to the eastern plateau, great flocks of partridges were seen. Just such flocks as these, exhausted from the long flight across the Red Sea, had lit at the feet of the children of Israel during the journey out of Egypt, furnished a much needed source of food.

From the jungle along the river bank would sound occasionally the roar of a lion and the growl of a bear, along with the deep grunt of the wild boar. Oddest of all the region's inhabitants, however, was the jerboa, which was not much more than the span of two hands in height, but had hind legs as long as its body and a tail even longer. When flushed in the thick grass or thickets, it seemed to fly through the air in a startling series of leaps.

Occasionally, when a deep, turbulent brook was encountered, the party was forced to pause and build a bridge across it. Since the water in these streams came from the hills, it was clear and cold, a welcome change from the muddy flow of the Jordan.

At Adamah, the swift current had undermined the steep western banks of the Jordan. Cliffs of earth were formed which sometimes tumbled into the river, blocking it and drying up the stream below for as much as a day or more. At such a time, Joshua and the children of Israel had crossed over dryshod near Jericho. Had Absalom chosen to send a force northward along the west bank of the Jordan to cross over at Adamah, he could have prevented David from reaching Mahanaim without fighting a battle that, in view of the meager forces at his command, might well have gone against him. But Hushai had cleverly lulled the rebellious prince into thinking that time was in his favor, and David and his men found only a ferryman at Adamah.

Moving on they came to the River Jabbok, which had its source in the uplands of the great eastern plateau separating the Jordan Valley from the vast wastes of the desert inhabited by fierce, roving tribes of the Bedawin. From the depths of the *Ghor* beside the Jordan, the mountains of Gilead had appeared forbiddingly high. But as they climbed steadily through the rolling country toward their goal of Mahanaim, the gentle slopes of the hills toward the eastern plateau offered no great impediment to their progress.

One afternoon, the column paused to rest upon a height which rose well above the others in the area. From this vantage point David could see the sparkling blue of the lake called Chinnereth to the northwest, with snow-capped Mount Hermon beyond it. And though Jerusalem itself was hidden by the hills of Canaan, David could picture the city with Absalom sitting upon his throne.

The mental picture brought a momentary feeling of doubt that the Lord would ever bring him back to his beloved city. But then he remembered and was comforted by the promise of the Most High, spoken through the mouth of Nathan, that his son would one day erect a great temple to the glory of God in Jerusalem. And when he turned away from the prospect in the distance to the more immediate beauty of the neighboring area, he could see in Gilead's rich pastures, heavily forested hills, and brawling streams an assurance that he and his people would be able to live comfortably there until such a time as he could retake the capital.

Once he had set up a headquarters at Mahanaim, David, characteristically, did not wait for the Lord to do his will for him. With the new-found energy that had come to him on the Mount of Olives outside Jerusalem, when he had humbled himself in his misery and hopelessness and had cried out to the Lord for help, he began at once the task of forging an army with which to defeat Absalom and regain his kingdom. And here the generosity that he had shown to fallen enemies and neighboring kings in the past proved to have been an excellent investment.

From Shobi, the son of King Nahash of Ammon, whom David had put over that district after his brother Hanun rebelled and caused the destruction of the Ammonite army, came both troops and supplies. From Lodebar, a neighboring principality, came Machir, the son of Ammiel. And from Rogelim in western Gilead came Barzillai. More important, all of these brought much needed supplies: sleeping mats and covers against the cool of the night in the hills above Mahanaim, basins of copper and earthenware, wheat, barley, flour, parched corn, beans, lentils, and "pulse," as the seeds of pod-bearing plants were called when dried and ground up to make a soup or gruel. Besides this, the visitors brought large quantities of honey, butter, cheese, sheep and goats for meat, and wine, lest the large army gathering slowly in the country around Mahanaim suffer from hunger.

The David who led these forces was a new man, fired with the knowledge that only his inspiration could fill the fighting men with the courage and zeal they would need to combat the considerably larger forces which Absalom was preparing to lead against them. Except for the mercenaries, the fighting men of Israel, who had once followed David in the long string of victories which had turned twelve often warring tribes into a mighty and powerful nation, were largely disbanded. Many were now too old to fight. The volunteers coming in from the outlying areas in obedience to David's summons had to be organized into a disciplined army which would not fling down its arms and flee in panic at the first sight of the chariots Absalom was sure to throw against them as his front line of advance.

Captains had to be appointed over the units of a thousand into which the troops were divided. These units, in turn, had to set captains over the divisions of a hundred, which were the tactical units of the army. The spearmen who would make up the first rank must be taught how to set the butts of their long-handled and iron-pointed weapons in the ground so that, when chariots were hurled against them, the points would penetrate the breasts of the horses, impaling them and killing them before the vehicles were able to crush the front line under their heavy wheels. Behind these would be ranged the bowmen, who must be taught to loose their arrows in waves over the heads of the front lines of the spearmen, so that the missiles could rain down from above upon the attacking troops.

Since most of the Benjaminites, who were the most skilled wielders of the sling in all Israel, had been against David from the beginning because of their allegiance to Saul, he could be fairly sure that they would make up a strong part of the forces Absalom would hurl against him. This fact had to be taken into consideration when he planned the disposition of his forces; the massing of men in ranks had to be avoided, lest the wielders of the sling be able to bring them down from some distance away.

As all these factors and many others could spell the difference between victory and defeat, a great deal of study and consideration was required in planning the coming campaign.

After his first survey of Mahanaim, David had given up any idea of fortifying the city further and making a stand there. For the type of defense he had in mind, the hill country back of Mahanaim was far more suitable. In such a terrain, the enemy could be cut up into small groups. These could then be destroyed one at a time, in the classic maneuvers of guerrilla warfare which David had brought to perfection during his years as a brigand chieftain in the wild country between Philistia and Judah.

As a headquarters and base of operations, however, Mahanaim was practically perfect. A great spring burst from the earth nearby and overflowed into a large pool to afford an ample supply of water. Many large government buildings were still standing which the energetic and capable Abner had erected in an attempt to make Mahanaim the capital of Israel under Ishbosheth. These housed a large portion of the army, and there was ample room nearby for the rest to set up their tents.

The presence of so large a number of people, the constant arrival of new troops from outlying areas, and the training of the soldiers in preparation for battle kept everyone occupied. As the army began to take on the appearance of a disciplined force, David ordered it divided into three sections. The first, containing most of the fighting men of his old band, along with experienced warriors from other parts of the kingdom, was placed under the direct command of Joab. The second force under Abishai was composed of the less experienced, whose steadiness in battle could not be relied upon until it was seen how they reacted to the first attack of the enemy. A third and highly mobile force was made up of the mercenaries of the king's household under the command of Ittai, who could be trusted to move swiftly to whatever point of weakness might develop and bolster the forces there. But when David himself announced his intention of fighting with the troops as he had in the old days, he encountered immediate opposition from the elders who had fled with him. No one, however, pointed out to David the obvious fact that, in spite of the new sources of energy which he appeared to have tapped since they had left Jerusalem, he was much too old to fight in the ranks in active battle.

"Do not go out with those who do battle," they pleaded. "It matters not if half of us die, but you are worth ten thousand of us."

David could not deny that the over-all direction he could give, his ability to judge the course of a battle and order the disposition of troops to any point of grave danger, was far more important than the bearing of weapons. In the same way that he had saved Jerusalem when it was attacked by the Philistines in the Valley of Rephaim, his advisers argued, he could serve the people best now. And in the face of these arguments, David had little choice except to agree, though there was a particular reason why he wanted to be in the heat of the battle himself. When at last word came that Absalom had crossed the Jordan and was moving toward Gilead, David called all the troops together. He gave them their final instructions, and then closed with the admonition that was nearest to his heart: "Deal gently for my sake with the young man, even with Absalom."

All who were going out to fight heard this cry of a father for the life of his beloved, if wayward, son.

CHAPTER 7

"Would God I had died for thee, O Absalom, my son, my son!" II SAMUEL 18:33

THOUGH DAVID BOWED to the wishes of his advisers and remained behind when the three forces moved out to meet Absalom's attack, he watched the general progress of the fighting from the vantage point of a peak overlooking the battle area. At the very outset the tide went against Absalom. He had given the command of his forces to Amasa, a palace sycophant who was a cousin of Joab's but possessed little of the latter's ability. Lacking shrewd leadership and the advantage of years of discipline possessed by the regular forces of Israel, Absalom's troops were at a considerable disadvantage. Besides, Absalom himself was no military leader. He was merely an ambitious and vain young man who had gained a popular following by promising indiscriminately to reward liberally everyone who followed him. Even if he had won he would not have been able to fulfill these promises, but as the day wore on, it became more and more apparent that the matter was being effectively taken out of his hands.

In the narrow valleys and canyons behind Mahanaim, David's army expertly cut Absalom's far less experienced forces into small bands, then moved in to destroy them one at a time. By noon the battle was decided and Absalom's forces began to withdraw toward the Jordan Valley, a desperate maneuver which David's commanders shortly turned into a rout by swift marches around the flanks. While Joab was leading one such flanking party, a subcaptain rushed to bring him the startling news that he had seen Absalom a few moments before, hanging from a tree.

"Do you mean he has taken his own life?" Joab demanded.

"My lord Absalom was fleeing upon a mule," the soldier explained. "When the animal went under a tree, his long hair caught among the branches and jerked him from his seat. He hangs now from the limbs of the tree by his hair."

At one time, Joab had supported Absalom in his ambition to inherit his father's throne. But Joab had spent too many years in helping David unify the kingdom to let a vain fool like Absalom destroy everything he and David had accomplished, just because the ambitious prince was too impatient to wait for his father's death, when the crown would undoubtedly have gone to him. With Absalom now at his mercy, it was far better for Israel, from Joab's point of view, if the young prince were destroyed, lest the ageing David, moved by his love for Absalom, put him in a position once again where he could foment an insurrection.

"If you saw him there, why did you not stake him to the ground?" Joab demanded angrily. "I would have given you ten shekels of silver and a belt."

"Even though I received a thousand shekels of silver I would not lift my hand against the king's son," the soldier said. "In our own hearing, the king charged you and Abishai and Ittai, saying, 'Beware that none touch the young man Absalom.' "

"Go join the others, then," Joab directed. "I will be along shortly."

When Joab found Absalom a few moments later, the upstart prince was almost unconscious from fright and pain. The grizzled old commander of Israel's armies could easily have cut Absalom down with a sword slash through his long hair and saved his life. Instead, however, he took from his belt three iron-pointed darts, heavy missiles which, thrown by a strong man, could penetrate deep into a block of wood. Drawing back one of these, Joab hurled it with all of his strength and saw the point bury itself to the hilt in Absalom's breast.

Ignoring the dying man's scream of pain, Joab hurled a second dart and still a third. By the time the last missile found its target, there was only a gurgling moan from Absalom as his body jerked and thrashed in the convulsions of death.

David was sitting by the gate of Mahanaim, waiting for word from the battlefront, when a runner came with the message from Joab that Absalom was dead and the rebellion had been crushed. The news of victory meant nothing to the old king, however, in his grief over the death of his son.

"O my son, Absalom! My son, my son Absalom! Would God I had died for thee, O Absalom, my son, my son!" David cried out, tearing the skirt of his robe and smearing his face with ashes and soot in a paroxysm of grief and mourning.

The defeat and death of Absalom could easily have been the end of the whole revolt, had David pressed the victory with his customary vigor. But all the fire seemed to have gone out of him. He sat all day at the gate of the city, weeping and mourning for his dead son. As a result of his inaction, those who had supported Absalom in Israel were able to extricate themselves from the battle line and retreat across the Jordan, where they continued to stir up rebellion against David.

With the whole country in a state of grave uncertainty and no firm hand at the helm, it was Joab who came to the rescue, as he had on more than one occasion. Risking David's displeasure and his own safety, for it was known everywhere that he had slain Absalom while the rebel prince hung from the tree, Joab sought to bring order out of the chaos that was fast gripping the nation.

"Because you appear to love your enemies and hate your friends," Joab told David bluntly, "you have brought shame to your servants who saved your life and the lives of your sons, your daughters, your wives, and your concubines. By your actions you declare that you have regard for neither princes nor servants, and that if Absalom had lived and all of us died, it would have pleased you well."

David raised his head and looked numbly at the man who had been his friend and closest counselor since that day when he had killed Goliath in the valley of Elah. But Joab had also slain David's son, an act for which the king could never really forgive him.

"What would you have me do?" he asked dully.

"Arise and speak comfort to your followers," Joab told him bluntly. "Else I swear that if you fail to do this, not one will stay with you, and it will be worse for you than all the evil that has befallen you from your youth until now."

Even in the depths of his grief, David could see that Joab was right in reminding him of his duty to Israel. Now, perhaps more than ever before, the nation needed a firm hand at the helm. "Call the people together," he said. "I will speak to them."

When the people gathered before the gate of Mahanaim, David thanked them for their loyal support. But even though they were cheered by his words of appreciation, none of them could fail to see that the vitality and purposefulness which had once characterized their king was now quenched, partly by age, it was true, but most of all by grief for his favorite son. When word of David's seemingly feeble hold upon the affairs of state reached the northern tribes, from which much of Absalom's strength had come, some dared to continue the rebellion, particularly under the leadership of a man named Sheba from the tribe of Benjamin.

Though his heart was heavy, David undertook the task of reuniting the nation, which was more helplessly divided now, it seemed, than it had been even in the days when Ishbosheth had ruled as king here in Mahanaim. His first act was to send Ahimaaz, the son of Zadok, to Jerusalem with a message for the chief priest and Abiathar.

"Speak to the Elders of Judah," he ordered the priests in his letter. "Say to them, 'You are my brethren, my very bones and my flesh. Why, then, are you the last to bring the king back home?' And say also to Amasa, 'Are you not of my bone and my flesh? God do so to me and mine, if you are not made chief captain of the army instead of Joab.' "

Amasa, the former commander of Absalom's forces, had fled across the Jordan after the defeat before Mahanaim. In offering him the position of chief captain, David was not only punishing Joab for killing Absalom against his orders, but at the same time seeking to lure a possibly powerful enemy into his camp, as he had with Abner in the time of Ishbosheth. Had David been his old self, he might have found reason for suspicion in the alacrity with which Amasa accepted the offer of amnesty and Joab's old position of chief captain. But with Sheba reported to be gaining adherents steadily, the king was forced to seek help wherever he could.

The coming over of Amasa to David's side appeared to remove much of the opposition which had developed during the short-lived and ill-fated rebellion of Absalom, particularly in David's own tribe of Judah. Soon a message arrived from the Elders saying, "Return with all your people."

A considerable company followed David to the river-crossing opposite Jericho. The Elders and a large group from Judah were camped at Gilgal across the stream. When he saw the size of the crowd, Abishai moved up to David's side and spoke to him urgently in low tones, so that Amasa would not be able to hear.

"At least a thousand men of Benjamin are there with Shimei," he said. "Remember how he cursed you and hurled stones when you were leaving Jerusalem? This could be a trap."

"Only a few of us will cross the river until the Elders of Judah have sworn allegiance to me once more," David said. "That way the others will be safe." He turned to Amasa. "Remain here and hold our forces ready. Abishai and Ittai will cross over with me."

Amasa was shrewd enough to realize what was in David's mind, but he made no objection. When a ferry from the other side grounded on the east bank, David and the two subcommanders entered it and were rowed across. The first to greet him as he stepped ashore was Shimei, who prostrated himself on the ground before the king.

"Let not my lord impute iniquity to me," Shimei begged humbly. "Neither remember what your servant did perversely the day my lord the king went out of Jerusalem, for I know I have sinned. Behold, therefore, I have come first this day of all my house to meet my lord the king."

"Shall not Shimei be put to death for cursing the Lord's Anointed?" Abishai demanded angrily.

David, however, had had enough of bloodshed. "What have I to do with you, the sons of Zeruiah, that you should always oppose me?" he demanded irritably of Abishai. "Do I not know that I am this day king over Israel?"

Abishai was silent before David's anger, and the king turned to the repentant Shimei. "You shall not die," he promised, and swore an oath that no harm would come by his hand to the Benjaminite or his family.

By showing mercy to his enemies, David hoped to weld the diverse factions in Israel once more into a whole, knowing that a policy of punishment and destruction for those who had followed the handsome and flamboyant Absalom would only harden their opposition to him. And as he had hoped, when it was demonstrated that he had chosen to be merciful, people began to flock about him as before, seeking his favor once again.

One man had stood by David, yet asked no favors in return. This was Barzillai, the tribal leader of Gilead who had placed all of his people and possessions at David's command. The old sheikh accompanied David as far as the Jordan, ready to help if there were further treachery on the part of the king's enemies in Benjamin and the northern tribes. But when it was apparent that David had regained control of the strongest part of the kingdom, the tribe of Judah, he asked leave to depart.

"Come over with me and I will care for you in Jerusalem," David begged the old chief, for he had become very much attached to him during the stay in Mahanaim. But Barzillai shook his head.

"How long do I have to live that I should go with the king to Jerusalem?" he said. "Today I am eighty years old and can no longer taste what I eat or what I drink, or hear the voices of singing men and singing women. Why should your servant be a burden to my lord the king? Let me turn back, I pray you, that I might die in my own city and be buried in the grave of my father and my mother."

David's weary soul longed to return with Barzillai to the peace of beautiful Gilead, with its forests, its streams, its hills and fertile valleys. But he could not rest while Israel was still in danger of being divided, so he embraced Barzillai in farewell and turned his face westward to the road leading to Jerusalem. As he moved along, more and more people of Judah joined the procession to usher their king back to his capital.

The Benjaminite Sheba, who had rallied part of Absalom's forces behind him to continue the rebellion, chose to take David's mercy toward his former enemies as a sign of weakness. Shrewdly utilizing the traditional distrust of the northern tribes for Judah, he rallied more and more support among dissident elements in the northern tribes. They must strike boldly, he told them, and carve out a kingdom for themselves, before David's forces were once again strong enough to hold the nation together.

CHAPTER 8

"So Joab and Abishai his brother pursued after Sheba." II SAMUEL 20:10

THE TASK of putting down Absalom's rebellion had sorely tried David's waning strength, and the loss of Absalom had been a near deathblow to his spirit. In the crisis brought about by the rebellion of Sheba and the northern tribes, he dallied where the younger David would have acted forthrightly. Only when word finally came that the rebel forces were gaining strength at an alarming rate did David yield to the entreaties of Abishai, Zadok, and Hushai, and send Amasa to gather the fighting men of Judah at Jerusalem within three days for a major attack upon Sheba's forces.

Amasa, however, had only pretended allegiance to David in order to save his own life. Still hoping to foment further the revolt which had almost toppled David from his throne, he delayed in gathering the troops of Judah together. But this time he had underestimated the king. David, though sick and weary, could still see that the situation demanded action. Without waiting for Amasa and the fighting men of Judah, he sent a force of veterans under Abishai, with the mercenaries of his own bodyguard, in a swift thrust into northern Israel—the type of tactic which long ago had gained him fame.

Though banished by David after Absalom's death, Joab was

waiting outside Jerusalem; once the troops were clear of the city, he joined his brother and took command. Meanwhile, Amasa heard that David had already sent forces northward to follow Sheba and hurried to join them. He met Joab and Abishai at the great spring in Gibeon, where long ago David had parleyed with Abner, and two dozen of the finest young men from both their armies had destroyed each other in a trial by combat. Amasa was wearing Joab's old uniform as chief captain, a deliberate affront to Joab. But when they met, the former commander pretended to be friendly and made as if to embrace him. Seconds later, Amasa lay on the ground dying from a sword thrust between the ribs.

Fortunately, the men who had followed Amasa knew Joab well, since the family of Zeruiah was one of the most prominent in all of Judah. Many of them, too, had fought under Joab. When Abishai raised a shout of "He that favors Joab and is for David, let him follow Joab," there was only a moment of indecision. Then someone in the crowd cried, "Joab and David," and the danger was passed.

With a large army now at their command, Joab and Abishai moved swiftly northward in pursuit of the fleeing forces under Sheba. Seeing their strength and certainty of purpose, people of the area through which they moved quickly gave up any thought of continuing the rebellion; many of them actually joined in the pursuit of Sheba. Finally, at Abel, in the foothills of Mount Hermon, Sheba and his considerably shrunken rebel forces chose to make a stand, but their cause was already lost. Rather than see their city destroyed by siege, the townspeople of Abel cut off the head of the rebel leader and sent it to Joab, thereby ending the revolt. With the rebellion put down so effectively by Joab's forthright measures, David had no choice save to reinstate him. But a gulf separated the two men who had once been so close, a gulf that widened steadily as the years passed.

David had hoped for a period of peace and prosperity after his troubles, but shortly after the siege of Abel was lifted, a great famine began in the land. When it continued for three years without relief, the people begged David to inquire of the Lord, through the priests and the prophets, as to how the nation might have offended the Most High and brought upon themselves the punishment of the famine. When the prophets were consulted, word came back that "The famine is because of Saul and his bloody house, and because he slew the Gibeonites."

Centuries before, immediately following the fall of Jericho, men from the cities of the Gibeonite confederation, including Gibeon, Kirjath-jearim, Beeroth, Lachish, and several others in the hill country a short distance northwest of Jerusalem, had sent representatives to Joshua. By pretending to have come from a great distance, they had appealed to Joshua's desire to placate any of the Canaanites who might endanger the rear of his army while he moved forward to conquer the central part of Canaan and had managed to gain from Joshua the promise that they would not be attacked. When it was then revealed that these cities were actually only a short distance away on the route of march which the Israelites planned to take, and not a threat to the rear flank, as they had led Joshua to believe, the Israelite leader had indignantly condemned the men of Gibeon to be "hewers of wood and drawers of water" for Israel, as a punishment for their deceit.

In the time of Saul, rivalry between Benjamin, Saul's tribe which dwelt nearby, and the Gibeonites had resulted in Saul's sacking the city. A large portion of its inhabitants were killed and the promise made to the Gibeonites by Joshua several hundred years before was broken. It was to this crime that the prophets now referred. In the belief that the famine was indeed a manifestation of God's wrath because he had not avenged the men of Gibeon against the house of Saul, David called for representatives from the Gibeonites to confer with him at Jerusalem.

The right of revenge for the killing of another was strictly guaranteed to members of the family or tribe to which the murdered man had belonged; so even though, in this case, an entire city was involved on the one hand, and the descendants of a single man on the other, the law was held to operate just as if only two people had been involved.

"In what way shall I make atonement that you may bless the inheritance of the Lord?" David asked the Gibeonites.

"We will have no silver or gold of Saul nor of his house," the men of Gibeon said. "Neither for us shall you kill any man in Israel."

"What do you say that I shall do for you, then?"

"Let seven of Saul's sons be delivered to us and we will hang them in Gibeah, his city" was the answer.

It was a bloody and terrible retribution upon the remaining members of the house of Saul. But believing it to be the will of the Lord, David did not hesitate, for the lives of thousands were at stake should the famine continue much longer.

"I will give them to you," he promised the Gibeonites. "But I will spare Mephibosheth, the son of Jonathan, because of the oath that was between me and Jonathan."

The men of Gibeon agreed to this stipulation, and David ordered turned over to them the two sons of Rizpah—the concubine of Saul over whom the controversy had arisen between Abner and Ishbosheth—and five sons which Saul's daughter, Merab, had borne to Adriel, the Meholathite. When the Gibeonites hanged the seven upon the hill of Gibeah, Rizpah went to the place of hanging. Spreading out sackcloth upon which she rested by night, she stayed there and did not allow the birds to rest upon the bodies by day or animals to disturb them by night.

When David learned what Rizpah had done, he ordered that the bones of Saul and Jonathan, which the men of Jabesh-gilead had taken from Beth-shan following the fall of Saul, should be gathered up along with the remains of the men who had been hanged and buried with honor in the sepulcher of Kish, Saul's father. And once the vengeance of the Gibeonites had been wreaked upon the descendants of Saul, the rains came once again upon the land as the prophets had foretold. The harvest was heavy and the pasture lands of the hillsides were green for the flocks and the herds.

Occupied as David had been with rebellion inside his own kingdom, he had not been able to watch the Philistines on the coast very closely. When the Philistine confederation once again gathered an army and attacked the tribe of Judah at a place called Gad in the hills before Gath, David went out to lead his own forces against them, in spite of his age and the ill health which had dogged him ever since the rebellion of Absalom.

The battle went in favor of the Israelites, and the strength of the Philistine confederation was destroyed once and for all. But after the battle, David suddenly fell to the ground in a faint. He was carried to his tent, and there his most trusted advisers and physicians told him that he must never again go out to battle. When a series of similar attacks followed, racking his steadily weakening body as the months passed, it became evident to all that the Light of Israel would soon be quenched.

CHAPTER 9

"Assuredly Solomon thy son shall reign after me, and he shall sit upon my throne?" I KINGS 1:13

WITH DAVID'S HEALTH visibly waning, a period of feverish political activity began in connection with the designation of one of his sons to succeed him as king of Israel. On one side was Bathsheba and her son, Solomon, supported by Zadok, the prophet Nathan, Benaiah, the captain of the king's household troops, Hushai, and many others among the Council of Israel who knew David had promised Bathsheba that Solomon would one day rule over Israel. In his grief over the death of Absalom and the turbulent period that had followed, David seemed to have forgotten that promise. Now, as he became more and more stuporous, Bathsheba feared that he might not issue the decree naming Solomon to succeed him before he lapsed into complete unconsciousness.

The Council of Israel was empowered to name the new king, but no one denied that David's preference would carry great weight, particularly since most of the council were old friends and companions of David from the days when he had fought successfully to make Israel a single unified nation. During these years, Solomon had been growing up from a serious and rather precocious little boy into a handsome young man whose unusual intelligence set him apart in the king's household, although his lack of skill in military arts and games often earned him the good-natured contempt of his brother princes. The latter were much more inclined to follow Adonijah, a powerful man of rather simple mind who, because he was a skilled warrior, stood high in the opinion of Joab and his brother Abishai, as well as in the eyes of a great number of the people.

Bathsheba sought to remind David of his promise to her concerning Solomon by bringing the young prince to his father's attention as much as possible. During the warm days of spring, David lay upon a litter in his pavilion upon the rooftop of the palace. In the brief periods when he had energy to speak, he taught Solomon the art of the poet and composer of songs. Wise in the nature of her husband, Bathsheba had chosen as the old king's nurse a lovely young girl called Abishag, who came from Shunem, a district in the north overlooking the beautiful Vale of Jezreel that was famous for the beauty of its women. But the spark she sought to stir in David was past all burning now. No longer did he sing love songs with the sweetest voice in Israel as once he had; instead his words were those of counsel to the young prince.

Observing how closely Bathsheba and her supporters guarded David, allowing only Solomon from among his sons to come into his presence, Joab realized that he must act quickly if he were to defeat this woman whom he had hated so bitterly ever since David's love for her had led to the death of Uriah. He could have wished for a more likely prospect for king than Adonijah, for David's eldest son already showed many of the same undesirable traits as Absalom had possessed. Adonijah had bought a chariot and set fifty men to run before him, announcing his coming whenever he passed through the city. But even the vanity of Adonijah was better, in Joab's opinion, than what he could expect at the hands of Bathsheba, who was sure to seek his death as soon as David was dead and Solomon chosen as king.

When David drifted into the deep stupor from which he roused only occasionally, and then rarely spoke more than a few words, Joab knew he would have to act quickly. Deciding to create a situation where David would be forced to name Adonijah king in order to avoid another civil war, Joab persuaded Adonijah to announce a special sacrifice to be followed by a great feast near the spring of En-rogel in the valley just south of the hill of Zion. He planned to have Adonijah announce himself as king during the feast and enter the city of Jerusalem in triumph to take the throne from his ailing father.

Since En-rogel was a favorite spot with the people of Jerusalem for celebrating religious feasts and private affairs, Adonijah could be sure of a large attendance from the city, as well as the presence of the king's sons, who were invited as special guests. He was careful, however, not to invite Zadok, the chief priest, or Nathan the prophet. Nor did he invite Benaiah, the captain of the king's guard, and others among the more powerful supporters of David in the Council of Israel, who were known to favor Solomon as the heir.

Nathan heard of the plot when invitations to attend the celebration came to influential men in his own town. He immediately saw through the flimsy screen of pretense under which Adonijah had cloaked his real intentions and acted at once. Journeying to Jerusalem, he sought out Bathsheba. Although she had once been the cause of Nathan's forthright denunciation of David, following the death of Uriah, Bathsheba was still the mother of the one man whom Nathan knew to have been chosen by God as the next king of Israel.

"Have you heard that Adonijah is claiming the kingdom for himself without letting our lord David know?" the prophet demanded.

Bathsheba had been too concerned about David's failing health to pay much attention to Adonijah's actions. But she saw at once the threat which they posed to the future of her son.

"Speak on," she implored the old prophet. "Tell me what I should do."

"Go to King David," Nathan instructed her, "and ask him if he did not swear to you saying, 'Assuredly Solomon, your son, shall reign after me and sit upon my throne.' 'Why, then,' you must ask him, 'does Adonijah reign?' "

"It will not be enough if only I speak to him," Bathsheba objected. "I am a woman, and only a man may speak in the Councils of Israel."

"I will join you while you are talking with the king and confirm your words," Nathan promised.

Abishag, the Shunammite nurse, was at the king's bedside when Bathsheba entered the chamber. David had been lying with his eyes closed, as he did much of the time now. For a moment Bathsheba feared that he was already dead, but the nurse reassured her.

"He lies like this much of the time," Abishag said in a whisper. "Sometimes he speaks under his breath words of the songs he sang when he was young. But when you rouse him, he knows what is happening."

Just then David opened his eyes and smiled at Bathsheba. "What is it you wish, O most beloved of my heart?" he asked, using a phrase that had been their private endearment through the years since he had taken her for his own.

"My lord, you swore to me by the Lord God saying, 'Assuredly Solomon shall reign after me and shall sit upon my throne,'" Bathsheba said. "But now Adonijah reigns and my lord the king does not know it. He has even slain oxen and fat cattle and sheep in abundance and has invited the king's sons and Joab, the captain of the army. But he has not invited your servant Solomon."

David's eyes closed; the temptation to pretend not to have heard was great, for much of his life had been spent in unifying Israel. He was tired now, and more than anything else, he wanted peace and rest until the Lord called him, but he had never shirked a responsibility put upon him by God. Insuring the future stability of Israel was a task he knew the Lord would not want him to evade even now in the declining days of his life.

Once he had hoped that Absalom would show the qualities Israel needed in a king, but he had been disappointed, and he did not delude himself that Adonijah would be able to hold together the disparate elements making up the nation. The days of battle were largely past, and what was needed now was not a warrior but a man of wisdom. Of all his sons, only Solomon possessed to the highest degree that particular qualification.

"My lord," Bathsheba's imploring voice brought David's thoughts back to the present. "The eyes of all Israel are upon you, that you should tell them who shall sit upon the throne of my lord the king after him. Otherwise, when my lord shall sleep with his fathers, I and my son Solomon shall be called offenders and be destroyed."

While Bathsheba was speaking, Nathan came into the room as he had promised. The grizzled old prophet did not waste words, lest the stupor in which David lay most of the time claim him again before they had accomplished their purpose.

"Have you said Adonijah shall reign after you and sit upon the throne?" he asked David. "Even now he has slain oxen and fat cattle and sheep for the people. He has called the king's sons, the captains of the troops, and the priests, to eat and drink with him and shout, 'God save King Adonijah!' But Zadok, Benaiah, your servant Solomon, and myself, Adonijah has not called. Is this done by my lord the king's permission, without your telling me who it is that shall sit upon the throne after you?"

Bathsheba had drawn away a little while Nathan was making his plea, so it would not appear that there was any plan behind their approaching David at the same time. When David whispered her name, she came to the other side of the couch.

"Call Zadok and Benaiah," he told her, and she went at once to get them.

"Take with you the servants of your lord," David directed, when Bathsheba returned with the two men. "Have my son Solomon ride upon my own mule and take him down to the spring Gihon. There let Zadok the priest and Nathan the prophet anoint him as king over Israel, and have trumpets sounded while the people shout, 'God save King Solomon!' Then you shall come up after him so that he may sit upon my throne, for he shall be king in my stead, as I have appointed him to be ruler over Israel and over Judah."

Benaiah, the squat leader of the stalwart Cherethites and Pelethites who made up the king's personal bodyguard, spoke: "As the Lord God has been with my lord, the king, even so may he be with Solomon," he said, "and make his throne greater than the throne of my lord King David."

Those who supported Solomon lost no time in carrying out David's instructions. Benaiah went to order every member of the king's guard on duty, while Zadok and Nathan sent out a call for the nobles of Israel who were in Jerusalem to gather at once beside Gihon. Bathsheba made Solomon ready for the ceremony. Unwittingly, Adonijah had helped their cause considerably by holding his feast near the spring En-rogel. With the greater part of his followers outside the city, it would be all the easier for Solomon to ascend the throne upon David's authority.

Soon a solemn group of people gathered around the spring of Gihon. There Zadok took a horn filled with oil and poured it upon Solomon's dark hair in the traditional rite of anointing, much as Samuel had done for David so long ago in his father's home at Bethlehem.

Solomon stood slender and straight as the fragrant oil soaked his hair and dripped down upon his shoulders. When Zadok finished speaking the words of blessing, Benaiah's trumpeters gave a great blast, and the people who had gathered hurriedly for the ceremony raised a shout of "God Save King Solomon!"

To Adonijah and the roisterers gathered around En-rogel farther down the Kidron Valley, the sound of the trumpets came but faintly. Joab heard it, however, and frowned.

"Why would trumpets be sounded in the city?" he asked Adonijah, with whom he was eating. "Perhaps your father is dead."

Reluctant to break off the festivities and return to Jerusalem, Adonijah continued to celebrate what he thought to be his own ascension to the throne of Israel. Nor did the celebrants at En-rogel suspect anything was amiss until Jonathan, the son of the priest Abiathar, brought word that David had designated Solomon king in his stead, and that the new king was already upon the throne.

Had Adonijah been the strong and forthright man that David had been in his younger days, he might still have rallied his supporters and taken the throne forcibly from Solomon. But when Adonijah vacillated and took no action at the news of Solomon's ascension to the throne, his supporters soon began to melt away like the snows from the slopes of Mount Hermon at the coming of summer. Fearing for his own safety, Adonijah finally ran to Jerusalem and threw himself upon the horns of the Altar of Sacrifice, the traditional place of refuge for any man in danger of his life.

Solomon could have destroyed his brother, had he chosen to violate the ancient right of refuge before the altar granted by tradition since the time of Moses. But here he exhibited the wisdom which David and wise old Nathan had seen in the young man, a wisdom which was to let him expand the kingdom of David even beyond the limits his father had achieved, and bring Israel to its highest glory.

"Let King Solomon swear to me this day that he will not slay his servant with the sword," Adonijah pleaded when he claimed sanctuary, and Solomon was quick to give him the assurance he desired.

"If my brother Adonijah will show himself a worthy man, not one hair of his head shall fall to the earth," Solomon decreed. "But if wickedness shall be found in him, he shall die."

With this assurance, Adonijah came away from the altar and was allowed to go to his home in peace. The brash attempt by David's oldest living son to unseat his father had failed as miserably as had that by Absalom. Solomon was now secure upon the throne of Israel.

CHAPTER 10

> *"Yea, though I walk through the valley of the shadow of death, I will fear no evil: for thou art with me."* PSALMS 23:4

FOR A WHILE AFTER Solomon's ascension, David's health improved. He was well enough to be carried to the audience chamber upon a litter to attend the solemn ceremony of investiture in which the Elders of Israel swore allegiance to the new king. One face was conspicuously absent from the ceremony, however, for Joab knew that Solomon and his followers would never forgive him for his part in the abortive attempt to place Adonijah upon the throne. When Adonijah fled to the sanctuary of the altar, Joab returned to his old home in Bethlehem. In supporting Adonijah over Solomon, the white-bearded old general of the armies had only been doing what he thought best for Israel and for his own fortunes, two goals which he had never considered separate. And having lost the conflict, he waited, like the good soldier he was, for the end to come.

When the colorful ceremony of investiture was finished, David spoke to the crowd. For a few moments, his voice regained its old vigor as he gave to the young king the credo which had guided him in his great career, first as warrior and later as king.

"I go the way of all the earth," he charged Solomon, who stood straight in the sunlight before the throne upon which the old king sat for the last time. "Be strong, therefore, and show yourself a man. Keep the charge of the Lord your God to walk in his ways and his judgment and his testimonies, as it is written in the law of Moses. Thus you will prosper in all that you do and wherever you turn. And the Lord will continue his word that he spoke concerning me saying: '*If thy children take heed to their way, to walk before me in truth with all their heart and with all their soul, there shall not fail thee a man on the throne of Israel.*'

"The God who is the rock of Israel also said to me: '*He that rules over men must be just, ruling in the fear of God. And he shall be as the light of the morning, even a morning without clouds when the sun rises, as the tender grass springs out of the earth in the clear sunshine after rain.*' And although my house be not so with God, yet hath God made with me an everlasting covenant ordered in all things, and certain. For this is all my salvation, and all my desire."

As the words died away, David's eyes closed and his shoulders slumped wearily. Abishag gestured to the bearers of the king's litter to take him away, and David made no objection. With the charge to Solomon finished, all strength seemed to have drained out of him, but his heart was at peace in the assurance that God had blessed him beyond his deserving.

It was true that David had sinned greatly in causing the death of an innocent man, the greatest sin a man can commit save only that of blasphemy against the name of God himself. But the prophecy of Nathan that blood would come upon his house because of that sin had been fulfilled, first in the death of the son of his illicit union with Bathsheba, and later, in the rebellion of his sons, Absalom and Adonijah. Now in Solomon, he knew, would be fulfilled the second promise of God, the promise that he had kept ever before him that his son would build a great temple to the glory of the Most High.

There were no more earthly duties to keep David now. As he was borne from the chamber where the investiture of Solomon had been carried out, his lips moved, but the words were so faint that only Abishag, the Shunammite, could hear them. And not even she could know that here in the final hours of his life as Israel's greatest king, David was speaking for the last time the words of assurance that had come to him upon the ridge overlooking the Valley of Elah, with Goliath's headless body still lying beside the brook where the giant had fallen.

That night David had looked into the future and had found himself afraid. But God had come to his aid then, as over and over again he had, with the words of assurance which had brought David safely through all the vicissitudes he had faced as both warrior and king:

The Lord is my shepherd; I shall not want.
He maketh me to lie down in green pastures:
He leadeth me beside the still waters.
He restoreth my soul:
He leadeth me in the paths of righteousness for his name's sake.
Yea, though I walk through the valley of the shadow of death,
I will fear no evil: for thou art with me;
Thy rod and thy staff they comfort me.
Thou preparest a table before me in the presence of mine enemies:
Thou anointest my head with oil; my cup runneth over.
Surely goodness and mercy shall follow me all the days of my life:
And I will dwell in the house of the Lord forever.

ACKNOWLEDGMENT

The Song of Ikhnaton sung by David in Chapter 5 of Book I is from *Our Oriental Heritage*, copyright 1935 by Will Durant, and used by permission of Simon and Schuster, Inc. The several verses and psalms appearing in the text other than the foregoing are from *The Bible to Be Read as Living Literature* by Ernest S. Bates, copyright 1936 by Simon and Schuster, Inc., and used by permission of the publishers. The author wishes to express his appreciation to Simon and Schuster for permission to use these excerpts, and to the authors of the books mentioned.

Jacksonville, Florida
October 10, 1961

ABOUT THE AUTHOR

Frank G. Slaughter was born in Washington, D. C., in 1908. At the age of only fourteen he entered college and graduated from Duke University in 1926 with a Phi Beta Kappa key. Four years later he graduated from Johns Hopkins Medical School, an "M.D." at the age of twenty-two. For many years, both as a civilian and then as a major and lieutenant colonel during World War II, Dr. Slaughter devoted himself to the practice of medicine. During these years he also began to write, and upon his release from military service at the end of the war, he decided to devote himself full time to the career of an author. Since the publication of his first book in 1941, Dr. Slaughter has become one of the most prolific men of letters of any century. In twenty-one years he has produced thirty-nine books, drawing his inspiration from fields as diverse as modern medicine, Renaissance history, and the timeless and unlimited sources of the Bible. In his own country and abroad, books such as *In a Dark Garden, The Road to Bithynia,* and *The Mapmaker* have given pleasure to more than 25,000,000 readers.

Dr. Slaughter is also well known as the author of novels dealing particularly with Bible times, such as *The Galileans, The Song of Ruth,* and *The Thorn of Arimathea.* His interest in spiritual affairs extends to on occasion filling a church pulpit in the pastor's absence. From this background of research and activity, *The Land and the Promise, David: Warrior and King,* and his story of the life of Jesus, *The Crown and the Cross,* have been written.

Dr. Slaughter lives now with his wife and two sons in Florida.